C0-CCE-679

INTRODUCTION TO
ELECTRONIC DATA
PROCESSING EQUIPMENT

McGraw-Hill Series in Information Processing and Computers

J. P. NASH, CONSULTING EDITOR

RICHARD W. HAMMING, ASSOCIATE CONSULTING EDITOR

INTRODUCTION TO ELECTRONIC DATA PROCESSING EQUIPMENT

Its Operation and Control

ROBERT V. OAKFORD

ASSOCIATE PROFESSOR OF INDUSTRIAL ENGINEERING
STANFORD UNIVERSITY

McGRAW-HILL BOOK COMPANY, INC.   1962

NEW YORK   SAN FRANCISCO   TORONTO   LONDON

INTRODUCTION TO ELECTRONIC DATA PROCESSING EQUIPMENT

47580

$10.00

THE MAPLE PRESS COMPANY, YORK, PA.

PREFACE

Data processing deals with, among other things, the flow of information through the business organization. The specialist in data processing is properly concerned with the pertinence of specific information to decisions that must be made by people in the business organization, and with the development and implementation of systems for maintaining records and channeling pertinent information to the decision makers.

A large part, but by no means all, of business data processing deals with numeric computations. Electronic computers and punched-card accounting equipment form an important set of tools for performing repetitive computational procedures. This book is concerned with the operation and control of these tools. Their control can be considered as a problem of communication between man and machine, because the man must program, i.e., define the time sequence of, the operations to be performed by the machine.

Specifically, this book has to do with identifying and describing certain elements of this communication problem that are common to various electronic data-processing equipments. A complete description would be an encyclopedic work, because it is technically true that each piece of equipment has its own language. However, there are certain subjects that are generally relevant. A study of number systems and coding systems based thereon is important, not only because they have a general value in data processing but also because they furnish a basis for representing the "natural language" of many data-processing equipments. The subjects of computer organization and control, of computer programming, and of program testing and error isolation are pertinent to use of stored-program computers by data processors. The subject of control of equipment by plug-board wiring is basic to the effective use of a large class of punched-card data-processing equipment. Finally, the algorithmic language, a language for describing computational procedures, introduces an alternative approach to the problem of communication between man and machine in the solution of data-processing problems.

The subject matter is discussed in terms of existing rather than hypothetical equipment. This has the disadvantage that some specific features of a given piece of equipment have been ignored. Offsetting this is the very real advantage that the reader will obtain a degree of facility of communication with a set of existing equipment. It is hoped that the knowledge acquired from this book will furnish the reader a solid foundation for further study of the subjects to which he will be introduced.

IBM equipment has been chosen as a basis for discussion for the simple reasons that it is representative and that the average reader is more likely to be exposed to IBM equipment than to any other kind.

This book has been adapted from a set of notes that the author has developed to introduce these subjects to upper division and graduate students in a course offered by the Industrial Engineering Department at Stanford University.

I should like to express my appreciation to Profs. W. G. Ireson and E. L. Grant for their encouragement and for giving me the opportunity to develop the course from which this book stems; to the many students whose questions and constructive criticisms were invaluable in the formulation of the manuscript; and to Mrs. Leah Schweizer for her conscientious work in the preparation of many sets of notes and the final manuscript.

R. V. Oakford

CONTENTS

1

WHAT IS DATA PROCESSING?

If an individual's social environment is sufficiently simple, he finds little or no need for written records. The infant, for example, has neither the need for nor the ability to use such devices as date books for recording future appointments or alphabetic indexes for recording names, addresses, and phone numbers. But as his environment becomes more complicated, he finds it desirable, if not essential, to augment his memory and recall facilities with written records. Similarly, it appears that the need for organized collection and dissemination of information increases with the complexity of the political and economic organization of a society.

Whatever the cause-and-effect relationship between social organization and information processing, it is true that a substantial portion of the material and manpower resources of an industrialized society is devoted to the collection, processing, and dissemination of information. If we consider a business enterprise, a governmental agency, or an educational institution to be a system of men, equipment, and materials organized for the purpose of efficiently accomplishing worthwhile objectives, the need for a flow of information throughout the system is intuitive. It is with the design of systems to provide an efficient flow of information throughout an organization that the specialist in data processing is concerned.

In general, data processing will be defined to comprise those activities which change the form or location of facts or data from which conclusions can be inferred. In particular, the data processor is concerned with the logic and the techniques for collection, storage, retrieval, and transformation of data and with the dissemination of information.[1] He is further concerned with the determination of

[1] Data are facts or figures that are known or assumed. Information is knowledge (including data) that has been acquired. No attempt will be made, therefore, to make a fine distinction between data and information; instead, the terms will be used interchangeably.

information requirements of an organization and the design of systems that will satisfy the requirements efficiently.

There are several allied fields which are concerned with similar problems or portions thereof. Specific examples include the communications field within electrical engineering, the field of systems and procedures within business and industrial management, and the field of accounting. The communications engineer may be especially interested in the problems associated with the design and use of electronic equipment for the accurate encoding, transmission, and decoding of information. The accountant may be especially interested in devising a system for estimating accurately the financial status of an organization at given points in time. The systems and procedures specialist may be particularly concerned with the organization of an administrative process. Since, in application, these fields are all concerned with the collection, transformation, and dissemination of information, it is not surprising that the designers of data-processing systems are frequently drawn from them.

1.1 Alphabetic and Numeric Information. Information is conveyed from person to person by combinations of sounds or symbols which have defined meanings of varying degrees of precision. This book will be concerned primarily with transmission of information in the form of symbols and combinations thereof. The familiar basic symbols used in writing the English language are, of course, the alphabetic characters, the numeric characters, the space, and the punctuation marks.

Numbers are of special interest because addition, subtraction, multiplication, and division are well-defined arithmetic operations that constitute a significant portion of business data processing. Moreover, there exist mechanical and electronic devices such as adding machines and computers that can perform these operations more rapidly than people can, and with fewer mistakes.

A number is of itself rarely meaningful without a verbal definition of what it measures. For example, a person analyzing his bank statement is interested in being able to identify properly the figures that indicate deposits, withdrawals, and balances. If, in addition, there are withdrawals for bank charges, he will certainly be interested in identifying not only the magnitude but also the reason for such charges. Such identifying information ultimately must be conveyed verbally.

There is a large portion of business information processing which is essentially verbal, and there are mechanical devices used for printing, reproducing, encoding, transmitting, decoding, and storing verbal information.

This book will be concerned primarily with that portion of business data processing which involves the principles and techniques of manipulating and identifying numeric information. Some attention will be devoted to the mechanical handling of alphabetic information, in so far as it is required to identify numeric information.

1.2 Formal and Informal Data Processing. Within most organizations there are both a formal flow and an informal flow of information. The properly organized formal data-processing system will channel information to various members of the organization on a "need to know" basis. The object is to furnish each person the information he needs in the performance of his delegated duties and to spare him the burden of extraneous information.

The informal data-processing system diverges from formal channels and distributes information on an "interesting to know" as well as a "need to know" basis. Transmission is often oral and frequently occurs during telephone calls or coffee breaks, at lunch hours, and at other semisocial or social times. Since there can be no control over this form of data processing, it will not be considered further.

1.3 Specializations within Data Processing. The activities which comprise data processing have been performed by organizations for hundreds of years. The term data processing was, however, given common currency with the adaptation of electronic digital computers to business problems of accounting, payroll, billing, inventory control, etc. Prior to this, such mechanical aids to computation as adding machines, desk calculators, bookkeeping machines, and punched-card accounting machines were used to speed up accounting calculations and to reduce human errors.

The first electronic digital computers were conceived and designed in the 1940s as a tool for performing calculations required in the solution of scientific problems. After they had been successfully employed for the original purpose, it became apparent that electronic computers could be useful in performing the calculations required in large-scale business accounting. With this in mind, the term *electronic data-processing machine* was applied to computers that were developed for application to commercial data processing.

Within the field of electronic numeric data processing there now exists a commonly accepted differentiation between scientific computation and management data processing. As the terms imply, scientific computation is primarily concerned with the numeric solution of problems arising in scientific research, engineering, etc., while management data processing is primarily concerned with the numeric solution of problems arising in organizational management. However, problems that call for identical numeric solutions may arise in either area.

To some extent, both equipment and personnel are used interchangeably within the two areas. The student who plans to use an electronic computer for either scientific computation or data processing must first learn how to communicate with it.

Within the area of management data processing, it is possible to define three further subdivisions on the basis of the type of equipment used as an aid in calculation. The first subdivision employs manually operated electromechanical devices such as adding machines, desk calculators, and bookkeeping machines. The second employs punched-card accounting equipment. The third employs automatic electronic data-processing equipment. The equipment discussed in this book will be limited to the last two subdivisions, and emphasis will be placed on the last.

1.4 A Data-processing System in Perspective. The basic justification of a data-processing system in an organization is that it will provide for the collection, storage, manipulation, and dissemination of the information required for effective operation. It is assumed that the cost of collecting and disseminating the data can be justified economically.

Most business data are generated by actions of individuals and are, in effect, a historical record of actions. It is reasonable to assume that each reader has performed actions that generated input for the data-processing system of a business organization. Consider in particular that portion of the system involved in the processing of charge sales records.

Normally both the customer and the salesman are involved in the preparation of the charge ticket. This initial record should identify the customer, the amount of money charged, the items purchased, and the date of the transaction. In addition, it may identify the person making the sale, the location of the sale, and other items that are of interest to the organization.

The amount of the charge will eventually be posted to the accounts receivable record maintained for this customer by the company and will appear on the statement of charges and credits that is mailed periodically to the customer.

In addition, the sales slip may be a basis for entry to the sales journal, to an inventory record, or to a salesman's commission record; and it may even serve as a shipping order. Its usefulness will depend to a great extent upon the judgment used in the design of the form and upon the accuracy of the information initially recorded.

A foundation will be laid in the next three chapters upon which the student can develop a simple system for computer processing of sales tickets. To do this, it will be necessary to learn to communicate with a computer. In Chap. 2 we shall consider the language of computers; in Chap. 3, the organization of a computer; and in Chap. 4, the writing of instructions for a computer.

Chapter 5 deals with the location and correction of errors in a set of instructions for a computer and with the manual aspects of operating a computer. Chapter 6 has to do with auxiliary equipment that may be encountered in a data-processing system. Chapter 7 treats the techniques that are available for reducing the manual effort required for the development of a computer program.

The specific information required for effective communication varies from computer to computer. This book will refer specifically to the operation of the IBM 650. Emphasis will be placed on its use in data processing. This is accomplished by the choice of examples, since the basic rules of communication are dictated by the construction of the computer rather than by the problem to be solved.

REFERENCE

Chapin, Ned: "An Introduction to Automatic Computers," D. Van Nostrand Company, Inc., Princeton, N.J., 1955.

PROBLEMS

1.1. Outline a system for manually processing the sales records of your local barber shop.

1.2. Outline a system for manually processing the credit-card sales of a major oil company.

1.3. Outline a system for manually collecting and storing the information required to prepare periodic grade reports and transcripts for the students in your college.

1.4. Discuss the relative importance of mechanizing the above systems.

2

CODING OF ALPHABETIC AND NUMERIC CHARACTERS

In order to communicate effectively with a given computer, we should learn the language of that computer. This is not absolutely essential, however, because mechanisms are available to effect translation between our language and that of a given computer. The reader who is anxious to get on with the study of the operation of the computer may wish to proceed directly to Chap. 3 and return to this chapter later.

Since the computer uses a language that is essentially numerical, this chapter will be devoted to a study of number systems and their use in the coding of alphabetic and numeric characters. First let us review some of the characteristics of our own language and its use in human communication.

Groups of human beings have developed the ability to communicate (make common) thoughts and feelings by combinations of vocal sounds—words—to which meanings have been commonly attributed. The collection of sounds common to a particular nation, tribe, or other group comprises the spoken language of that group. An alphabet is an ordered set of characters or symbols used in the written language.

An equivalence between the spoken and written language is developed if each spoken word has a counterpart represented by a combination of alphabetic characters and if the same meaning is commonly attributed to the spoken word and its written counterpart. In a sense, then, the written words form a set of symbols or a code for the spoken words.

The English language contains many ambiguities. A given combination of sounds may be equivalent to two or more combinations of alphabetic characters, e.g., to, too, two. Further ambiguities are

6

introduced by dialects, mispronunciation, and other deviations from a theoretical standard of speech and by personal idiosyncrasies of script. The dictionary furnishes a key to the code and a standard of pronunciation. It is an alphabetically ordered list of the words in a language together with the accepted meanings and pronunciations of each.

In the process of learning to speak, read, and write a language, the individual stores in his memory the knowledge required to associate a sound combination with a letter combination and a "working knowledge" of the accepted meaning or variety of meanings of words. "Habit patterns" stimulate the physical actions involved in forming the sound combinations in speech or in forming the letter combinations in writing. With practice and use, the normal individual can become adept in the communication (transmission and reception) of ideas with the spoken and written language. He learns to convert or translate from oral to written language and vice versa. In the process his memory is used for both short-term and long-term storage of information (knowledge).

Information may be said to be communicated with complete accuracy from one individual to another if and only if the sounds or symbols evoke in the mind of the recipient ideas that are identical to those that the sender is attempting to describe. Consequently, accurate communication of information is probably rarely attained. For practical purposes, such communication is considered to be sufficiently accurate if the ideas conveyed to the recipient are consistent with those of the sender.

Although the human language is replete with ambiguities, communication among human beings is satisfactorily accomplished. This success is attributable not so much to the logical organization of our language but rather more to its redundancy and to the ability of the user to reason and consequent ability to formulate questions that will lead to the resolution of ambiguities and uncertainties in communication.

A computer does not have the power to reason. We shall find, therefore, that the computer language is both limited and precise. Correspondingly, the components of our number systems are limited and precise, and the arithmetic operations defined thereon are logical and precise, a notable exception being division by zero. It should not be surprising, therefore, that the computer language can be represented in numeric form. We shall find that both our alphabetic characters and our numeric characters are represented as numbers in computer language.

NUMBER SYSTEMS

2.1   Decimal Integers.   Most of us have had little reason to become familiar with any number system other than the decimal system, although we may have some degree of familiarity with the Roman numeral system.   The latter is cumbersome and is not used widely. In particular it is ill suited for the arithmetic operations of addition, subtraction, multiplication, and division, whereas the decimal system is amenable to such manipulations.

There are other number systems that are amenable to arithmetic manipulation.   Of these, we shall find that the binary system is frequently used in the representation of characters included in computer language.   Before introducing a new number system, let us review briefly the basis of the decimal system.

The 10 basic numerals used in writing decimal numbers are the Arabic numerals 0, 1, 2, 3, 4, 5, 6, 7, 8, 9.   The base or radix of the system is equal to the number of basic numerals.   Any integer larger than 9 is represented by some combination of the basic numerals. The rule for determining the combination can be expressed algebraically by the equation

$$N = a_n(10^n) + a_{n-1}(10^{n-1}) + \cdots + a_2(10^2) + a_1(10) + a_0 \quad (2.1)$$

where N is the decimal integer, each coefficient a_i is a basic numeral, and $n + 1$ is not less than the number of digit positions in the integer.

This representation has a direct relationship to the way a number is written, displayed in a cash register, or displayed in the register of a desk calculator.   The right-hand coefficient a_0 corresponds to the units position, the next coefficient a_1 corresponds to the tens position, etc. For example,

$$0352 = 0(10^3) + 3(10^2) + 5(10) + 2 = 300 + 50 + 2 \quad (2.1a)$$

The above representation of decimal integers may appear needlessly cumbersome, but familiarity therewith will aid in the following study of other number systems.

2.2   Binary Integers.   The binary number system has just two basic numerals, normally represented by 0 and 1.   This system is of particular interest, because it is directly analogous to the two-positional (on-off, or flip-flop) electronic elements that constitute a major segment of computer circuitry.[1]

---

[1] The relationship between the binary number system and computer circuitry is developed in Refs. 3 and 4.

The arithmetic operations are the same for binary as for decimal numbers, but the addition and multiplication tables are different. They are very short, however, and can be readily mastered.

The addition table is simply

$$0 + 0 = 0 \qquad 0 + 1 = 1 \qquad 1 + 1 = 10$$

The multiplication table is

$$0 \times 0 = 0 \qquad 0 \times 1 = 0 \qquad 1 \times 1 = 1$$

Given these tables, we may perform the arithmetic operations by strict analogy to the decimal system. The arithmetic operations of addition, subtraction, multiplication, and division are illustrated in the following examples, which may be checked by reference to the addition and multiplication tables above.

	Decimal	Binary	Decimal	Binary
1. Addition	2 +3 5	10 +11 101	6 +7 13	110 +111 1101
2. Subtraction	5 −3 2	101 −11 10	13 −7 6	1101 −111 110
3. Multiplication	5 ×3 15	101 ×11 101 101 1111	6 ×7 42	110 ×111 110 110 110 101010
4. Division	$3\overline{)9}$ 3	$11\overline{)1001}$ 11 11 11 11 0	$9\overline{)45}$ 5	$1001\overline{)101101}$ 101 1001 1001 1001 0

Even after checking the above manipulations against the addition and multiplication tables to ensure that they are formally correct, we are apt to be left with a natural inclination to refer to the decimal equivalents thereof to gain a feel for the magnitudes expressed and confidence in the correctness of the manipulations.

2.3 Binary-to-Decimal Transformation. A binary number can be converted to its decimal equivalent by considering the place value of each of the digits used to represent the number:

Binary	*Decimal*
1	$1 = 2^0$
$1 + 1 = 10$	$1 + 1 = 2 = 2^1$
$10 \times 10 = 100$	$2 \times 2 = 4 = 2^2$
$10 \times 100 = 1000$	$2 \times 4 = 8 = 2^3$

Hence, multiplication of a binary number by binary 10 has the effect of multiplying its decimal equivalent by 2. Thus the position values of the digits in a binary number are represented in the decimal system by powers of 2.

It is convenient to think of a binary number as though it were written in a register (as on a desk calculator) with the decimal-equivalent position value of each digit written above it.

Decimal-equivalent position value........	2^3	2^2	2	1
Binary number........................	1	1	1	1

If each digit position is multiplied by its weight and the resulting products are summed, the decimal equivalent is generated:

$$(1 \times 2^3) + (1 \times 2^2) + (1 \times 2) + 1 = 15$$

Note that the arithmetic was performed in the decimal system. Had it been done in the binary system, the binary number would have been simply regenerated:

$$(1 \times 1000) + (1 \times 100) + (1 \times 10) + 1 = 1111$$

The transformation of a binary integer to its equivalent decimal integer can be represented by an expression analogous to Eq. (2.1):

$$N = a_n(2^n) + \cdots + a_2(2^2) + a_1(2) + a_0 \qquad (2.2)$$

where N is a decimal number and each coefficient $(a_n, \ldots, a_2, a_1, a_0)$ is either 0 or 1, i.e., one of the basic digits. The indicated arithmetic operations are performed in the decimal system.

The relationship (2.2) can be alternatively represented in the form of a register in which the decimal-equivalent position value of a digit is placed directly above the digit, e.g.,

Decimal-equivalent position value.........	2^3	2^2	2	1
Digits....................	a_3	a_2	a_1	a_0
$N =$	$8a_3 +$	$4a_2 +$	$2a_1 +$	a_0

Thus we have a basis for converting any binary number to its decimal equivalent.

2.4 Decimal-to-Binary Transformation. Since the transformation of a decimal integer to its binary equivalent is the inverse of the binary-to-decimal conversion described above, it could reasonably be expected to involve successive divisions by 2. The algorithm (computing procedure) for the conversion of a decimal 13 to a binary 1101 is illustrated in Table 2.1.

In step 0, the decimal number 13 is divided by 2, the base of the binary system. The remainder 1 is equal to a_0. In step 1, the quotient from the previous division (6) is divided by 2. The remainder 0 is equal to a_1. The process is repeated until a quotient of 0 is obtained.

Table 2.1

Step	Dividend	Divisor	Quotient	Remainder	a_i
0	13	2	6	1	a_0
1	6	2	3	0	a_1
2	3	2	1	1	a_2
3	1	2	0	1	a_3

Since further divisions would generate only leading zeros, the process is stopped.

The general validity of this transformation is obvious when it is recalled that each a_i in Eq. (2.2) is multiplied by a power of 2. For example, the binary equivalent of a decimal integer N is represented by the expression

$$N = a_3(2^3) + a_2(2^2) + a_1(2) + a_0$$

The problem now is to find the value of each a_i (a_3, a_2, a_1, a_0).

	Division	Quotient	Remainder
$N = [a_3(2^2) + a_2(2) + a_1]2 + a_0 = 2q_1 + a_0$	$N/2$	q_1	a_0
$q_1 = [a_3(2) + a_2]2 + a_1 = 2q_2 + a_1$	$q_1/2$	q_2	a_1
$q_2 = a_3(2) + a_2 = 2q_3 + a_2$	$q_2/2$	q_3	a_2
$q_3 = 0(2) + a_3 = 0 + a_3$	$q_3/2$	q_4	a_3

The decimal equivalent of a binary number less than 1 can be represented by the expression

$$D = \frac{a_{-1}}{2} + \frac{a_{-2}}{2^2} + \cdots + \frac{a_{-m}}{2^m} \qquad (2.3)$$

where D is a decimal fraction, each a_i is 0 or 1, and a_{-1} is the first posi-

tion to the right of the binary point.   For example, the decimal equivalent of the binary number 0.101 is

$$D = \tfrac{1}{2} + \tfrac{0}{4} + \tfrac{1}{8} = .500 + .000 + .125 = .625$$

The binary equivalent of a decimal fraction can be generated by a
series of successive multiplications by 2, as follows:

$$2D = a_{-1} + p_1 = a_{-1} + \frac{a_{-2}}{2} + \cdots + \frac{a_{-m}}{2^{m-1}}$$

$$2p_1 = a_{-2} + p_2 = a_{-2} + \frac{a_{-3}}{2} + \cdots + \frac{a_{-m}}{2^{m-2}}$$

.

.

.

Since each a_i is either 0 or 1, it always appears in the units position
of the product.   For example, decimal .5625 is shown to be arithmetically equivalent to binary .1001:

$$
\begin{array}{lll}
2 \times .5625 = 1.125 & a_{-1} = 1 \quad \text{and} & p_1 = .125 \\
2 \times .125 = 0.250 & a_{-2} = 0 \quad \text{and} & p_2 = .250 \\
2 \times .250 = 0.500 & a_{-3} = 0 \quad \text{and} & p_3 = .500 \\
2 \times .500 = 1.000 & a_{-4} = 1 \quad \text{and} & p_4 = 0
\end{array}
$$

Continuation of the process would only generate zeros.

There is a one-to-one relationship between the decimal integers and
the binary integers.   For each decimal integer there is a corresponding
binary integer.   But there is not a one-to-one relationship between
the decimal fractions and the binary fractions.

It can be shown by induction, and the following examples illustrate
that there is an arithmetically exact decimal-fraction equivalent for
each binary fraction (e.g., .1, .01, .001, . . .), provided we are allowed
a sufficient number of decimal places:

$$
\begin{array}{ll}
\tfrac{1}{2} = .5 & \tfrac{1}{16} = .0625 \\
\tfrac{1}{4} = .25 & \tfrac{1}{32} = .03125 \\
\tfrac{1}{8} = .125 & \tfrac{1}{64} = .015625
\end{array}
$$

There are, however, many decimal fractions that have no arithmetically exact binary representation regardless of the number of binary
places permitted.

It is well known that there are many rational fractions that have
no arithmetically exact decimal-fraction representation, e.g., $\tfrac{1}{7} \cong$
.142857142857 . . . .   Similarly, the decimal fraction .3 has no arith-

metically exact binary equivalent, e.g., decimal $.3 \cong .010011001100$
. . . . In each case the difference between the original value and
that of its alternative representation becomes smaller and smaller
as the number of digit positions is increased in the alternative
representation.

Thus, we may say that as the number of digit positions is increased,
the precision of representation of an inaccurate transformation is
increased; i.e., the smaller the difference between the original value
and its transformation, the greater the precision of representation of
the transformation.

So long as we are talking about arithmetic equivalence of or difference between two values, no problems attend increased precision of
representation. However, there are practical considerations that
attend the precision of representation. These include rounding or
truncation errors induced when there is a limit on the permissible
number of digit positions. The subject of rounding and truncation
errors will be deferred until Sec. 3.23. At the moment we shall
address ourselves to the question of inferences that are commonly
based upon the precision of representation.

Consider the arithmetic identity, decimal $.50 =$ binary $.10$. While
the arithmetic identity of the two values is unquestioned, common
practice assigns a different precision to the two representations. Let
us assume that these two values are alternative representations of a
measurement of a value V and that the precision of the measuring
device is sufficient to justify either representation. Then the range of
possible values of V may be inferred from the precision of representation, provided that it is known whether the value shown was arrived
at by truncation or by rounding.

First consider the case of truncation. If decimal $.50$ represents a
truncation of the decimal value V, then $.50000 \ldots \leq V \leq .50999$
. . . , or $V = .50^{+.01}_{-0}$. Thus, the precision of representation of the
measurement of V is $.01$. In general, if the measurement of the value
V is justifiably represented as a decimal number D that has been
truncated to d decimal places, it follows that $D \leq V < D + 10^{-d}$.

Now consider the case where binary $.10$ represents a truncation of
the binary representation of V to two binary places; then binary
$.1000 \ldots \leq V \leq$ binary $.10111 \ldots$, or $V =$ binary $.10^{+.01}_{-0}$; or an
equivalent decimal representation is $.50000 \ldots \leq V < .75000 \ldots$.
Hence the precision indicated by two binary places is somewhat less
than the precision indicated by two decimal places. It will be impos-
sible to attain identical precision for the alternative representations of
decimal and binary fractions, but the precision indicated by d decimal

places and $\dfrac{d}{\log 2} = \dfrac{d}{.3}$ binary places is comparable; e.g., decimal .01 and binary .000001 indicate comparable precision.

Next consider the case of rounding. If a decimal number V is to be rounded to d decimal places, then $V + (5 \cdot 10^{-(d+1)})$ is truncated to d decimal places. Thus, if decimal .50 represents V after rounding, then $.49500 \ldots \leq V \leq .50499 \ldots$, or $V = .50 \pm .005$ and the precision of representation is decimal .01. If binary .10 represents V after rounding, then binary $.011000 \ldots \leq V \leq$ binary $.100111 \ldots$, or $V = $ binary $.10 \pm .001$ and the precision of representation is binary .01.

Thus, truncation and rounding lead to comparable precision of representation, but this is not to be construed as meaning that they are equally desirable for purposes of numeric computation.

The foregoing discussion is intended to furnish a basis for determining a justifiable precision in the representation of decimal fractions by binary equivalents. This should not be confused with the problem of determining the number of decimal places that must be carried in arithmetic operations in order to avoid loss of accuracy. The subject of rounding errors will be discussed in Sec. 3.23.

2.5 The Base-b Number System. The procedure outlined for conversion between the decimal and binary systems can be generalized. If 2 is replaced by b, then Eqs. (2.2) and (2.3) become

$$N = a_n(b^n) + \cdots + a_2(b^2) + a_1(b) + a_0 \tag{2.4}$$
$$D = a_{-1}(b^{-1}) + a_{-2}(b^{-2}) + \cdots + a_{-m}(b^{-m}) \tag{2.5}$$

where N is a decimal integer, D is a decimal fraction, b is the base of the number system, a_i is less than b, and the basic numerals are 0, 1, 2, $\ldots$, $b - 1$.

It follows immediately that the computing procedures for conversion between the decimal and base-b systems are analogous to those outlined for the conversions between the decimal and binary systems.

To convert a decimal integer N to its equivalent base-b integer:

1. Divide N by b. The remainder equals a_0.
2. Divide the quotient from step 1 by b. The remainder equals a_1.
3. Divide the quotient from step 2 by b. The remainder equals a_2.

$$\cdot$$
$$\cdot$$
$$\cdot$$

The division is repeated until a zero quotient is obtained.

To convert a decimal fraction D to its equivalent base-b fraction, perform the following sequence of operations:

1. $bD = a_{-1} + p_1$
2. $bp_1 = a_{-2} + p_2$

.
.
.

The process is repeated until sufficient accuracy of representation is obtained. Each a_i is an integer; therefore it appears in the units position of the product.

Conversion of a base-b number to its decimal equivalent is accomplished by appropriate substitution in formulas (2.4) and (2.5). When the above conversions between the decimal system and a base-b system are performed, all arithmetic is done in the decimal system.

It is not necessary to restrict Eqs. (2.4) and (2.5) to conversions between the decimal system and a base-b system. They apply equally well for conversions between arbitrarily chosen pairs of number systems. For example, the formulas could be used for direct conversion between numbers from the base-5 and the base-2 number systems by performing the arithmetic operations in the base-5 system.

2.6 The Base-5 Number System. The base-5 or quinary number system is of particular interest, because it is one used in the 650. The basic numerals are 0, 1, 2, 3, and 4.

The addition table for the quinary number system is illustrated in Table 2.2. An element in the table is the quinary sum of the numerals that identify the row and column in which the element is located.

Table 2.2 Addition Table for Quinary Numbers

Addend	Augend				
	0	1	2	3	4
0	0	1	2	3	4
1	1	2	3	4	10
2	2	3	4	10	11
3	3	4	10	11	12
4	4	10	11	12	13

The multiplication table for the quinary number system is illustrated in Table 2.3. An element of the table is the quinary product of the numerals that identify the row and column in which the element is located.

It should be noted that the elements in each table are shown as quinary numbers. The correctness of an element can be verified by converting it to its decimal equivalent, using the general formula (2.4) with b equal to 5.

Fortunately, we shall not be required to do arithmetic in the base-5 number system. Learning the addition and multiplication tables in this system would be somewhat more formidable than learning the binary tables. In fact, the computer does not do arithmetic in the base-5 system, but it is used as a basis for displaying decimal numbers as illustrated in Fig. 2.4.

Table 2.3   Multiplication Table for Quinary Numbers

Multiplier	Multiplicand				
	0	1	2	3	4
0	0	0	0	0	0
1	0	1	2	3	4
2	0	2	4	11	13
3	0	3	11	14	22
4	0	4	13	22	31

2.7   The Octal Number System.   The basic octal digits are 0, 1, 2, 3, 4, 5, 6, and 7. The relationship between the octal digits and the three-digit binary integers is frequently useful for coding purposes. The development of this relationship is left as an exercise for the reader (see Probs. 2.1 and 2.2).

CODING OF INFORMATION FOR MECHANICAL TRANSMISSION

The use of alphabetic and numeric characters as a system for coding verbal information is so common to most of us that the characters are regarded as part of the language rather than a basis for coding the spoken language. The written or printed word furnishes an effective means of storing information for transportation to a recipient who may be removed in either time or location from the sender. The telephone and the radio furnish rapid means of transmitting the spoken word over great distances.

Other useful communications systems are incapable of directly transmitting either the spoken or the written word, so the alphabetic characters, numerals, and punctuation marks must be coded in symbols that are adaptable to the transmission system.

An example is the semaphore code, which defines the alphabetic characters and the space by the relative positions in which two flags are held by a signalman. The eight permissible positions of a flag are indicated in Fig. 2.1. The key to the flag-position code is shown in Table 2.4. It is assumed that positions 1 through 3 are to the right of the signalman when he is facing the reader. Since the two flags are identical, the combination 0 and 2 may be indistinguishable from 2 and 0. Similarly, at long range, 0 and 2 is indistinguishable from 2 and 2. Consequently, only 29 combinations are usable, and the key matrix is symmetric, i.e., condition 43 is the same as 34. It is of interest that the above discussion has translated the semaphore code to a numeric code.

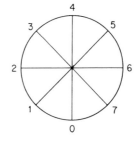

FIG. 2.1. Semaphore flag positions.

The international Morse code, used in the transmission of information by radio or by blinker lights, defines the alphabetic and numeric characters and certain punctuation marks in terms of sequences of dots, dashes, and intervals (see Table 2.5). Formally, the dot is defined to be a pulse of sound (or light) lasting approximately $\frac{1}{24}$ second. The dash is a pulse lasting three times as long as the dot. The interval between letters is equal to one dash, while that between words is twice one dash.

Table 2.4 Key to Semaphore Code

Flag-1 position	Flag-2 position							
	0	1	2	3	4	5	6	7
0		A	B	C	D	E	F	G
1	A		H	I	K	L	M	N
2	B	H		O	P	Q	R	S
3	C	I	O		T	U	Y	
4	D	K	P	T			J	V
5	E	L	Q	U			W	X
6	F	M	R	Y	J	W		Z
7	G	N	S		V	X	Z	

The precision indicated by the definitions can be approximated by experienced operators, but fairly rough approximations are understandable by a person experienced in receiving Morse code.

Further mechanization of the transmission and reception of information is achieved by the teletype system. The message is typed on a teletypewriter, a machine that prints the information on a sheet of paper and simultaneously punches the appropriate code for each letter in a paper tape, as illustrated in Fig. 2.2.* The punched paper tape actuates a transmitter that emits electric impulses. At the

Table 2.5 Excerpt from the International Morse Code

Character	Morse code
A	. —
B	— . . .
C	— . — .
D	— . .
E	.
1	. — — — —
2	. . — — —

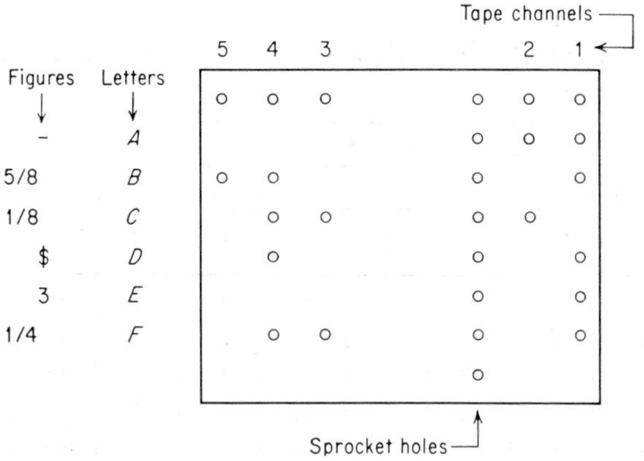

receiving end, the teletypewriter decodes the electric impulses and automatically types the message on a sheet of paper. Consequently, two people with no knowledge of the code system can carry out an exchange of information while the intervening translation from

Tape channels

Figures	Letters	5	4	3	2	1
		o	o	o	o	o
–	A				o	o
5/8	B	o	o			o
1/8	C		o	o	o	
$	D		o			o
3	E					o
1/4	F		o	o		o

Sprocket holes

Fig. 2.2. Five-channel teletype (Baudot) code.

printed language to machine language and back is performed almost simultaneously by machines.

The Morse code is not adaptable for teletypewriter control because the time required for transmission of a character varies with the number of dots and dashes used to represent a given character.

* The art of printing telegraphy dates back to the inventions of Hughes and Baudot in 1874.

Simpler mechanisms are obtainable if each character is represented by a code that can be transmitted in a uniform time interval. Each sprocket hole shown in Fig. 2.2 is associated with the time interval required for transmission of the code for a single character. This time interval is in turn divided into five equal successive intervals, corresponding to the tape channels. A punch in a channel will allow current to flow during the associated time interval. The absence of a punch will prevent the flow of current.

The equivalence between this five-channel "on-off" code and a five-digit binary code is apparent if the absence of current is represented by a 0 and the presence of current is represented by a 1. There are 32 possible five-digit binary numbers. The number of possible characters on the teletypewriter is almost doubled by reserving one of the 32 numbers for a "figures" shift code. Referring to Fig. 2.2, a "figures" code must be preceded by a "figures" shift code.

2.8   Coding of Information for Machine Storage and Retrieval. The written or printed language is the basic method for storing information. Filing and indexing systems have been developed to facilitate the retrieval of information stored in printed form. In such systems the sorting, indexing, filing, and retrieval of documents is performed manually.

There are certain types of information, however, that may be adapted economically to mechanical or electronic storage and retrieval systems. The social security records maintained by the United States government undoubtedly constitute the largest electronic file. Large corporations have found it practical to use electronic and electromechanical systems for filing accounting data. There is, therefore, a very large amount of information stored in files that depend upon electronic and electromechanical systems for retrieval.

The information input to such a file must be in machine language on material of a form that the machine is designed to handle. The term *machine language* is used to indicate a coding system that can cause the machine to perform certain predetermined functions. In this sense, the machine language furnishes a basis for communication. The commonly used input media are punched cards, punched paper tapes, and magnetic tapes. Examples of commonly used coding systems are discussed below.

2.9   The IBM Punched-card Code.[1]   The IBM punched-card code (Fig. 2.3) provides for the representation of alphabetic characters,

---

[1] The code is more properly referred to as the Hollerith code. In the decade 1880 to 1890, Dr. Herman Hollerith, while employed by the U.S. Census Bureau, developed a punched-card system for tabulating census data. The IBM code is based on the code used in that system.

decimal numerals, and some special characters by the relative positions of punches in a card. (The term *alphanumeric* is often used to refer to character groups that contain both alphabetic and numeric characters, e.g., 1st.)

The card is $3\frac{1}{4}$ by $7\frac{3}{8}$ inches. It has 80 columns, numbered from left to right at the bottom of the card. Each column can be used to identify uniquely any character provided for by the code. Hence each card can contain 80 characters of information.

The card is divided into 12 horizontal rows. The two top rows of the standard IBM card (Fig. 2.3) are without printing. The remaining rows are identified by the numbers 0, 1, 2, . . . , 9 printed in each

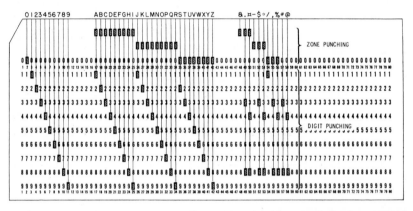

Fɪɢ. 2.3. IBM card, and character coding. (*Reprinted by permission from "IBM Reference Manual—Functional Wiring Principles," A24-1007-0, copyright 1956 in original notice by International Business Machines Corporation.*)

column. It is common practice to refer to the rows in terms of punches. A punch in the top row is referred to as a 12 punch. One in the next row is called an 11 punch. The remaining punches correspond to the digits printed in the columns.

The code identifies a character with a specific combination of punches. The characters provided for by the code are shown at the top of Fig. 2.3. The combination of punches that uniquely identifies each character is shown in the column below.

It will be noted that the alphabetic characters are defined by a zone punch (12, 11, or 0) and a digit punch (1 through 9). The numerals are defined by a digit punch (0 through 9). The 0 punch is used as both a zone and a digit punch, but there is no ambiguity in the code.

As presented above, the punched-card code would be interpreted on the basis of the relative location of bits of information. A bit is defined to be the smallest identifiable unit in a coding system. In this case, a single punch is a bit. It will be seen in Chap. 6 that a card-reading machine can interpret the code on the basis of the relative time at which electric impulses are emitted. The punch in a column provides a path for the pulse emission, and the relative location provides for the time differential.

Not all IBM machines are designed to interpret all the characters defined in Fig. 2.3; consequently, communication among machines within a system may be limited.

2.10 The IBM 650 Code for Displaying Decimal Digits. The punched card is the basic input medium for the 650. As the card is read by the card-reading unit, the punched-card code for a decimal digit is translated to a code that represents the equivalent quinary (base-5) integer in terms of weighted binary bits.

The coding system is illustrated in Table 2.6. The 10 decimal digits and their quinary equivalents appear in columns 1 and 2. The corresponding combinations of binary bits, the codes for the decimal digits, are shown in the last column of the table. The weight associated with each bit position is shown at the top of the column containing the bit. This code is also referred to as a biquinary code because the fives position of the quinary code assumes one of only two values while the units position assumes one of five values.

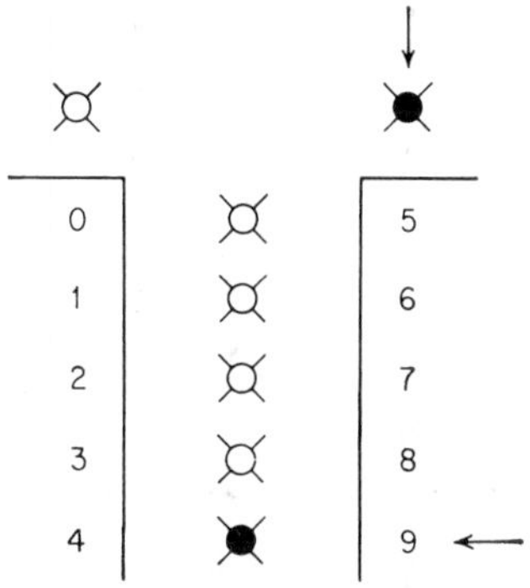

FIG. 2.4. Use of lights to display the 650 coding of decimal digits.

The decimal equivalent of the weighted binary code is calculated as the sum of the products obtained by multiplying each bit value by its associated weight. For example, the sum of the products for the last row in the table is $(1 \times 5) + (1 \times 4) = 9$.

Figure 2.4 illustrates the use of seven lights to identify the decimal number displayed. If exactly one of the two columns of figures is selected because the light above it is on and if exactly one of the five rows of figures is selected because the light in that row is on, the indicated decimal digit is shown at the intersection of the selected row and column. It can be seen that a number is uniquely identified (i.e., a code is valid) if and only if one column indicator light and one row indicator light are on.

Similarly, a simple arithmetic check may be used to determine whether an arbitrary combination of seven binary bits is one of the

10 combinations defined in Table 2.6.   In each of these combinations, the sum of the two left-most bits is 1 and the sum of the five right-most bits is 1.   Of the 128 possible combinations of seven binary bits, only the 10 shown in the table satisfy both of these sum checks.   If either of the two sum checks is not satisfied, the code is invalid because it does not uniquely define one of the 10 specified decimal digits.   A computer can perform the sum checks automatically and verify the validity of a code each time it is used.

Table 2.6   IBM 650 Code for Displaying the Decimal Digits

Decimal digit	Quinary integer	Weighted binary code 05 01234
0	00	10 10000
1	01	10 01000
2	02	10 00100
3	03	10 00010
4	04	10 00001
5	10	01 10000
6	11	01 01000
7	12	01 00100
8	13	01 00010
9	14	01 00001

This code is said to be single-error detecting because a single change in a valid code will result in an invalid code.   A single error occurs if just one binary bit is changed—from 0 to 1, or vice versa.   (Double or triple errors will be detected unless they result in a valid code.) The code is not single-error correcting, because it does not contain sufficient information to identify the bit in which a single error occurs. Such codes are possible, and their formulation will be discussed later in the chapter.

2.11   The IBM 650 Code for Alphanumeric Characters.   The 650 coding described thus far provides only for the representation of the decimal digits.   Alphanumeric characters are represented by the two-digit decimal coding system shown in Table 2.7.   It should be noted that the units position of this code is identical with the digit punch in the punched-card code and that the tens position of this code is a translation of the zone punch.   The 12 punch is translated to a 6, the 11 punch to a 7, etc.

A two-digit equivalent of each decimal digit is provided for uniformity in the event an alphanumeric term is encountered.   For example, the term N3PB would be translated as 75 93 77 62.

A blank in an alphanumeric term is represented by 00.

2.12   The IBM 705 Magnetic-tape Code.   The IBM 705 and the 650 use the same coding system for storing alphanumeric characters on magnetic tape.   Each character is represented by a combination of seven binary bits as illustrated in Table 2.8.

Table 2.7   IBM 650 Code for Alphanumeric Characters

Units position	Tens position			
	6	7	8	9
0				0
1	A	J		1
2	B	K	S	2
3	C	L	T	3
4	D	M	U	4
5	E	N	V	5
6	F	O	W	6
7	G	P	X	7
8	H	Q	Y	8
9	I	R	Z	9

If we visualize length and width of the tape to correspond to length and width of the table, the seven bits representing a single character are located in channels or lanes across the width of the tape.   The codes for successive characters are located along the length of the tape.

A one (1) in the code can be thought of as indicating the presence of a magnetic spot in the corresponding tape channel.   The absence of a 1 (equivalent to binary 0) is equivalent to the absence of a magnetic spot in the corresponding channel.

For each character, the sum of the seven bits comprising its code is always even.   This condition is sufficient to make the code single-error detecting.   The check bit is included in the code to satisfy this condition.

The remaining six information bits furnish a direct correspondence to the punched-card character coding.   With the exception of zero (0), the weighted sum of the four digit bits is equal to the sum of the digit punches in the card code.   The 0 is coded with a weighted sum of 10 so it can be distinguished from a blank.

The two zone bits are sufficient to distinguish the four zone-punch conditions: no zone punch, a 12 punch, an 11 punch, and a 0 punch.

2.13   The Hamming Code: [1] **Single-error Detecting.**   It has been noted that the seven-bit binary coding systems defined for the 650

---

[1] For a complete discussion, refer to R. W. Hamming, Error Detecting and Error Correcting Codes, *Bell System Technical Journal*, vol. 29, pp. 147–160, 1950.

Table 2.8   IBM 705 Magnetic-tape Character Coding

| Character | Digit bits | | | | Zone bits | | Check bit |
| | Bit weights | | | | | | |
	1	2	4	8	A	B	C
0		1		1			
1	1						1
2		1					1
3	1	1					
4			1				1
5	1		1				
6		1	1				
7	1	1	1				1
8				1			1
9	1			1			
A	1				1	1	1
B		1			1	1	1
C	1	1			1	1	
D			1		1	1	1
E	1		1		1	1	
F		1	1		1	1	
G	1	1	1		1	1	1
H				1	1	1	1
I	1			1	1	1	
J	1					1	
K		1				1	
L	1	1				1	1
M			1			1	
N	1		1			1	1
O		1	1			1	1
P	1	1	1			1	
Q				1		1	
R	1			1		1	1
S		1			1		
T	1	1			1		1
U			1		1		
V	1		1		1		1
W		1	1		1		1
X	1	1	1		1		
Y				1	1		
Z	1			1	1		1
&					1	1	1
.	1	1		1	1	1	1
¤			1	1	1	1	
-						1	1
$	1	1		1		1	
*			1	1		1	1
/	1				1		
,	1	1		1	1		
%			1	1	1		1
#	1	1		1	1		1
@			1	1			

(Table 2.6) and for magnetic tape (Table 2.8) are both single-error detecting. The method of checking the validity of a code is different; but, in each case, a single error results in an invalid combination of bits, i.e., a combination not defined in the code. This section will be devoted to a discussion of the principle by which single-error detecting codes are formulated.

The term *message* will be used to refer to the code for a single character, and the term *code* will be used to refer to the set of messages for a specified set of characters. If a set of binary integers (e.g., 000, 001, 010, . . . , 111) are used as messages in the code for a set of characters, then each message will differ from each other message in at least one position and each character will be uniquely identified. However, if a single error occurs in transmission of a message, it is likely that error will convert that message to another message in the code.

For example, the binary integers 00, 01, 10, and 11 can be used to code four characters. A single error occurs when the value of a single bit is changed, i.e., a single 0 to a 1 or vice versa. Thus, a single error in any message of such a code will result in another acceptable message. This situation can be shown graphically by representing the messages as points in the xy plane. The four points in the plane that are permissible as messages correspond to the four vertices of the unit square, and a single error corresponds to a move from one permissible point to another.

If the rules for devising the code are modified so that it is required that each message shall differ from each other message in at least two positions, then it will be possible to detect the occurrence of a single error. In terms of points in the two-dimensional plane, the added restriction requires that the messages be at diagonal vertices of the square, i.e., the permissible messages are either 00 and 11 or 01 and 10, but not all four. A single error in a message in this code will result in an undefined message or, in terms of the example, will specify an unpermitted location. Thus, such a code is said to be single-error detecting because the occurrence of a single error in the transmission (or, in fact, the origination) of a message from this code can be detected.

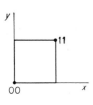

Such a code is said to be redundant because only two messages are defined, whereas there is sufficient information to code four messages. The redundancy is the price paid for single-error checking, and it yields a return only when a single error occurs.

It is interesting to note that in one set of permissible messages (00 and 11) the sum of the bits in each message is even and that in the other set (01 and 10) the sum of the bits in each message is odd. It turns out that this is in fact a clue to the rule for converting a code in which each message is unique to a single-error detecting code. The number of bit positions required to define unique binary messages for N characters is, of course, the smallest integer K such that $2^K \geq N$. If one more bit is added to each message in such a way that the sum of the bits in each message is odd, then each message will differ from every other message in at least two bit positions and the code will be single-error detecting. The added bit is commonly referred to as a check bit or, alternatively, as a parity bit.

To prove the foregoing statement, let us consider any pair of messages satisfying the following conditions:

1. Each message has $K + 1$ bits.
2. The messages are unique.
3. The sum of the bits in each message is odd.

Assume that two messages, each containing $K + 1$ bits, differ in only one bit position. But this leads to a contradiction of condition 3, because if the sum of the bits in one message is odd, then the sum of the bits in the other message must be even if they differ in only one bit position.

If the two messages are unique, they must differ in at least one bit position; and since they cannot differ in just one bit position, they must differ in at least two.

Thus, a code in which all messages satisfy the above conditions is single-error detecting. It is not true, however, that a code must satisfy these conditions to be single-error detecting. For example, we could change the word *odd* in condition 3 to read *even*, or we could eliminate condition 3 and modify condition 2 to be read: Each pair of messages differs in at least two digit positions. However, the above set of conditions is desirable for the following reasons:

1. The single-error detecting code will be efficient, i.e., minimize redundancy.
2. The odd-sum check simplifies automatic checking of messages.
3. A code is easily formulated.

2.14 The Hamming Code: Single-error Correcting. Consider a code that satisfies the following pair of conditions:

1. Each message contains K binary bits.
2. Each pair of messages differs in at least three bit positions.

It can be demonstrated that any such code is single-error correcting, which means that each message contains sufficient information that a single error not only can be detected by inspection but can also be corrected.

The accompanying diagram geometrically illustrates the foregoing proposition. With only three bits, the permissible messages in a code that satisfies condition 2 correspond to the coordinates of diagonal vertices of the unit cube, e.g., 000 and 111 (or 100 and 011, etc.). A single error in a message from such a code is equivalent to a translation along the edge of the cube to an unpermitted vertex. However, its new position will be closer to that of the correct message than of 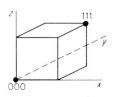 any other permitted message. Hence, the erroneous message may be corrected by selecting the message corresponding to the closest permitted vertex. It may be observed that such a code is also double-error detecting; however, it cannot be used for both purposes simultaneously.

While the foregoing argument may justify the validity of the proposition, it does not provide an orderly method for formulating a single-error correcting code and for isolating and correcting errors.

With messages composed of binary bits it is sufficient to locate the bit position at which the single error occurred; then the method of correction follows immediately, namely, replace the bit in that position with its one complement.

It is apparent that more redundancy will be required in each message of the single-error correcting code than in each message of the single-error detecting code. But how many check bits are required and what is the rule for assigning their values? Possibly some clues can be obtained from examining the codes suggested by the illustration.

The alternative permissible codes each contain two messages (see Table 2.9). First note that only one bit is required to code two characters. Hence, in each three-bit message two bits are redundant. The left-most bit, in the column headed I, will be called the information bit; the remaining two bits, in the columns headed A and B, will be called check bits.

Next, observe that there are exactly four conditions to be identified for each message, if the code is to be single-error correcting:

1. No single error in a message
2. A single error in bit A
3. A single error in bit B
4. A single error in bit I

Table 2.9

Code	Message	
	1	2
	IAB	IAB
1	000	111
2	001	110
3	101	010
4	100	011

It is known that two binary bits are sufficient to code the four conditions. This suggests that the three bits be partitioned into two submessages, each of which is single-error detecting and such that each combination of outcomes of sum checks on the two submessages is uniquely associated with one of the four conditions to be identified. Table 2.10 defines one such relationship, and there are many others that are possible. A value of O in the table signifies that the sum of the bits in the associated submessage is odd, while a value of E in the table signifies that the sum of the bits in the submessage is even.

Thus, submessage 1 is assigned bits I and B, and submessage 2 is assigned bits I and A. It remains to assign values to the bits in such a way that the specified outcomes will be realized for each of the two messages in the code. This will be accomplished by satisfying the conditions $A + I$ is odd and $B + I$ is odd in each message in the code,

Table 2.10

Condition identified	Submessage	
	1	2
(1) No single error in message	O	O
(2) Single error in bit A	O	E
(3) Single error in bit B	E	O
(4) Single error in bit I	E	E

while I has the value 1 in one message and the value 0 in the other. The two messages satisfying these conditions are $IAB = 100$ and $IAB = 011$.

To generalize the foregoing procedure for defining a single-error detecting code, it is observed that three submessages can have eight combinations of outcomes, four submessages can have sixteen combinations of outcomes, . . . , and K submessages can have 2^K combinations of outcomes.

In each case one outcome must be reserved to identify the condition of no single error in the message; thus single errors in $2^K - 1$ bits can be identified. Since each of the K submessages must be single-error detecting, K bits must be reserved as check bits, one for each submessage. It follows that K check bits will provide single-error correction (or, alternatively, double-error detection) for $2^K - K - 1$ information bits.

In particular, three check bits will provide single-error detection for four information bits, which in turn will provide a code for 16 messages, each of which will be single-error correcting. Let us assume that the form of a message in the code is to be $I_1 I_2 I_3 I_4 \, ABC$, where the I's identify information bits and A, B, and C identify check bits. Table 2.11 defines one of the many possible patterns of relating errors in individual bits to the outcomes of single-error detection on submessages.

Table 2.11   Outcomes of Submessage Single-error Detection

Condition identified	Submessage		
	1	2	3
(1) No single error in message	*O*	*O*	*O*
(2) Single error in bit C	*O*	*O*	*E*
(3) Single error in bit B	*O*	*E*	*O*
(4) Single error in bit I_4	*O*	*E*	*E*
(5) Single error in bit A	*E*	*O*	*O*
(6) Single error in bit I_3	*E*	*O*	*E*
(7) Single error in bit I_2	*E*	*E*	*O*
(8) Single error in bit I_1	*E*	*E*	*E*

Thus, submessage 1 contains bits I_1, I_2, I_3, and A; submessage 2 contains bits I_1, I_2, I_4, and B; and submessage 3 contains bits I_1, I_3, I_4, and C. The four information bits can assume the values of the binary integers 0000, 0001, . . . , 1111 and satisfy the condition that each message differs in at least one bit position. Then the values of bits A, B, and C must be assigned so that each submessage will be single-error detecting, i.e., the sum of the bits in the submessage will be odd if no single error has occurred. A complete seven-bit single-error correcting code is shown in Table 2.12.

The procedure for correcting a single error is the reverse of that for formulating the code.   When a message from the code is received, the sum of the bits in each submessage is calculated, and the combination of outcomes determines a line in the table of message conditions identified.

Table 2.12   Seven-bit Single-error Correcting Code for the Decimal Digits

Decimal	Information bit weights				Check bits		
	I_1	I_2	I_3	I_4	A	B	C
0	0	0	0	0	1	1	1
1	0	0	0	1	1	0	0
2	0	0	1	0	0	1	0
3	0	0	1	1	0	0	1
4	0	1	0	0	0	0	1
5	0	1	0	1	0	1	0
6	0	1	1	0	1	0	0
7	0	1	1	1	1	1	1
8	1	0	0	0	0	0	0
9	1	0	0	1	0	1	1

2.15 Checking Groups of Characters. Other checks may be devised to indicate the occurrence of an error in the transmission of a block of characters.   One of the most obvious is the sum check.   If,

Table 2.13   Single-error Correction by Row and Column Check Bits

Decimal digit	Information bits	R check
1	0001	0
2	0010	0
3	0011	1
4	0100	0
5	0101	1
6	0110	1
7	0111	0
8	1000	0
9	1001	1
C check	1110	0

for example, a block of 10 digits is to be transmitted over a telegraph line, their sum is calculated and transmitted.   The sum of the 10 digits received is calculated and compared with the check sum received.

ATTENTION TREASURER
IMPORTANT NOTICE

AFTER APPLYING THE ATTACHED REMITTANCE, PLEASE SEND DUPLICATE INVOICE WITH PROOF OF DELIVERY OF ANY OPEN ITEM ON OUR ACCOUNT OVER 60 DAYS OLD.

YOUR CO-OPERATION WILL BE GREATLY APPRECIATED.

THANK YOU.

HOCHSCHILD, KOHN & CO.
BALTIMORE, MD. 21201

E. B. CAGLE
CONTROLLER

If the sums agree, it is assumed that transmission is correct. If they disagree, an error is implied.

Another check, illustrated in Table 2.13, provides an odd-sum check on each column as well as on each row of a block of characters. The value of each R (row) check bit is chosen so that the sum of the five bits in each row is odd. The value of each of the four C (column) check bits is chosen so that the sum of the bits in each of the four columns of information bits is odd.

If a single R check bit is changed, the sum check will fail (sum will be even) in that row, but not in the four columns. If, instead, any other single bit is changed, the sum checks will fail for both the row and the column containing that bit. The erroneous bit can thus be isolated and the correction is then obvious.

2.16 Redundancy. The preceding sections have been devoted to the discussion of coding systems that were devised to detect and to correct errors in messages. The systems were such that the computer could be designed to detect certain types of errors that it is prone to make. The existence of such codes is tacit recognition that machines as well as humans are not infallible.

In each case a price was paid for the additional capability of the coding system. This price can be related to the redundancy in each message. The additional bit that is added to each message in a single-error detecting code is redundant as long as the message is accurate, because the information contained in that bit is used only when an error occurs. Nevertheless, there will be a cost for carrying the extra bit that will be reflected either in extra equipment or in wasted time. If a four-bit code is increased to five bits to provide single-error detection and if the bits in a message are transmitted in parallel, a corresponding increase of 25 per cent in transmission lines and in certain equipment must be provided in the transmission system. If, instead, the bits in a message are transmitted serially (one after the other over a single line), there will be a reduction of 20 per cent in the rate at which messages can be transmitted.

In deciding how much should be expended for error detection and/or correction, we should consider two costs. One is the cost of providing a given level of protection against the occurrence of and lack of detection of errors; the other is the expected cost of errors at that level of protection. For example, as the speed of computers increases and with it the cost per unit of lost time when an error is detected, single-error correcting becomes an economical replacement for single-error detecting. Ideally, we should choose the level of protection that minimizes the sum of the two costs. The actual determination of that level is not an easy task, and in the case of hardware it is primarily a problem for the designer.   However, the user of the equipment may have to consider such a problem in making choices among alternative equipments because he will pay for whatever features are included in the equipment he chooses.

A fact that is not so well recognized is that the analyst and the programmer also face decisions about the inclusion of redundant information in the results obtained in the solution of a problem.   The value of redundancy is recognized by the accountant in his double-entry bookkeeping system.   He builds into his system various redundant totals that aid him in the detection and isolation of errors.   It is recommended that this principle be kept in mind in the analysis and programming of solutions to all types of problems.

In Chap. 5 it will be recommended that rather large amounts of redundant information be produced during the program test phase of developing a computer program.   Such information is produced to facilitate detection and isolation of errors in the program and will be of value only if errors are actually detected.   It is not recommended that as much redundant information be produced in later production runs.   The decision as to just what is produced must be made in the context of a particular problem.

There has been much emphasis placed on the accuracy and reliability of electronic computers as well as on their speed.   For the most part this emphasis is justified; however, along with the high unit cost of computer time, it may tend to divert us from the fact that the computer is designed to detect automatically special kinds of errors only. There are many other kinds of errors that the machine does not detect automatically.

These include errors in data to be processed, errors in the definition of or analysis of the problem, errors in the logic of the program, and errors introduced by rounding (see Sec. 3.23) in arithmetic operations. Such errors must be anticipated by the analyst and the programmer, and redundancy should be built into the solution to the extent that it is justified for protection against expected losses.

This redundancy can take several forms.   One is the production of redundant information to be checked by a human being.   A second is the duplicate processing of data with two different systems, each of which should lead to correct results, but by different paths, as it were. A third is the inclusion of various tests on input data, intermediate results, and output information for the purpose of detecting certain exceptional values that would lead to erroneous results or actions. There are undoubtedly many other types of redundancy that the ingenious analyst will think of to protect against errors that are peculiar to a specific situation.

There will be, of course, a cost for such redundancy. The cost may be reflected in additional computer time, in human effort, or in a combination of the two. The cost of the protection that one purchases should be weighed against the expected losses. With the sheer volume of data that a computer is capable of processing in a short period of time and completely out of range of human observation, many errors that were previously detected by experienced observers may now go undetected.

A representative of a computer manufacturer once made a claim that their computers had never made an undetected error. He, of course, was referring to the types of errors their computer was designed to check, and in any event such a statement is as difficult to refute as it is to substantiate. It is interesting to speculate what the cost may have been of undetected errors of the kind that the computer is not designed to detect.

2.17 Other Coding Systems. The coding systems used vary among computer systems. The foregoing discussion serves to introduce the reader to the specific coding systems used in the 650. He will be expected to acquaint himself with such coding systems, as required, by reference to literature available from the manufacturer of a specific computer. The discussion also lays a foundation or the reader to develop coding systems that will be useful in computer solutions of data-processing problems.

REFERENCES

1. Brillouin, L.: "Science and Information Theory," Academic Press, Inc. New York, 1956.
2. Ore, Oystein: "Number Theory and Its History," McGraw-Hill Book Company, Inc., New York, 1948.
3. Phister, Montgomery: "Logical Design of Digital Computers," John Wiley & Sons, Inc., New York, 1958.
4. Richards, R. K.: "Arithmetic Operations in Digital Computers," D. Van Nostrand Company, Inc., Princeton, N.J., 1955.

PROBLEMS

2.1. Prepare the addition and multiplication tables for the octal (base-8) numbers.

2.2. Write the binary equivalents of the basic octal digits.

2.3. Determine the octal equivalent of the decimal number 536.625.   Convert the result to its binary equivalent, using the octal-to-binary table prepared in Prob. 2.2. Check the transformations by converting the binary result to its decimal equivalent.

2.4. Demonstrate that the quinary integer 224 can be converted directly to its octal equivalent using the equation

$$N_8 = a_2 b^2 + a_1 b + a_0$$

providing all arithmetic is done in the octal number system. In the octal system,

$$N_8 = 31a_2 + 5a_1 + a_0$$

Check the result by conversion to the decimal equivalent.

2.5. Show that the seventh (high-order) binary position is included in the code of Table 2.6 for error detection purposes only.

2.6. Prove that at least five binary bits are required as a basis in a single-error detection code for the decimal digits. (*Hint:* Of the binary integers 0 through 15, the sum of the bits in each of eight integers is odd.)

2.7. Translate the name Robert T. Jones to 650 and to 705 alphanumeric code.

2.8. Convert the decimal fraction .13 to its equivalent in the binary, quinary, and octal systems. Carry each conversion only to the number of places justified by the accuracy of representation of the decimal fraction.

2.9. Devise a single-error correcting code containing six information bits.

2.10. Three independent parameters of a chemical process, which are sensed at given intervals, are measured in Boolean terms, e.g., acid or base, positive or negative, temperature $\geq K$ or temperature $< K$, etc. These data are to be transmitted from the plant to the data-processing center via leased-wire transceiving equipment. In answering the following questions, identify the three parameters by the characters X, Y, and Z. Each message transmitted is to communicate the state of X and Y and Z. Assume the sequence in which the parameters are sensed is always X, then Y, then Z.

a. What is the total possible number of different messages?

b. Write out a table of the possible messages.

c. Devise a binary code for transmitting these messages which will make it possible to detect a single error. Display your code for each message and explain the error detection procedure.

d. Devise a code which could be used for single-error correction or for double-error detection. Prepare the following tables:

(i) The error test outcomes for single errors
(ii) The error test procedure plan
(iii) Your code for each of the possible messages

e. Demonstrate (with any *one* of the messages) that the code you presented in (*d*) would provide for detecting a double error. Also, explain the consequences of applying the single-error correction procedure to a message containing the errors.

3

ELECTRONIC COMPUTER ORGANIZATION

This chapter will be devoted to a discussion of computer organization and control. Computer organization, as used here, refers to the five basic components comprising the computing system and to their interrelationships in performing elementary computer operations. The purpose of the discussion is to give the reader a general understanding of the functioning of a computer.[1]

3.1 Basic Components and Their Functions. A complete computational system—manual, mechanical, or electronic—comprises five basic components:

1. A memory unit
2. An arithmetic unit
3. A control unit
4. A data input unit
5. A data output unit

For limited computations, the human faculties suffice for all the functions performed by these components. Input data may be received aurally, visually, or mentally. Arithmetic operations can be performed mentally. The sequence of operations can be controlled mentally. The results may be audibly or visibly disseminated or retained as input for a subsequent operation. For complex computations, it is generally necessary to supplement the human memory with pencil and paper. In addition, pencil and paper or some equivalent thereto are often used for conveying input and output data and for specifying the sequence of arithmetic operations to be performed. In

[1] Readers who are interested in a more detailed discussion of the logical design of computers are referred to Refs. 3 and 4.

some situations it is economical to substitute for the human brain a manually operated computing mechanism, such as an abacus, slide rule, adding machine, or desk calculator. The stored-program general-purpose digital electronic computer combines the five basic components and is a powerful tool for performing repetitive numeric computations.

An electronic computer performs arithmetic operations at electronic speeds (order of microseconds to milliseconds), in contrast with electro-mechanical speeds (order of a second to tens of seconds). The language of a digital computer is a discrete or digital number system. It was shown in the section on coding that both the alphabetic and numeric characters are represented numerically within the computer. A stored-program computer is capable of performing a sequence of

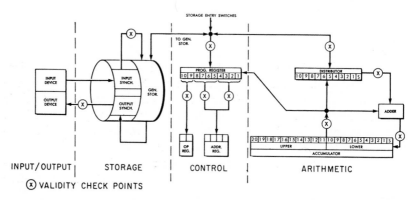

Fig. 3.1. Schematic of IBM 650 Computer. (*Reprinted by permission from "IBM 650 Data Processing System Bulletin—General Information, Console Information, Operation, Special Divisions," G24-5000-0, copyright 1958 in original notice by International Business Machines Corporation.*)

operations by interpreting and executing a sequence of instructions that have been stored in the memory unit. If the operator can arbitrarily modify the sequence of operations without modifying the basic computer design, the computer is said to be general-purpose; otherwise, it is said to be special-purpose.

The organization of the 650 is schematically illustrated in Fig. 3.1. The arrows in the diagram show the paths and directions of data flow. Punched cards containing input information are fed into the input device where the input information is translated to the 650 code and transferred to the input synchronizer, a special segment of the memory unit. From the input synchronizer the information is automatically transferred to the general memory (storage) at the appropriate time. The information thus entered to memory may be either instructions to

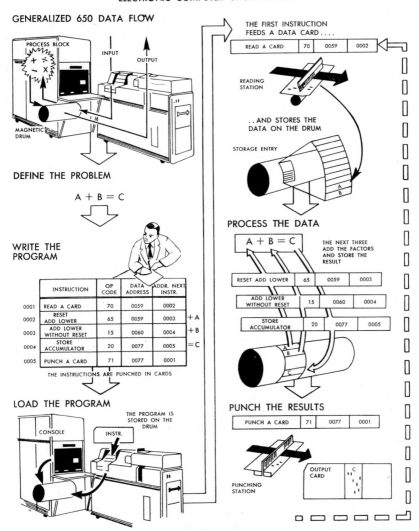

Fig. 3.2. Generalized 650 data flow. (*Reprinted by permission from "IBM 650 Data Processing System Bulletin—General Information, Console Information, Operation, Special Divisions," G24-5000-0, copyright 1958 in original notice by International Business Machines Corporation.*)

be executed by the computer or data to be processed as specified by a sequence of instructions. Information (normally instructions) can be transferred to the program register in the control unit from general memory or from the arithmetic (process) unit. Note that the path to the program register is one way—in. Instructions are interpreted in the control unit and the specified computer functions (input, output, arithmetic, and data transmission) are initiated at the appropriate time.

Arithmetic operations are performed in the arithmetic (process) unit. Information can be transferred from memory to the arithmetic unit and vice versa. The information may be an instruction to be modified by arithmetic operation or it may be data to be processed.

Information can be transferred from general memory to the output synchronizer, a special segment of memory, from which information is automatically transferred to the output device where translation from 650 code to punched-card code is effected. The output information may be instructions, constants, or information derived by processing input data.

The STORAGE ENTRY SWITCHES provide for manual entry of information into general memory, the program register, or the arithmetic unit. They play an important part in the execution of a sequence of instructions, because the initial instruction of a sequence is normally entered into the computer via the STORAGE ENTRY SWITCHES.

The sequence of events in the solution of a data-processing problem is illustrated schematically in Fig. 3.2. The first requirement is to become familiar with the computer and the language for communication therewith. Next, the data-processing problem is defined. (Note that the computer does not define the problem.) Then it is necessary to write a sequence of instructions (program) that can be interpreted by the computer and that will cause the computer to perform the desired operations. The instructions are transferred to punched cards and entered to memory via the input device.

The data are entered to memory and then processed as the instructions are executed; finally, the results are transferred from memory and punched via the output device.

In this chapter we shall discuss the components of the 650, the operations that it is designed to execute, and the writing of simple sequences of instructions.

THE MEMORY UNIT

3.2 The Memory Register.   The memory unit is used for orderly recording of data so that they are accessible to the machine. Whether the memory unit is a magnetic drum, a magnetic tape, a magnetic disk, a matrix of magnetic cores, or a combination thereof, it can be thought of as a set of registers, each analogous to a set of dials on a desk calculator.

It will be assumed that each register has 11 positions—one position for each digit of a 10-digit decimal number and one position for a sign (plus or minus) indicator, as shown in Fig. 3.3. The digits in each position shown in Fig. 3.3 will be used henceforth as reference numbers for the memory-register positions, except that the high-order position will be referred to as position 10 rather than 0. In Fig. 3.3, register position 1 contains the digit 1, register position 2 contains the digit 2, etc. It should be noted that while there is provision for the number to have a sign, there is no provision for a decimal place. As with the desk calculator, the sequence of operations must provide for keeping track of the decimal place. The 650 computer treats the contents of a register as a signed 10-digit decimal integer.

The number in a register is commonly referred to as a word and alternatively as the contents of the register. If the number of digit positions of each memory register is fixed, as is assumed in the example, the computer is said to be of fixed word size. In some computers the

| 0 | 9 | 8 | 7 | 6 | 5 | 4 | 3 | 2 | 1 | $\pm$ |

FIG. 3.3. Schematic of a memory register.

word size is variable, and the end of a word is indicated by a characteristic symbol.

If the memory is thought of as a sequence of fixed-size registers, a corresponding sequence of integers can be used as addresses to identify the locations of the registers. If there are no more than 10,000 registers, the sequence of four-digit integers 0000 through 9999 can be used to uniquely identify or locate each register. An important control feature of the stored-program computer is its ability to locate a register specified by an address, then to write or store data in the register or to read or copy data from the register.

When a word of data is copied into a register, the previous contents of the register are normally erased before the new information is entered. This corresponds to the clearing of the dial on a desk calculator before a new number is entered. When a word of information is copied from a register, the contents of the register normally are not destroyed in the copying process. The contents of the register are therefore the same before and after being copied from. This corresponds to the reading of a desk-calculator register.

3.3 A Magnetic-core Register. A magnetic core resembles a tiny washer, approximately $\frac{1}{16}$ inch in outside diameter. For the purpose of this discussion, the core is considered to have just two states, mag-

netized or unmagnetized.   Hence a single magnetic core can be used
to represent a binary bit—the magnetized state corresponding to the
binary digit 1 and the unmagnetized state to the binary digit 0.
Seven cores can therefore be used to represent a seven-digit binary
integer.   In particular, a seven-bit (weighted binary) code from
Table 2.6 can be represented by seven binary cores set to the appro-

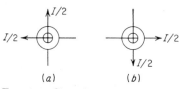

(a)   (b)

Fig. 3.4. Changing the state of a
core.   (a) Current flow to set core
to the 0 state.   (b) Current flow to
set core to the 1 state.

priate combination of states.   For
that code, seven cores will be required to represent the code for a
single decimal digit; hence, seven
cores will be required for each register position.[1,2]

To control its state, each core is
threaded with a pair of wires, as
illustrated in Fig. 3.4.   Assume that
the core is set to the 0 state when
the vertical wire carries an impulse of current $I/2$ flowing upward
and the horizontal wire simultaneously carries an impulse $I/2$ flowing
to the left; and that the core is set to the 1 state when both current
flows are reversed; i.e., the vertical wire carries an impulse $I/2$ flowing
downward and the horizontal wire carries an impulse $I/2$ flowing to
the right.   An important factor in the operation of the core memory is

Fig. 3.5. A digit position of a core register.

that a single impulse $I/2$ in either wire, in either direction, will not
change the state of the core.   Figure 3.5 illustrates a case in which
the core with weight 4 is being set to the 1 state while the states of the
remaining cores are unaffected.

[1] The reader will recall from Chap. 2 that four information bits plus a check
bit are sufficient to provide a single-error detecting code for the decimal digits.
The seven-bit code is used here (and later) for illustrative purposes because it is
the code that is displayed to the 650 user.   A five-bit code is actually used to
store a digit in a register position on the magnetic drum.

[2] In many computers, the memory is designed to store binary integers rather
than coded decimal integers, in which case each register position requires a single
core.   Thus, 36 cores will accommodate a binary integer of the same order of
magnitude as a 10-digit decimal integer.   This yields an appreciable saving in the
cost of memory.

In addition to setting the state of individual cores, it is necessary that it be possible to copy from one core (or set of cores) to a second, i.e., to determine the state of one core and duplicate its (original) state in the second. To copy from a core, it is necessary to sense its state. In the process of sensing, a core is always set to the 0 state. In order that data will not be destroyed when a core is copied, provision is made for restoring each core to its original state after sensing. The wires required for sensing and restoring the state of a core are not shown in Figs. 3.4 and 3.5.

Now let us consider a procedure for copying from a digit position of one register into the corresponding digit position of another register, assuming that the seven-bit code is used. Each of the two digit positions may be represented by a set of seven cores, as illustrated in Fig. 3.5. Let us assume that the original state of the register position to be copied corresponds to the binary integer 10 00001 and that the seven cores are to be copied sequentially, working from right to left. The copying will thus be performed in eight successive time intervals.

In the first time interval, all seven cores of the register position to be copied into will be simultaneously set to the 0 state. This may be accomplished by simultaneously impulsing the horizontal wire and the seven vertical wires threading the cores (see Fig. 3.5) with currents $I/2$ flowing to the left and upward, respectively.

In the second time interval, the state of the right-most core (weight 4) to be copied is sensed. If it is in the 1 state (as is assumed in this example), it will be set to the 0 state and hence must be reset to the 1 state by simultaneously impulsing its horizontal and vertical wires with currents $I/2$ flowing to the right and downward respectively (Fig. 3.5). The corresponding core to be copied into will be set to the appropriate state if these reset impulses are also channeled to the horizontal and vertical wires threading that core.

In each succeeding time interval, the process of interval 2 is repeated. The state of the core to be copied from is sensed; then that core is reset and the corresponding core is set to the appropriate state. If, however, the core to be copied from is in the 0 state originally, sensing will not change its state; hence the reset impulses are not required, nor are the set impulses for the core being copied into, since it was set to the 0 state in the first time interval.

The same result will obtain if the pair of vertical wires threading the corresponding pair of cores are automatically impulsed with current $I/2$ (flowing downward) at reset time of each time interval and if the pair of horizontal wires threading the corresponding pair of cores are impulsed with current $I/2$ (flowing to the right) only if the 1 state is sensed.   It will be seen that this procedure has some advantage when we next consider copying from one register into another.

The 11-position register of Fig. 3.3 can be represented by the matrix array of cores shown in Fig. 3.6.   Each of the 11 rows of the matrix is a set of seven cores corresponding to each of 11 register positions.   The matrix shown is being impulsed at time interval 2 so that the 4 bit is set to the 1 state in register positions 1, 2, 5, 6, 7, and 10 simultaneously.   The 4 bits in the remaining positions (3, 4, 8, and 9) remain at the 0 state.   This implies that in the second time interval all the 4 bits for the 11 register positions are simultaneously set to their final

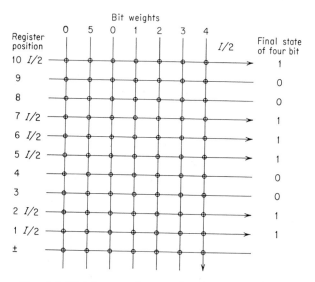

Fig. 3.6. Matrix array for a 10-decimal-digit register.

state.   During the third time interval, all the 3 bits for the 11 register positions are set to their final state, etc.

Such a procedure for storing data in registers is said to be serial (or sequential) by bit position and parallel by register position.

Each additional memory register requires a replication of the core matrix illustrated in Fig. 3.6.   A 100-register memory can be visualized as a bank of 100 such matrices.   Such a bank would require 1100 horizontal wires, 700 vertical wires, and the additional wires necessary for sensing and restoring the cores.   When we consider the number of extra cores and wires required for two extra bit positions, the need for using an efficient code becomes apparent.   From the computer's point of view, the five-bit code for the decimal digits is as satisfactory as the seven-bit code; and from the manufacturer's point of view, it is more economical. For the computer operator, the display of the seven-bit code is easier to translate to its decimal equivalent than a display of the four information bits from the five-bit code. In the 650, a five-bit code is used in memory and a seven-bit code is used for display.

In a fixed-word-size memory, all registers have the same number of positions; e.g., all registers in the 650 have 10 digit positions and a sign position as illustrated in Fig. 3.3. The individual registers in the bank of 100, referred to above, could be identified by the set of integers 00 through 99, where each integer is associated with a set of 11 horizontal wires and 7 vertical wires threading the cores. The integers thereof become addresses for the bank of registers. The horizontal and vertical wires serve identical functions for each register; hence they need not be addressed individually for the benefit of the user of the computer.

In a variable-word-size computer, each digit position is addressable by the user. The 1100 digit positions referred to above as a bank of 100 registers might then be identified by the addresses 0000 through 1099. In addition, a code, identifiable by the computer, is used to indicate the end of a word.

The term *random-access memory* can be defined now. The access time to a register is the time required by the computer to locate a register in memory and copy from it or into it. If at an arbitrary instant the access time to a memory register is independent of the register specified, then the memory is said to be random-access. The core memory described above would be considered random-access. It will be seen that the magnetic-drum memory of the 650 is not a truly random-access memory.

3.4 A Magnetic-tape Memory.

To visualize a magnetic tape as a memory unit, consider first a tape that is approximately ½ inch wide and 2500 feet long. The tape may be metal or, more likely, it will be plastic with a thin coating of metallic oxide. Next, visualize the matrix of cores illustrated in Fig. 3.6 as a matrix of spots on the tape, as in Fig. 3.7.

Tape channels							Register positions
1	2	3	4	5	6	7	
o	o	o	o	o	o	o	1
o	o	o	o	o	o	o	2
o	o	o	o	o	o	o	3
o	o	o	o	o	o	o	4
o	o	o	o	o	o	o	5
o	o	o	o	o	o	o	6
o	o	o	o	o	o	o	7
o	o	o	o	o	o	o	8
o	o	o	o	o	o	o	9
o	o	o	o	o	o	o	10
o	o	o	o	o	o	o	±

Fig. 3.7. Arrangement of a signed 10-digit word on magnetic tape.

The seven-bit code for a single character is distributed across the width of the tape in seven columns, commonly referred to as channels. The 11 rows corresponding to the 11 register positions are distributed along the length of the tape.   Figure 3.7 illustrates the possible positioning of the 77 bits required for a signed 10-digit word, corresponding to the register illustrated in Fig. 3.6.

The tape is wound on a reel.   Codes are copied from the tape or written on the tape as it passes under a READ-WRITE head (see Fig. 3.8). The functions performed by the wires that thread the individual cores in the core matrix are performed by wires attached to the READ-WRITE heads.

It becomes apparent that addressing the location of a word of data on a magnetic tape is less direct than addressing the wires threading a

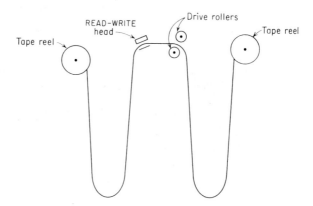

FIG. 3.8. A schematic magnetic-tape unit.

set of cores in a fixed location.   In the latter case, an address system that identifies individual wires, or groups thereof, is sufficient.   With the magnetic tape, the address must be identified as the tape passes under the READ-WRITE head; hence the movement of the tape must be synchronized with the operation of the READ-WRITE head.   This problem is further complicated by the fact that there will be regions in the tape that must be skipped because the magnetic film is imperfect or the tape has been broken and spliced.

A practical method of reducing the complications introduced is to divide the tape into blocks, with a specified number of words, say 50, per block.   Each block has a unique address, and each address is preceded by a block marker or code that signals the computer to identify a block number after a fixed time delay.

In practice, the assignment of block addresses may be accomplished in two steps.   The first step involves running the tape forward the entire length and recording a constant magnetic level in the process. This has the effect of erasing the tape.

In the second step the tape is rewound.   As it is rewound, an automatic check is made for tape blocks that contain no imperfection.   As

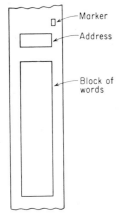

illustrated in Fig. 3.9, each tape block must be long enough to accommodate a block marker, a block address, and the block of words, previously assumed to be 50.   Each length of tape, without imperfections, satisfying the foregoing requirements is assigned a block address and a block marker.   Each time an imperfection is encountered before a block marker is assigned, the block inspection starts anew after the imperfection is passed.

Once the calibration is completed, data may be recorded in the blocks that have been defined. Retrieval of data that have been stored in a specific block of words will involve a sequential search of the tape until the appropriate block of words is located.   It follows that magnetic-tape storage may be referred to appropriately as sequential- or serial-access memory rather than as random-access memory.

Fig. 3.9. Schematic diagram of a tape block.

3.5 A Magnetic-drum Memory.   The magnetic drum is a metal cylinder that is mounted for rotation about its axis.   The unit illustrated in Fig. 3.10 has a single band of memory registers located sequentially around the circumference of the drum.   Let us assume that there are 50 registers to a band, that they are sequentially numbered 00 through 49, that each register is equivalent in memory capacity to the core matrix of Fig. 3.6, and that the word size is fixed. This may be thought of as a 50-word tape block wrapped around a cylinder.

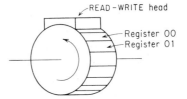

Fig. 3.10. A schematic magnetic-drum memory unit.

As in the case of the core memory bank, the set of integers 00 through 49 furnishes the user a set of addresses for the 50 registers.   A specified register can be read from or written into only when it passes under the READ-WRITE head, i.e., once each drum revolution.   Address identification depends upon precise synchronization between the rotation of the drum and a timing circuit that serves to establish the point in time at which an arbitrarily selected register will pass under the READ-WRITE head. At this same point in time, the READ-WRITE head must be activated to copy or record.

The access time to a given register depends not only on the time required to perform switching (connect the appropriate sets of wires) but also on the circumferential distance between the register and the READ-WRITE head when switching has been accomplished. Hence, the access is sequential within a band of memory registers. The switching time may be of the order of 1 word time, but the delay time may range from 0 to 50 word times. A word time is defined to be t/n, where t is the time required for one drum revolution and n is the number of words in a circumferential band. In the 650, t is 4.8 milliseconds and n is 50; hence a word time is .096 millisecond.

The number of registers in the magnetic-drum memory unit may be increased by adding registers to the band or by increasing the number of bands. If more registers are added to the band, it is probable that the circumference of the drum will be increased proportionately and the rate of rotation will be reduced for mechanical reasons, the probable result being a corresponding increase in average access time. If the length of the cylinder is increased to provide for additional bands of registers, each band having its own READ-WRITE head, there need be no appreciable increase in access time.

The 650 magnetic-drum memory comprises 2000 fixed-word-size registers addressed sequentially from 0000 through 1999. There are 40 bands, each having its own READ-WRITE head. The registers in the first band are addressable at 0000 through 0049; those in the second band, at 0050 through 0099; . . . ; and those in the fortieth band, at 1950 through 1999. It is as though 40 of the bands illustrated in Fig. 3.10 were mounted side by side. It is common practice to regard the register with the lowest address in a band as the first register in that band. The input synchronizer and the output synchronizer[1] are two sets of registers (10 each) that are also on the magnetic drum. No addresses are assigned to these registers.

A five-bit code is actually used to represent a decimal integer stored in a memory-register position. Internal machine operations are performed on the basis of this code or translations thereof. For our pur-

---

[1] The input synchronizer serves as a temporary repository for data as they are translated from the punched-card code to the 650 code. The output synchronizer serves as a temporary repository for data as they are translated from the 650 code to the punched-card code. Since the input-output devices are electromechanical, hence relatively slow, these temporary repositories are used to free the computer for processing during translation time.

poses, it will be convenient in future discussions to consider the contents of a register as a decimal integer, e. g., $0987654321 \pm$. In addition to being convenient, this convention is practical. Our problems are normally expressed in decimal numbers and alphabetic characters, our thinking will be done in terms of such characters, and the contents of the registers are displayed so that they are translatable to decimal integers.

THE 650 ARITHMETIC UNIT[1]

The 650 can perform the arithmetic operations of addition, subtraction, multiplication, and division upon pairs of decimal integers. To be precise, we should state that the operations can be performed on the codes for decimal integers, but such a refinement is not only inconvenient but also unnecessary. Future discussion will therefore be presented as though the operations are performed directly in the decimal system.

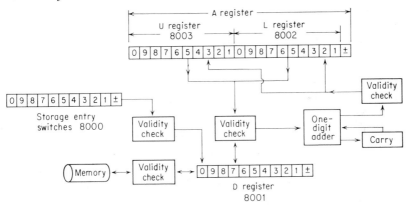

Fig. 3.11. Schematic of 650 arithmetic unit.

Figure 3.11 illustrates schematically the paths of data flow between the 650 memory and the arithmetic unit and of data flow within the arithmetic unit. Note that data pass through a validity check point each time they are copied. At these check points the validity of each binary code is checked. If an invalid code is encountered, a signal is sent automatically to the computer control unit. The way this signal may be used to stop the computer or, alternatively, to initiate a course of action specified by the user will be discussed in Chap. 4.

The A register has 20 digit positions and a sign position, thus

[1] For discussion of the circuitry of arithmetic units, see Refs. 3 and 4.

providing capacity to store the product of two 10-digit numbers. The A register is used to accumulate sums as they are generated by the one-digit adder. It will be shown in the discussion of multiplication and division that products are generated in the A register by successive additions and that quotients are generated by successive subtractions.

The D register has 10 digit positions and a sign position, as do the memory registers. A word can be copied from a memory register into the D register and vice versa. The D register serves as an auxiliary register in arithmetic operations. It is also used when data are to be transferred from the A register to memory, since no direct path exists between the A register and memory.

Since data must be copied from the A register 10 digits at a time, it is addressed as two registers. The 10 high-order positions are referred to as the U (upper accumulator) register, and the 10 low-order positions are referred to as the L (lower accumulator) register. It is worth noting that as an accumulator the A register always operates as a single 20-digit unit, whereas it is addressed as two independent registers when data are copied from it. With a single exception, described in the discussion of the division operation, the sign of the A register applies to both U and L registers. The errors that can arise from treating the A register as two independent registers will be discussed in detail in each of the arithmetic operations.

The D, L, and U registers have been assigned the addresses 8001, 8002, and 8003, respectively, whereas the 2000 memory registers were assigned addresses 0000 to 1999. The D, L, and U registers are not located on the rotating magnetic drum; instead, they are stationary. Relative to the average access time of 25 word times for memory registers, the access time to the D register is considered to be 0 word time, and the access time to the U and L registers does not exceed 1 word time.

In the 650 arithmetic operations all numbers are treated as integers. If a problem actually involves decimal fractions, then the user must provide in his instructions to the computer a procedure for keeping track of the implied position of the decimal point. Specific procedures associated with positioning of decimal points will be alluded to in the discussions of addition, multiplication, and division. These procedures generally take advantage of the shifting feature of the A register.

The 20-digit contents of the A register may be shifted to the right or the left an arbitrary number of spaces. The sign position is not affected by shifting. Any digits shifted out of either end of the A register are completely lost, while positions vacated are filled with zeros.

Our attention will now be directed to the specific execution of each arithmetic operation in the 650.

3.6 The Addition Operation. In a sense, the 650 "knows" how to add pairs of decimal digits and it "knows" about the generation and use of carries in addition. At least the one-digit adder can generate sums of pairs of decimal digits and generate a carry if the tens position of the sum of the pair of digits is 1. The manner in which a pair of integers is added in the computer bears a distinct resemblance to the manner in which most individuals would add a pair of integers, e.g.,

		Register
0000111110	Carry	
0123456789 +	Augend	A
0123456789 +	Addend	D
0246913578 +	Sum	A

The individual would normally write the numbers one under the other by aligning the units position of the two numbers, whereas the 650 requires that the pair of numbers be positioned in a specific pair of registers—the A (accumulator) register and the D (distributor) register.

The procedure in the computer is to send the pair of digits from the units position to the adder first, copy the units position of the sum from the adder into the units position of the A register, and record the carry for addition to the sum of the pair of digits in the tens position. The pair of tens-position digits are next sent to the adder; their sum plus the carry digit is determined; the units position of the sum from the adder is copied into the tens position of the A register; and the carry is recorded for addition to the pair of digits from the hundreds positions. This procedure is repeated until all pairs of register positions have been added and the sum has been copied in the A register.

Since the D register has 10 digit positions while the A register has 20, the units position of the D register may be aligned with that of the L register (or the U register) for the purpose of choosing pairs of digits to be sent to the adder. Addition with alignment to the L register is referred to by the symbolic operation code ALO, an abbreviation for the term *add to the lower accumulator.*

Addition with alignment to the U register is referred to by the symbolic operation code AUP, an abbreviation for the term *add to the upper accumulator.*

It is worth noting that the terms *add to the lower accumulator* and *add to the upper accumulator* are really misnomers. In each case the number in the D register is added to the 20-digit number in the A register. Situations in which unfortunate consequences follow from failure to recognize this fact are discussed below in examples that lead to an A register condition referred to as underflow.

The addition operation provides for adding the number from any addressable register to the number in the A register. In the execution of the addition operation, the number from the specified register is first copied into the D register; then the addition process described above is carried out. The location of the number that is to be added to the A register is identified by appending the address of the register containing the number to the operation code, e.g.,

$$\text{ALO} \qquad dddd$$
$$\text{AUP} \qquad dddd$$

where $dddd$ is the address of the appropriate register. If the register containing the number to be added to the A register is located in memory, then $dddd$ will assume some value 0000 to 1999. If the register is located in the arithmetic unit, then $dddd$ will assume some value 8001 to 8003.

The results of these two addition operations can be illustrated readily by considering the number in the A register as the sum of two numbers. Let N_1 be the 10-digit number contained in the D register, let N_2 be the 10-digit number in the L register, and let N_3 be the 10-digit number in the U register. It will be convenient to adopt the convention $C(dddd)$ to refer to the contents of a register located at address $dddd$. Thus,

$C(8003) = C(\text{U}) = N_3$ i.e., the contents of register 8003 (U) is N_3
$C(8002) = C(\text{L}) = N_2$ i.e., the contents of register 8002 (L) is N_2
$C(8001) = C(\text{D}) = N_1$ i.e., the contents of register 8001 (D) is N_1

The letters A, U, L, and D will be used to indicate the corresponding registers.

It follows that $C(\text{A}) = (N_3 \times 10^{10})^* + N_2 = [C(\text{U}) \times 10^{10}] + C(\text{L})$. N_3 and N_2 have the same sign (except in a special case after division, to be discussed later) and this sign is that of the A register.

Consider now four examples.

Example 3.1   ALO 8001

This is equivalent to $(N_3 \times 10^{10}) + N_2 + N_1$. This may be expressed alternatively as $C(\text{A}) + C(\text{D}) \to \text{A}$, or as $[C(8003) \times 10^{10}] +$

* $10^{10} = 10,000,000,000$ is used to obviate writing long strings of zeros.

$C(8002) + C(8001) \to$ A.   The symbolic statements are interpreted: the algebraic sum of the numbers in the A register and the D register is copied into the A register.

In particular, consider the case that

$C(\text{A}) = 59 \times 10^9 = (5 \times 10^{10})$
$\qquad\qquad\qquad\qquad + (9 \times 10^9) = 00\ 0000\ 0005\ 90\ 0000\ 0000+$
$C(\text{D}) = 3 \times 10^9 \qquad\qquad\qquad = \qquad\qquad\quad 30\ 0000\ 0000+$
$C(\text{A}) + C(\text{D}) = 62 \times 10^9 = (6 \times 10^{10})$
$\qquad\qquad\qquad\qquad + (2 \times 10^9) = 00\ 0000\ 0006\ 20\ 0000\ 0000+$

But this is equivalent to

$$(5 \times 10^{10}) + [(9 + 3) \times 10^9] = (6 \times 10^{10}) + (2 \times 10^9)$$

or
$$[C(\text{U}) \times 10^{10}] + C(\text{L}) + C(\text{D}) \to \text{A}.$$

Example 3.2   AUP 8001

This is equivalent to $[(N_3 + N_1) \times 10^{10}] + N_2$, or $C(\text{A}) + [C(\text{D}) \times 10^{10}] \to$ A, or $[C(8003) + C(8001)] \times 10^{10} + C(8002) \to$ A.

In particular, consider the case that

$C(\text{A}) = (8 \times 10^{10}) + 3 \qquad\qquad = 00\ 0000\ 0008\ 00\ 0000\ 0003+$
$C(\text{D}) = 3 \qquad\qquad\qquad\qquad\quad = 00\ 0000\ 0003+$
$C(\text{A}) + [C(\text{D}) \times 10^{10}]$
$\qquad = [(8 + 3) \times 10^{10}] + 3 = 00\ 0000\ 0011\ 00\ 0000\ 0003+$

Example 3.3   ALO *dddd*

This is equivalent to $C(dddd) \to$ D; $C(\text{A}) + C(\text{D}) \to$ A.   The contents of the register located at *dddd* (e.g., 1325) are copied into the D register; then the contents of the D register are added to the contents of the A register.

Example 3.4   AUP *dddd*

This is equivalent to $C(dddd) \to$ D; $C(\text{A}) + [C(\text{D}) \times 10^{10}] \to$ A. The contents of the register located at *dddd* are copied into the D register; the D register is aligned with the U register; the addition is performed; the sum is stored in the A register.

In Example 3.1, the sum exceeded a 10-digit number, i.e.,

$$N_2 + N_1 = (9 + 3) \times 10^9 = 12 \times 10^9 > 10^{10} - 1$$

A carry from the L register to the U register resulted, thus emphasizing that the A register acts as a 20-position unit in addition. When an addition or subtraction causes a carry from the L register to the U register, it is said that an *overflow* from the L register to the U register has occurred. A carry from the L register to the U register does not result in ambiguity if the contents of the A register are considered as a 20-digit number.

It will be seen in Chap. 4 that it is frequently convenient to consider the contents of the U register and those of the L register as two independent numbers. When this is the case, an overflow from the L register to the U register will lead to ambiguous results.

3.7 Overflow from the A Register. When the AUP operation is executed and $[(N_3 + N_1) \times 10^{10}] + N_2 \geq 10^{20}$, an overflow from the A register occurs because the sum exceeds a 20-digit number.

Example 3.5   AUP 8001

$$C(\text{A}) = (6 \times 10^{19}) + 123 \qquad = \quad 60\ 0000\ 0000\ 00\ 0000\ 0123+$$
$$C(\text{D}) = 4 \times 10^{9} \qquad\qquad = \quad 40\ 0000\ 0000+$$
$$C(\text{A}) + [C(\text{D}) \times 10^{10}] = 10^{20} + 123 = 1\ 00\ 0000\ 0000\ 00\ 0000\ 0123+$$

The carry from the left end of the A register causes an overflow signal to be sent to the control unit. This signal may be used to stop the computer or it may be alternatively used to initiate action specified by the user of the computer. This will be discussed later in connection with the BOV (branch on overflow) operation.

3.8 Addition of Numbers with Opposing Signs. Thus far, the signs of the A register and the D register have been considered to be positive. This is not a necessary restriction, and it played no part in the operations being illustrated. If the signs are not the same, the correct algebraic sum (with regard to sign) will be copied into the 20 digit positions of the A register and the appropriate sign will be entered into the sign position of the A register.

For example, let $C(dddd) = -5$ and $C(\text{A}) = +3$; then execute the operation ALO *dddd*.

Example 3.6   ALO *dddd*

$$C(dddd) \to \text{D} \quad = \qquad\qquad\qquad 00\ 0000\ 0005-$$
$$C(\text{A}) \qquad\qquad = 00\ 0000\ 0000\ 00\ 0000\ 0003+$$
$$C(\text{A}) + C(dddd) = 00\ 0000\ 0000\ 00\ 0000\ 0002-$$

3.9 Underflow from the U Register. A condition referred to as *underflow* may occur when an addition is performed and the signs of the two registers differ. Underflow corresponds to a borrow from the units position of the U register. This is exemplified by executing the operation AUP *dddd*, using the values of the above example.

Example 3.7   AUP *dddd*

$$C(dddd) \rightarrow \text{D} \qquad\qquad = 00\ 0000\ 0005-$$
$$C(\text{A}) \qquad\qquad\qquad = 00\ 0000\ 0000\ 00\ 0000\ 0003+$$
$$C(\text{A}) + [C(dddd) \times 10^{10}] = 00\ 0000\ 0004\ 99\ 9999\ 9997-$$

This again serves to emphasize that the A register operates as a 20-position unit. As in the case of a carry from the L to the U register, no ambiguity results from an underflow if the contents of the A register are considered as a 20-digit integer. But ambiguity will result from underflow if the contents of the A register are being considered as two independent 10-digit integers, i.e., if the number in the U register is considered to be independent of the number in the L register.

The conditions under which underflow may occur may be analyzed in terms of the numbers N_3, N_2, and N_1; where $N_3 = C(\text{U})$, $N_2 = C(\text{L})$, $N_1 = C(dddd)$, and N_3 and N_2 always have the same sign.

If the AUP *dddd* operation is being executed, underflow will occur if and only if $N_2 \neq 0$, $|N_1| > |N_3|$,* and the signs of the A register and the register located at *dddd* differ. All three of these conditions must be satisfied for underflow to occur when the AUP *dddd* operation is executed.

If the ALO *dddd* operation is being executed, underflow will occur if and only if $N_3 \neq 0$, $|N_1| > |N_2|$, and the signs of the A register and the register located at *dddd* differ. Again, all three conditions must be satisfied for underflow to occur.

3.10 Alignment of Decimal Points in Addition. It was stated earlier that the 650 performs integer arithmetic. Integers were used in all the foregoing examples of addition, but this restriction is not so serious as it might first appear. Assume, for example, that the number 00 8765 4321+ has been copied into the register located at *dddd*. This certainly appears to be an integer. For our purposes in the solution of a problem at hand, we may assume the number is actually 8765.4321+. In short, we may assume that a decimal point is located between the fourth and fifth register positions. If this number is to be added to an integer, it will be necessary to position the integer in the A register so that the units position of the integer is in position 5 of either the L or the U register.

---

* The notation $|N_1| > |N_3|$ is read: the magnitude of N_1 is greater than the magnitude of N_3.

Example 3.8

$C(\text{A}) = 5$	00 0000 0000 00 0000 0005+
Shift $C(\text{A})$ left four positions	00 0000 0000 00 0005 0000+
$C(dddd) = 8765.4321$	00 8765 4321+
$C(\text{A}) + C(dddd) \to \text{A}$	00 0000 0000 00 8770 4321+

The requirement of aligning the decimal points of a pair of numbers before addition is common to longhand arithmetic. Since numbers can be positioned in the A register by shifting the contents thereof to the right or to the left, it is possible to align the units positions of a pair of integers, hence the decimal points, before adding them. The shift operations and operation codes will be discussed later.

3.11   The Reset and Add Operation.   In the preceding examples it has been assumed in each case that one of the two numbers to be added was already in the A register. Frequently it will be necessary to add a pair of numbers, neither of which is in the A register. In this event, we might clear the A register to 0, add the first of the two numbers into the A register, position this number for alignment of decimal points, and then add the second of the two numbers to the A register. The sum of the two numbers then resides in the A register.

The operation codes RAU and RAL are abbreviations, respectively, for *reset the A register and add to the U register* and *reset the A register and add to the L register*.

The operation RAU *dddd* implies the following sequence of events:

$$C(dddd) \to \text{D}; 0 \to \text{A}; [C(\text{D}) \times 10^{10}] + 0 \to \text{A}$$

First the number from *dddd* is copied into the D register. Next the A register is reset to 0; i.e., each of the 20 digit positions is set to 0 and the sign position is set to plus. Finally, the D register is aligned with the U register and addition is performed. When the addition is completed, the number in the U register is identical to the number in the D register, which in turn is identical to the number in register *dddd*, from which it was copied.

The operation RAL *dddd* implies the following sequence of events:

$$C(dddd) \to \text{D}; 0 \to \text{A}; C(\text{D}) + 0 \to \text{A}$$

This operation differs from the RAU *dddd* operation only in that the D register is aligned with the L register, instead of the U register, before the addition is performed.

3.12   Add Magnitude to the A Register.   The operation AML *dddd* implies the following events:

$$C(dddd) \to D; |C(\text{D})| + C(\text{A}) \to \text{A}$$

The number from register *dddd* is copied together with sign into the D register; then the D register is aligned with the L register. When the addition is performed, the sign of the D register is ignored and the number therein is added to the A register as a magnitude (i.e., as a positive number). The notation $|C(\text{D})|$ is interpreted as the magnitude or absolute value of the contents of the D register.

The operation RAM *dddd* implies the following events:

$$C(dddd) \rightarrow \text{D}; \; 0 \rightarrow \text{A}; \; |C(\text{D})| + 0 \rightarrow \text{A}$$

This operation differs from AML *dddd* in that the A register is reset to 0 before the addition is performed. After the operation is executed, the contents of the D register (sign included) are equal to the contents of *dddd*. The U register contains zeros; the number in the L register is equal in magnitude to that in the D register; but the sign of the A register will be positive regardless of the sign of the D register.

3.13 The Subtraction Operation. Since subtraction is a special case of addition [e.g., $h - k = h + (-k) = -(-h + k)$], it is not too surprising that each addition operation code has a counterpart subtraction operation code. The subtraction operations are summarized below.

SLO *dddd*: $C(dddd) \rightarrow \text{D}; \; C(\text{A}) - C(\text{D}) \rightarrow \text{A}$

SUP *dddd*: $C(dddd) \rightarrow \text{D}; \; C(\text{A}) - [C(\text{D}) \times 10^{10}] \rightarrow \text{A}$

RSL *dddd*: $C(dddd) \rightarrow \text{D}; \; 0 \rightarrow \text{A}; \; C(\text{A}) - C(\text{D}) \rightarrow \text{A}$

RSU *dddd*: $C(dddd) \rightarrow \text{D}; \; 0 \rightarrow \text{A}; \; C(\text{A}) - [C(\text{D}) \times 10^{10}] \rightarrow \text{A}$

SML *dddd*: $C(dddd) \rightarrow \text{D}; \; C(\text{A}) - |C(\text{D})| \rightarrow \text{A}$

RSM *dddd*: $C(dddd) \rightarrow \text{D}; \; 0 \rightarrow \text{A}; \; C(\text{A}) - |C(\text{D})| \rightarrow \text{A}$

The operations summarized above are analogous to the addition operations, to which the reader may refer for translation of the symbolic descriptions. It is left as an exercise for the reader to determine the conditions that will lead to underflow when a subtract operation is executed.

3.14 The Nines Complement of a Number. In the discussion of underflow, it was shown that the 650 A register is a *direct-reading* accumulator. The term direct-reading is used to indicate that the accumulator displays the appropriate magnitude and sign of both positive and negative numbers.

Most desk calculators do not have direct-reading accumulators. The reader who is familiar with such a calculator will recall that when a sum is calculated for a sequence that contains both positive and negative integers, the accumulator may or may not display the magnitude of the sum directly. If the positive numbers are entered to the accumulator by depressing the ADD key and the negative numbers are entered by depressing the SUBTRACT key, the correct magnitude will be displayed when the sum is positive; but the tens complement of the magnitude will be displayed when the sum is negative.

The mechanical reason behind this can be demonstrated in terms of a one-position rotary accumulator that can assume the values 0, 1, 2, . . . , 9, as illustrated in Fig. 3.12. The accumulator displays the integer 0 as though it had just been reset. Next the integer 2 is added (Fig. 3.12b) to the accumulator. After the integer 2 has been added, the integer 3 is subtracted (Fig. 3.12c) from the accumulator. In each case, the direction of rotation of the wheel depends upon whether the number has been added (plus) or subtracted (minus), while the amount of rotation depends upon the magnitude of the number.

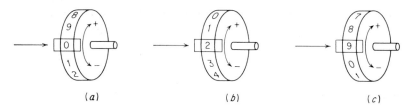

(a)   (b)   (c)

FIG. 3.12. Schematic of a one-position rotary accumulator. (a) Initial setting. (b) After +2. (c) After +2−3.

The integer 9 is displayed as a result of the successive rotations of the wheel. The latter rotation causes the wheel to move one position past 0 in the negative direction. The correct answer in this case can be calculated by subtracting the integer displayed from 10 and assigning the result a minus sign, i.e., $-(10 - 9) = -1$. In other words, the correct answer is obtained by taking the tens complement of the number displayed and reversing the sign.

The user of a desk calculator must recognize when a sum or difference is negative and take the appropriate action to obtain the correct magnitude and to assign the negative sign. This is accomplished rather simply by an individual when a sum or difference involves only two numbers. If a subtraction is indicated, the rule is to change the sign of the subtrahend and add, e.g.,

$$a - b = a + (-b) = -[b + (-a)]$$

If the sum involves two numbers with different signs, the individual determines the larger of the two numbers by inspection; he then subtracts the smaller magnitude from the larger and assigns the result the sign of the larger magnitude, e.g., $a - b = -(b - a)$.

This approach is not practical in an automatic computer for two reasons. The first is that the computer cannot determine which is the larger of two magnitudes without taking the difference; i.e., it cannot make such a determination by inspection. The second is that the process of borrowing [e.g., $22 - 9 = 10 + (12 - 9) = 13$] is "awkward" for an electronic accumulator.

Both these difficulties may be overcome by using the nines complement to represent the negative integer when a sum involves two integers with different signs. A set of logical rules that might be adapted are discussed below. First the tens complement and the nines complement of an integer will be defined.[1]

Let N be any positive integer less than 10^k. The tens complement of N is equal to $10^k - N$. The nines complement of N is equal to $(10^k - 1) - N$. For the 20-position A register of the 650, the value of k must be at least 20. The use of the tens complement in addition and subtraction operations can be demonstrated in terms of a two-position accumulator (k equals 2) without any loss in generality.

It is apparent that 99 is the largest integer that can be displayed in a two-position accumulator. When $k = 2$, the tens complement of 99 is $100 - 99 = 1$. The nines complement of 99 is $99 - 99 = 0$. It should be noted that the calculation of the tens complement will involve borrowing, whereas the calculation of the nines complement precludes any requirement for borrowing. Hence the nines complement will be used in the development of a logical set of rules for the determination of magnitudes and signs of sums or differences of pairs of integers having the same or different signs.

Let a and b both be positive integers less than 100. This assumption does not restrict the generality of the following discussion.

1. If a subtract operation is to be executed, change the sign of the subtrahend and execute the addition operation as indicated in (2); e.g., $a - b = a + (-b) = -[b + (-a)]$; and if b has a negative sign, $[a - (-b)] = a + b$.
2. If the add operation is to be executed, first compare the signs of augend and addend.
   a. If both signs are the same, add the magnitudes and assign the common sign to the sum; i.e., $a + b = +(|a| + |b|)$ or $-a - b = -(|a| + |b|)$.
   b. If the signs of the augend and addend are different [e.g., $a + (-b)$], take the nines complement of the magnitude of the integer with the negative sign; then add the nines complement to

[1] In general, if $0 \leq x \leq y$, the complement of x with respect to y is $y - x$. The complement with respect to y of the complement of x with respect to y is $y - (y - x) = x$; thus the complement is self-inverse.

the positive integer. The rules for determination of magnitude and sign will be developed in the three cases below.

Let $S = a - b$. The sign of S is positive if $a > b$. The sign of S is negative if $a < b$. It is customary to let the sign of S be positive when $S = 0$, i.e., when $a = b$.

Let
$$S_c = a + \text{nines complement of } b$$
$$= a + [(10^2 - 1) - b] = (a - b) + 99$$

Now consider the three cases $a > b$, $a < b$, and $a = b$.

If $a > b$, then $S_c \geq 100$; the sign of S is positive; and

$$S = (a - b) = S_c - 99 = (S_c + 1) - 100$$

For example, let $a = 55$ and $b = 45$; then $S = 10$.

$$S_c = 55 + (99 - 45) = 109$$
$$S = (S_c + 1) - 100 = (109 + 1) - 100 = +10$$

In terms of a two-position register, when $a > b$ there will be a carry from the left end of the accumulator that can be used to indicate that the sign of the sum is positive and to augment S_c by 1 as required. The accumulator then displays the correct magnitude and sign.

$$
\begin{array}{c}
\text{Carry} \\
\text{signal}
\end{array}
\;
\begin{array}{ccc}
-1 & 0 & 9 \\
 & + & 1 \\
\hline
0 \quad 1 & 0 & +
\end{array}
$$

If $a < b$, then $S_c < 99$, the sign of S is negative, and

$$S = -(b - a) = -(\text{the nines complement of } S_c)$$
$$= -[99 - (a - b + 99)] = -(b - a)$$

For example, let $a = 42$ and $b = 57$; then $S = -15$.

$$S_c = 42 + (99 - 57) = 84$$
$$S = -(99 - 84) = -15$$

In terms of a two-position register, when $a < b$ there will be no carry from the left end of the accumulator, in which case the magnitude of S is the nines complement of S_c and the sign is negative.

$$
\begin{array}{ccll}
0 & 8 & 4 & \text{No carry} \\
- & 9 & 9 & \text{Nines complement} \\
\hline
 & 1 & 5 & -
\end{array}
$$

If $a = b$, a problem arises only because it is customary to assign a positive sign when S is 0 but there is no carry impulse. The 650 does assign a positive sign to a 0 resulting from either an add or a subtract operation.

The reader may also be concerned about the use of overflow (carry) from the left end of the accumulator to indicate a positive sign. This use of the overflow can be logically distinguished from that used to indicate the generation of a sum that exceeds the capacity of the accumulator. The latter will occur only when the signs of the addend and augend are the same, while the former will occur only when the signs differ.

3.15 The Shift A Register Operations. Before continuing with the arithmetic operations multiply and divide, let us define the operations provided for shifting the contents of the A register to the left and to the right. The symbolic operation code SLT is an abbreviation for *shift the contents of the A register to the left.* The number of positions that the contents will be shifted is controlled by the magnitude of the units position of a four-digit integer appended to the operation code, e.g., SLT *dddx*. The integer *dddx* must be the address of a register, but the register located at *dddx* is not affected by the execution of a shift operation. The digit x may be assigned the value 0, 1, . . . , 9. It determines the amount of the shift. If x is 0, no shift will occur. If x is 9, the contents of the A register will be shifted nine positions to the left. Any digits shifted out of the A register are lost, while the positions vacated at the right end of the A register are filled with zeros.

The operation SRT *dddx* is analogous to SLT *dddx* except that the contents of the A register are shifted to the right x positions.

3.16 Shift A Register and Round. The symbolic operation code SRD is an abbreviation for *shift the contents of the A register to the right and round.* The operation SRD *dddx* is similar to SRT *dddx*, but there are two important differences. If x is 0, the contents of the A register are shifted 10 places to the right, instead of 0 as in SRT *ddd*0. Regardless of the value of x, rounding is performed after the shifting is completed. This is accomplished automatically by the addition of a 5 to the last digit shifted off the right end of the A register, e.g.,

$$
\begin{array}{lll}
C(\text{A}) = & 0987654321 & 0987654321 \ 0- \\
\text{SRD } 0005 & 0000009876 & 5432109876 \ 5- \\
& & + \ 5 \\
& 0000009876 & 5432109877 \ 0- \\
\end{array}
$$

The addition is performed without regard to sign of the A register, just as it would be done by an individual in rounding a number manually.

3.17 Shift A Register Left and Count Shifts. The symbolic operation code scT is an abbreviation for *shift the contents of the A register to the left and count the number of shifts that must be performed until the high-order position of the U register contains a digit other than 0.* The number of shifts that can be executed is limited. In no case can it exceed 10. It is further restricted by the magnitude of x in the specification of the operation, scT *dddx*. The number of shifts cannot exceed x except when x is 0, in which case the maximum is 10.

If the high-order position of the U register does not contain a digit other than 0 before or after x shifts have been made, shifting stops and an error signal is sent to the control unit. This signal is referred to as a shift-and-count overflow signal. It may be used like the A register overflow signal to stop the computer or to initiate alternative operations as discussed in the BOV operation.

After the shifting has been terminated, a count C is entered into the two low-order positions of the L register. The count C is determined as follows:

1. If x is 0, then C is equal to the actual number of shifts.
2. If x is not 0, then C is equal to $10 - x$ plus the number of shifts.

The scT operation is rather specialized as compared with the operations previously introduced. It is used particularly in performing floating-point arithmetic, which will be discussed after the arithmetic operations of multiplication and division.

3.18 The Multiplication Operation. Multiplication is performed in the 650 accumulator by a process of successive additions that is almost directly analogous to the longhand procedure for multiplication. The multiplier must have been stored in the U register by a preceding operation. The multiply operation is symbolically specified by the term MPY *dddd*, where *dddd* is the address of the register containing the multiplicand.

Example 3.9

Multiply $C(aaaa)$ by $C(bbbb)$. Assume that $C(aaaa) = 35 \times 10^8$ and that $C(bbbb) = 32 \times 10^8$.

Operation	U register	L register	D register
RAU *bbbb*	32 0000 0000	00 0000 0000 +	32 0000 0000 +
MPY *aaaa*	11 2000 0000	00 0000 0000 +	35 0000 0000 +

The product of two 10-digit integers is displayed as a 20-digit integer in the A register, and the appropriate sign is displayed in the sign position.

The basic scheme for multiplication, in the 650, of 35×10^8 by 32×10^8 is as follows: The contents of the A register are shifted to the left one position; then the multiplicand 35×10^8 is added to the A register three times. The number of additions is controlled by the (multiplier) digit shifted out of the A register. When this has been completed, the contents of the A register are again shifted to the left one position; then the multiplicand is added to the A register twice. This is followed by eight successive shifts of the contents of the A register one position to the left. These eight shifts correspond to the eight zeros indicated by the factor 10^8 in the multiplier. The scheme can be illustrated by the following analogy to longhand arithmetic. The difference is that the procedure starts with the high-order position of the multiplier and proceeds from left to right.

35 0000 0000	35×10^8
32 0000 0000	32×10^8
35 0000 0000	70
35 0000 0000	105
35 0000 0000	1120×10^{16}
3 5000 0000	
3 5000 0000000000000	
112 0000 0000000000000	

The specific sequence of operations executed automatically by the 650 is outlined below. This sequence is completed for each multiplication regardless of the number of zeros in the 10-digit multiplier. The computer cannot make the short cuts that an individual would when zeros are encountered. The number of additions required to generate a product is equal to the sum of the 10 digits in the multiplier.

In the description that follows, two registers are introduced that are not included in the illustration of Fig. 3.11. Each of these registers has only one digit position, and neither has an address. One is referred to as a shift counter because it is used to record the number of left shifts of the A register as they are executed. The other is referred to as an index register, and it is used to count the multiplier digit down to 0 as successive additions of the multiplicand to the A register are performed.

Execution of the MPY *aaaa* operation involves stepping through the following sequence of operations:

1. Transfer the contents of *aaaa* to the D register and set the shift counter to 0.
2. Shift the contents of the A register one position to the left and copy the multiplier digit shifted out the left end into the index register.
3. Test the index register.   Is it equal to 0?
   a. If it is, go to step 6.
   b. If it is not, go to step 4.
4. Align the D register with the L register and add the integer in the D register to the integer in the A register, both regarded as positive quantities, i.e., $|C(\text{D})| + |C(\text{A})| \rightarrow \text{A}$.
5. Decrease the index register by 1, then go back to step 3.
6. Test the shift counter.   Is it set at 9?
   a. If it is not, increase it by 1, then go back to step 2.
   b. If it is, go to step 7.
7. Does the sign of the A register equal the sign of the D register? (These signs have not been affected by the foregoing operations.)
   a. If they are equal, set the sign of the A register to plus.
   b. If they are different, set the sign of the A register to minus.
8. The multiply operation is complete.

While the foregoing operations are performed automatically, the description of the sequence is typical of the logical description of a computer program, a subject pursued in Chap. 4.

Example 3.10 illustrates the consequence of leaving a residual in the L register when a multiply operation is executed.

Example 3.10

Multiply the contents of the D register by the contents of the U register without clearing the L register.

Let $\qquad$ $C(\text{A}) = 00\ 0000\ 0004\ 00\ 0000\ 1234+$
Let $\qquad$ $C(\text{D}) = \qquad 00\ 0000\ 0002 -$
The operation is MPY 8001.
The result is $C(\text{A}) = \quad 00\ 0000\ 1234\ 00\ 0000\ 0008 -$.

The L register is not cleared automatically before execution of the operation MPY *dddd*.   Instead, the absolute value of the "product" is $[|C(\text{U})| \times |C(dddd)|] + [|C(\text{L})| \times 10^{10}]$, where *dddd* contains the multiplicand.   This feature can be used in generating a sum of products, if the sum is sure to be less than 10^{10} and all intermediate products have the same sign.   On the other hand, it can lead to erroneous results when the residual in L is inadvertent.   If the residual is large enough, an overflow may occur that will affect the multiplier.

3.19 The Decimal Point in Multiplication. It has been stated earlier that the 650 treats all numbers as integers but that it is possible to position an *implied* decimal point by the appropriate use of the shift A register operations. The position of the *implied* decimal point after multiplication is illustrated in Example 3.11.

Example 3.11

Perform the multiplication $C(0000) \times C(0050)$, assuming that

$$C(0000) = 00000XX.XXX \qquad \text{e.g., } 0000012.345$$
$$C(0050) = 000000X.XXX \qquad \text{e.g., } 0000001.234$$

Round the result to two decimal places. The implied decimal points are shown in the example, but they do not appear in the actual registers.

The strings of X's are used to represent a number for the purpose of indicating that only the number of digit positions in the number is known in advance but that the value the number will assume in a particular operation is not known in advance. Each 0 shown indicates that the corresponding digit position will always be 0 for all values to be considered in a particular problem. Each X indicates that the corresponding digit position may be any one of the digits 0, 1, . . . , 9.

Operation	U register	L register	D register
RAU 0000	$00000XX.XXX$		$00000XX.XXX$
MPY 0050		$0XXX.XXXXXX$	$000000X.XXX$
SRD 0004		$0000\ 0XXX.XX$	$000000X.XXX$

The number of digit positions in the product can be no greater than the sum of the digit positions in the multiplicand and the multiplier. The number of decimal places d in the product is equal to the sum of the decimal places in the multiplicand d_1 and the multiplier d_2. The number of shifts $s = d - d_p$, where d_p is the number of decimal places to be shown in the product. The SRD operation causes automatic rounding after shifting is completed.

3.20 The Division Operation. There are two division operations available in the 650. One, DIV $dddd$, transfers the contents of $dddd$ to the D register and then divides the 20-digit integer in the A register by the 10-digit integer in the D register. The quotient is copied into the L register and the remainder stays in the U register.

It is at this point that the U register may have its own sign. The U register, containing the remainder, will have the sign of the dividend.

The A register (hence the L register) will have the appropriate sign for the quotient. This condition continues until a reset (e.g., RAU, RSL, etc.), multiply, or another divide operation is executed, at which time the sign of the A register again becomes the common sign for both U and L registers.

The second division operation, DVR *dddd*, differs from the first in that the remainder is not saved; instead, the U register is reset to zeros after the quotient is generated. After the divide and reset upper operation, from which the code DVR stems, the quotient is in the L register, the U register is set to zero, and the sign of the A register is the sign of the quotient.

The two division operations can be described symbolically as follows, with Q indicating quotient and R indicating remainder:

DIV *dddd*: $C(dddd) \rightarrow$ D; $C(\text{A}) \div C(\text{D})$; $Q \rightarrow$ L, $R \rightarrow$ U
DVR *dddd*: $C(dddd) \rightarrow$ D; $C(\text{A}) \div C(\text{D})$; $Q \rightarrow$ L, $0 \rightarrow$ U

The division is performed by successive subtractions of the divisor from the dividend. This is essentially the way the individual performs longhand division. The principal difference is that the individual knows the multiplication table and takes advantage of this knowledge in the digit-by-digit determination of the quotient. Another difference is that the individual ignores the high-order zeros. The following example is performed the way the 650 would do it:

```
                                    2020202020
      00  0000  0022   )00 0000 0004 4444444444
                        −0 0000 0002 2
                        −0 0000 0002 2
                        −0 0000 0002 2
                        +0 0000 0002 2
                            0000 0000 04
                           −0000 0000 22
                           +0000 0000 22
                             000 0000 044
                            −000 0000 022
                            −000 0000 022
                            −000 0000 022
                            +000 0000 022
                             00 0000 0004
                                   .
                                   .

                             0000000004
                            −0000000022
                            +0000000022
                             0000000004
```

The sequence of steps listed below illustrates the logic followed by the 650 in the automatic execution of the symbolic operation DIV *dddd*. As in multiplication, allusion is made to two auxiliary one-position registers not shown in Fig. 3.11. One register is used as a shift counter. It will be seen that the contents of the A register are shifted (one position) to the left exactly 10 times each time a division operation is executed. The other register, referred to as the trial digit counter, is used to maintain a count of the number of subtractions required to determine a given digit in the quotient.

Before the divide operation is specified, the dividend must be properly positioned in the A register; then the divide operation is executed as follows:

1. Copy the divisor from register *dddd* into the D register. Copy the sign of the dividend into the U register sign position. Set the shift counter to 0.
2. Compare the sign of the dividend (the sign of the U register) with the sign of the divisor (the sign of the D register).
   a. If they are the same, enter a positive sign in the sign position of the A register.
   b. If they are different, enter a negative sign in the sign position of the A register.
3. Shift the contents of the A register one position to the left. Set the trial digit counter to 0.
4. Align the D register with the U register, then subtract the magnitude of the contents of the D register from the magnitude of the contents of the A register, i.e., $|C(\text{A})| - |[C(\text{D}) \times 10^{10}]| \rightarrow \text{A}$.
5. Did the last subtraction result in an overdraw; i.e., is $|C(A)| - |[C(\text{D}) \times 10^{10}]| < 0$?
   a. If not, go to step 6.
   b. If so, restore the last withdrawal; i.e., execute $|C(\text{A})| + |[C(\text{D}) \times 10^{10}]| \rightarrow \text{A}$, copy the trial digit counter into the units position of the A register, then go to step 7.
6. Is the trial digit counter equal to 9?
   a. If not, increase the counter by 1, then go back to step 4.
   b. If so, signal a *quotient overflow* and halt execution.
7. Is the shift counter equal to 9?
   a. If not, increment the counter by 1, then go back to step 3.
   b. If so, 10 shifts have been executed and division is complete.[1]

When the division operation is completed, the quotient is in the L register and the remainder with its sign is in the U register.

[1] If the operation code is DVR instead of DIV, the U register is reset to 0 automatically; then the division operation is complete.

3.21   Quotient Overflow.   If either division operation, DIV *dddd* or DVR *dddd*, attempts to generate a quotient with more than 10 digit positions, the 650 will stop automatically because the L register would not be able to contain such a quotient.

If DIV *dddd* or DVR *dddd* were to be executed when $|C(\text{A})/C(dddd)| \geq 10^{10}$, a quotient overflow would occur.   This is equivalent to stating that a quotient overflow will occur whenever division is attempted and $|C(\text{U})| \geq |C(dddd)|$.

It follows that quotient overflow can be avoided by making sure that $|C(\text{U})| < |C(dddd)|$ whenever DIV *dddd* or DVR *dddd* is to be executed.   It is important to keep in mind that in the foregoing inequalities, the contents of both registers are integers.   If the contents of *dddd* are 0, quotient overflow can be avoided only by not executing the division operation.   If the contents of *dddd* are not 0, quotient overflow can be avoided by shifting the contents of the A register (the dividend) to the right until $|C(\text{U})| < |C(dddd)|$.

The foregoing inequality is surely satisfied if the dividend is positioned in the A register so that all the nonzero digit positions in the dividend lie to the right of all the nonzero digit positions in the divisor when register *dddd* is aligned with the U register, e.g.,

Dividend in the A register: 0 0 0 0*XXXXXX   XXXXXXXXXX*
Divisor in *dddd*:   *XXXX*0 0 0 0 0 0

3.22   The Decimal Point in Division.   The location of an *implied* decimal point in a quotient generated in the 650 may be determined just as it would if the division were performed manually.   The number d_q of decimal places in the quotient is equal to the number d_n of decimal places in the dividend minus the number d_d of decimal places in the divisor, i.e., $d_q = d_n - d_d$.

To increase the number of decimal places in the quotient, we must either increase the number of decimal places in the dividend or decrease the number of decimal places in the divisor.   The usual procedure, when division is performed manually, is to add trailing zeros to the dividend as required.   When division is performed in the computer, the desired number of trailing zeros can be added to the dividend by shifting it to the left in the A register before executing the division operation.   The number of positions that the dividend may be shifted left is limited by the restriction (discussed in Sec. 3.21) that $|C(\text{U})| < |C(dddd)|$.

Example 3.12 illustrates a simple division problem and shows the status of the U, L, and D registers after execution of the indicated operations.   The dividend is copied from register 1500 into the A register by executing RAL 1500.   At this point, it is noted that the implied number of decimal places is seven for the dividend and five for the divisor. The SLT 0002 operation adds two low-order zeros to the dividend, thus assuring four decimal places in the quotient. The maximum quotient 99999 is obtained from $999.99/.01$. The form of the remainder is deduced from two observations. First, the remainder must be smaller than the divisor. Second, the remainder must have at least as many low-order zeros as the divisor and the dividend have in common.

Example 3.12

Calculate B/C to four decimal places.

Assume that $0.00 \le B \le 999.99$ is located in register 1500 in the form $XXX.XX00000$ and that $0.01 \le C \le 999.99$ is located in register 1501 in the form $00XXX.XX000$.

Operation	U register	L register	D register
RAL 1500		$X\,XX.XX0\;0\;0\;0\;0$	$XXX.XX\;0\,0000$
SLT 0002	XX	$X.XX\;0\;0\;0\;0\;0\;0$	$XXX.XX\;0\,0000$
DIV 1501	$00XXXXX00\,0$	$0\;XX\;XXX.XXXX$	$0\,0X\;XX.XX000$

3.23 Truncation Errors, Rounding Errors, and Floating-point Numbers. The numbers operated on in a computational process may be divided into two classes. The numbers in one class are exact; the numbers in the other class depart from the exact value by an error term which is caused by truncation or rounding of the exact number.

The numbers in the latter class may be described by the relationship $X = x + E$, where X is the exact value, x is the value operated on, and E is a random error. The numbers in the former class may be thought of as a special case where E is known to be 0. For example, the number 2 in the expression $(X + Y)/2$ may be thought of as having a 0 error term, whereas the values assigned to the variables X and Y may be thought of as having random error terms.

The error term may have been introduced prior to execution of the computational process. For example, most measuring devices will have only finite precision; hence the departure of the number recorded from the value measured may be considered a random variable. In addition, a measuring device may have a constant bias or error built into it. An example is a tape measure that has had the first inch removed from it, so that the graduations always read 1 inch higher than the length they actually represent.

Also, errors may be introduced or aggravated during the computational process because of physical limitations of fixed-word-size memory (e.g., 10 digit positions) and fixed-decimal-point restrictions. Such limitations may lead to truncation or rounding of individual values, which action may affect the accuracy of the result of the computation. It should be noted that the meanings of the terms truncation and truncation error, as used in this discussion, differ from the meanings commonly attributed to them in numeric analysis.

The effect of such errors in individual numbers on the accuracy of the result of a computational process involving a long series of arithmetic operations is not well understood. Consequently the following discussion will consider the effect of such errors in the result of arithmetic operations on pairs of numbers, and the bounds of the error in the result of a long series of arithmetic operations.

Truncation and rounding will be defined in terms of a unit interval; hence, it will be convenient to consider the case of truncation and of rounding decimal numbers to integers. However, it will be seen that the same argument holds for truncation or rounding to d decimal places by introducing a multiplying factor 10^{-d}. The following discussion is for the case $d = 0$.

A decimal value V is truncated to an integer I by deleting the decimal-fraction portion of V. Unless otherwise specified, it is assumed that V is positive. Thus $V = I_t + E_t$, and E_t will be referred to as the truncation error. When V is positive, $I \leq V < I + 1$, it follows that $0 \leq E_t < 1$.

A decimal value V is rounded to an integer I by truncating $V + \frac{1}{2}$. Thus, $V = I_r + E_r$, and E_r will be referred to as the rounding error. When V is positive, $I - \frac{1}{2} \leq V < I + \frac{1}{2}$, it follows that $-\frac{1}{2} \leq E_r < \frac{1}{2}$. More specifically, this procedure should be referred to as rounding up. If we defined rounding down in an analogous manner, i.e., truncating $V - \frac{1}{2}$, then we would see that an undesirable bias would be introduced, because with positive V, $I + \frac{1}{2} \leq V < I + \frac{3}{2}$. Hence the term rounding, as used here, implies rounding up.

It is intuitive that a truncation is implied by a number that represents a measurement with a device having finite precision. Alternatively, a truncation may be a consequence of physical limitations of the computing device. To study the effect of truncation or rounding introduced in the computing process on the relative error of the result, it will be assumed in the following discussion that this is the only source of error.

It is also assumed that E_t is a random variable from the interval 0 to 1 with a uniform probability distribution. Then the expected value of E_t is $m_t = \frac{1}{2}$, and the standard deviation of E_t is

$$s_t = \sqrt{\tfrac{1}{12}} = .287228$$

Similarly, it is assumed that E_r is a random variable from the interval $-\frac{1}{2}$ to $\frac{1}{2}$ with a uniform probability distribution. Then the expected value of E_r is $m_r = 0$, and the standard deviation of E_r is $s_r = \sqrt{\frac{1}{12}}$.

The bias in an approximation will be defined to be the expected value of the error term, and the standard deviation of the error term is a measure of the precision of the approximation. Thus, truncation yields a biased approximation, while rounding yields an unbiased approximation. However, both approximations have the same measure of precision.

Consider the errors induced when $V = I + E$ and arithmetic operations are performed on I instead of V. In particular, let $X = x + E_x$ and $Y = y + E_y$, where X and Y are nonnegative true values and x and y are the integer approximations operated upon. Then E_x and E_y are random errors in the approximations.

$$X + Y - (x + y) = E_x + E_y$$
$$XY - xy = xE_y + yE_x + E_xE_y$$
$$\frac{X}{Y} - \frac{x}{y} = \frac{yE_x - xE_y}{y(y + E_y)}$$

If the means and standard deviation defined above are used, the expected errors and standard deviations of the results of arithmetic operations on the above pair of values are as follows, if it is assumed that the errors in the two factors are independent:

Operation	Expected error		Standard deviation
	Truncation	Rounding	
Addition	1	0	$\sqrt{\frac{2}{12}}$
Multiplication	$[(x + y)/2] + \frac{1}{4}$	0	?
Division	$(y - x)/y(2y + 1)$	0	?

Now consider the error that will be generated when a sequence of arithmetic operations is performed on N values. If it is assumed that error terms in the N values are statistically independent, the expected error of the result will be 0 if each approximation is the result of rounding. Although true, the implication of this statement may be unduly optimistic for the person not familiar with statistics. In the first place, the assumption of independence of the error terms may be unwarranted. Furthermore, the actual error may be large even though its expected value is 0. Hence, we should like to know the distribution function of the error of the result, so that we can determine the likelihood that it falls within a specified range of values. Short of this, we shall settle for an upper bound on the magnitude of the error.

In the case of the sum of N integer approximations of decimal numbers, the limit on the magnitude of the error of the sum is N if the integer approximations resulted from truncation and is $N/2$ if they resulted from rounding. In either case, the standard deviation of the error of the sum is $s_{ES} = \sqrt{N/12}$. Thus, if N is relatively large (i.e., 30 or more) and if many such sums are generated, the central-limit theorem of theoretical statistics leads us to expect that about two-thirds of the time the error in the sum of N rounded approximations would fall in the interval $-\sqrt{N/12} \le E_{sr} \le \sqrt{N/12}$, and the error in the sum of N truncated approximations would fall in the interval $N/2 - \sqrt{N/12} \le E_{st} \le N/2 + \sqrt{N/12}$.

Except for the expected error induced by rounding, it would be extremely difficult to make statistical statements about the error of a product of N factors. However, something can be said about the bounds of the relative error of the product.

Consider the case $\left(\dfrac{X}{x}\right)^N = \left(1 + \dfrac{E}{x}\right)^N$, where E is the error in x and E/x is the relative error in x. Let $r = E/x$ and consider $(1 + r)^N$.

$$(1 + r)^N = 1 + Nr + \frac{N(N - 1)}{2} r^2 + \frac{N!}{3!(N - 3)!} r^3 + \cdots$$
$$+ Nr^{N-1} + r^N$$
$$< 1 + Nr + \frac{(Nr)^2}{2} + \frac{(Nr)^3}{3!} + \cdots \le e^{Nr} \cong (2.718)^{Nr}$$

Thus, if P is the actual product and p is the calculated product, then $P/p \le e^{NE/x}$. If the error in the product is E_p, then a bound on the magnitude of the relative error of the product p is given by

$$\frac{E_p}{p} = \frac{P}{p} - 1 \le e^{NE/x} - 1$$

Table 3.1 shows how the bound on the relative error of a product of N factors varies with NE/x. The first column of the table contains a selected set of values of NE/x. The second column shows the contribution of the first two terms of the expansion to the relative error of the product. The third column shows the upper bound on the magnitude and the relative error of the product.

Table 3.1 shows that the first two terms of the expansion account for most of the relative error in the product. In particular, when $NE/x \le .10$, the first two terms of the expansion account for about 99.8 per cent of the relative error in the product. Furthermore, when $NE/x \le .02$, the relative error in the product will not exceed NE/x by more than 1 per cent. Thus, if the relative error of each factor is sufficiently small, N can be quite large and the relative error of the product will still be small.

When arithmetic is being performed manually, the number of digit positions and the relative location of the decimal point can be adjusted to provide for retaining a specified number of significant digits in each intermediate result. But when we are restricted to a fixed register size (e.g., 10 digit positions) and a fixed location of the decimal point within the register, the number of significant digit positions and hence the relative error in intermediate results may vary widely. In many data-processing problems, these restrictions will cause no difficulty.

Table 3.1

NE/x	$(NE/x)(1 + NE/2x)$	$e^{NE/x} - 1$
1.00	1.50000	1.71828
.50	.62500	.64872
.25	.28125	.28403
.10	.10500	.10517
.05	.05125	.05127
.02	.02020	.02020
.01	.01005	.01005
.001	.00100	.00100

For example, when the range of possible values for each datum of a data set is known in advance and when the sequence of operations to be performed on the data set is sufficiently small, an analysis may be made to determine whether the restrictions of fixed register size and fixed location of the decimal point will lead to intolerable error in the results.

The consequences of the restriction of fixed word size can be greatly alleviated by performing double precision arithmetic. This term implies that each number is considered as consisting of two parts, $D = (a \times 10^{10} + b)10^{-d}$, where d is the number of decimal places in the 20-digit number, a is the high-order 10-digit positions, and b is the low-order 10-digit positions. The two parts of a 20-digit number are stored in separate registers, and the computer is programmed to perform arithmetic operations upon pairs of such numbers and to detect overflow, e.g., $(a \times 10^{10} + b)(c \times 10^{10} + d)10^{-(d_1+d_2)}$.

The restriction of fixed location of the decimal point can be eliminated by performing floating-point arithmetic. A floating-point number[1] is a 10-digit number $ccmmmmmmmm \pm$, where the two high-

[1] There are several conventions for representing floating-point numbers; the one presented here is commonly referred to as the "excess-50" convention.

order positions, cc, specify the relative location of the decimal point and the remaining positions contain the eight most significant digits of the number being represented. The sign of a floating-point number is the sign of the number being represented.

More specifically, let $\pm F$ be a signed number to be represented as a floating-point number. The excess-50 convention for its representation is

$$\pm F = \pm .mmmmmmmm \times 10^{cc-50}$$

The exponent is stated "excess-50" to obviate the need for a second minus sign. The following are examples of the representation of a selected set of numbers in the floating-point convention defined above:

Number	Floating
-1234567890	$6012345678 -$
0	$0000000000 +$
$.0012345000$	$4812345000 +$
$-.1234567890$	$5012345678 -$

The restrictions on a floating-point number, as defined above, are:

1. F is assigned the value 0 when $0 < |F| < .10000000 \times 10^{-50}$ and is undefined when $|F| \geq 10^{50}$.
2. A floating-point number is truncated to eight significant-digit positions.

These restrictions need not be serious if care is used in calculating the excess-50 exponent. If not, very large numbers may be inadvertently converted to very small numbers and vice versa.

Some computers are designed to perform arithmetic operations on floating-point numbers directly. Otherwise, the computer may be programmed to perform arithmetic operations on floating-point numbers. In the latter case, the computer time required to perform floating-point arithmetic is much greater than that required for fixed-point arithmetic.

Floating-point multiplication and division are important because of the arithmetic precision of the products and the quotients generated. If it is assumed that the relative error of each factor in a floating-point multiplication is $\leq 10^{-8}$, then the relative error of the product is of the order of 10^{-8}. It is easy to demonstrate that the relative error in the quotient of two such factors is of the order of 10^{-8}.

Unfortunately, nothing can be said in general about the relative error of a sum involving both positive and negative numbers. Since such a sum may vanish, the relative error thereof may become infinite.

The previous discussion presented methods of bounding the relative error in a sum of positive numbers, and this bound is equally good for fixed-point and floating-point arithmetic. A method was presented for bounding the magnitude of the relative error of a series of multiplications, in which case negative numbers can be introduced as factors in the multiplication.

However, very little can be said about the relative accuracy of long sequences of mixed arithmetic operations. For example, we should not assume that the same relative accuracy will result from computing $4 \sum_{i=1}^{N} x_i - 2N$ and from computing $\sum_{i=1}^{N} (4x_i - 2)$ even though floating-point arithmetic is used. The actual results of alternative floating-point computations for 2480 values of $0 \leq x_i < 1$ were

$$\Sigma x_i = 1223.8746$$
$$4\Sigma x_i - 4960 = -64.5016$$
$$\Sigma (4x_i - 2) = -64.377721$$

The two results differ in the third significant digit. The true value of Σx_i was in fact 1223.9058674400, and relative errors in the last two computed values were .0018 and .000018, respectively. Thus it is illustrated that the relative error in the difference of two relatively large numbers may be much greater than relative error of either of the factors.

We should remember that floating-point arithmetic does not ensure results that are accurate to eight significant digits. In fact, one criticism of floating-point arithmetic is the apparent accuracy of results even though unjustified. The apparent accuracy may be precluded by errors in measurement of the original data. Furthermore, the apparent accuracy may obscure the fact that the relative error has become quite large, because addition involving a large positive and a large negative number results in a sum whose magnitude is relatively small.

THE CONTROL UNIT

The control unit controls the sequence of functions performed by the computer. It is here that operation codes and addresses are interpreted and that the switching of computer circuitry is initiated. In the discussion of the arithmetic unit we specified certain operations that can be executed by the 650. These operations were specified in terms of a symbolic operation code and a four-digit operand address. At this point we shall specify the form of a 650 instruction; then we shall discuss the interpretation of instructions in the control unit.

Table 3.2 650 Operation Codes*

Operation code		Class	Function of $dddd$	Operation performed
Numeric	Symbolic			
00	NOP	Miscellaneous	None	None
01	HLT	Miscellaneous	None	Halt instruction execution
10	AUP	Arithmetic	Locates operand	$C(\text{A}) + [C(dddd) \times 10^{10}] \rightarrow \text{A}$
11	SUP	Arithmetic	Locates operand	$C(\text{A}) - [C(dddd) \times 10^{10}] \rightarrow \text{A}$
14	DIV	Arithmetic	Locates operand	$C(\text{A}) \div C(dddd) \rightarrow \text{L}$; remainder $\rightarrow \text{U}$; restriction: $|C(dddd)| > |C(U)|$
15	ALO	Arithmetic	Locates operand	$C(\text{A}) + C(dddd) \rightarrow \text{A}$
16	SLO	Arithmetic	Locates operand	$C(\text{A}) - C(dddd) \rightarrow \text{A}$
17	AML	Arithmetic	Locates operand	$C(\text{A}) + |C(dddd)|\dagger \rightarrow \text{A}$
18	SML	Arithmetic	Locates operand	$C(\text{A}) - |C(dddd)| \rightarrow \text{A}$
19	MPY	Arithmetic	Locates operand	$\pm\{[|C(\text{U})| \times |C(dddd)|] + [|C(\text{L})| \times 10^{10}]\} \rightarrow \text{A}$
20	STL	Data transmission	Specifies memory location	$C(\text{L}) \rightarrow \text{D} \rightarrow dddd$
21	STU	Data transmission	Specifies memory location	$C(\text{U}) \rightarrow \text{D} \rightarrow dddd$
22	SDA	Data transmission	Specifies memory location	D address of $\text{L} \rightarrow D$ address of D; $C(\text{D}) \rightarrow dddd$
23	SIA	Data transmission	Specifies memory location	I address of $\text{L} \rightarrow I$ address of D; $C(\text{D}) \rightarrow dddd$
24	STD	Data transmission	Specifies memory location	$C(\text{D}) \rightarrow dddd$
30	SRT	Data transmission	Digit position specifies number of shifts	Shift $C(\text{A})$ to right
31	SRD	Data transmission	Digit position specifies number of shifts 0 indicates 10 shifts	Shift $C(\text{A})$ to right; then round
35	SLT	Data transmission	Digit position specifies number of shifts	Shift $C'(\text{A})$ to left
36	SCT	Data transmission		See Sec. 3.17
44	NZU	Logic	Alternative instruction address	Test magnitude of $C(\text{U})$; if nonzero, next instruction at $dddd$
45	NZE	Logic	Alternative instruction address	Test magnitude of $C(\text{A})$; if nonzero, next instruction at $dddd$

Table 3.2   650 Operation Codes* *(Continued)*

Operation code		Class	Function of *dddd*	Operation performed
Numeric	Sym-bolic			
46	BMI	Logic	Alternative instruction address	Test sign of A register; if minus, next instruction at *dddd*
47	BOV	Logic	Alternative instruction address	Test overflow circuit; if set, next instruction at *dddd*
60	RAU	Arithmetic	Locates operand	$C(dddd) \to$ D; reset A; $C(\text{D}) \to$ U
61	RSU	Arithmetic	Locates operand	$C(dddd) \to$ D; reset A; $-C(\text{D}) \to$ U
64	DVR	Arithmetic	Locates operand	Same as DIV, but U is reset to 0 after division
65	RAL	Arithmetic	Locates operand	$C(dddd) \to$ D; reset A; $C(\text{D}) \to$ L
66	RSL	Arithmetic	Locates operand	$C(dddd) \to$ D; reset A; $-C(\text{D}) \to$ L
67	RAM	Arithmetic	Locates operand	$C(dddd) \to$ D; reset A; $|C(\text{D})| \to$ L
68	RSM	Arithmetic	Locates operand	$C(dddd) \to$ D; reset A; $-|C(\text{D})| \to$ L
69	LDD	Data trans-mission	Locates operand	$C(dddd) \to$ D
70	RCD	Data trans-mission	Locates read band	Read a card into read band indicated
71	PCH	Data trans-mission	Locates punch band	Punch a card from punch band indicated
84	TLU	Miscellaneous		See Sec. 3.26
9x	BDx	Logic		See Sec. 3.26

* Refer to IBM manual for detailed discussion of each operation code.

† $|C(dddd)|$ is interpreted as the magnitude of the contents of *dddd*.

Later we shall introduce additional operations that can be executed by the 650.

3.24   Form of the 650 Instruction.   An *instruction* for the 650 is a 10-digit number with a sign, of the form *rr dddd iiii* $\pm$. Each of the three indicated sets of digits has specific restrictions:

1. *rr* must be a two-digit number that is a valid (defined) operation code. Each symbolic operation code has a two-digit equivalent; e.g., RAU is equivalent to 60. The numeric equivalents of the symbolic operation codes are defined in Table 3.2.

2. *dddd* must be a register address—0000 through 1999 or 8000[1] through 8003. These positions will be referred to as the operand address or as the *D* address.[2] For most operation codes, the operand address specifies the location of the operand, the data that are to be operated on. For some operation codes, only memory-register addresses (0000 through 1999) are permissible as operand addresses. For some operation codes the operand address does not locate an operand, e.g., SLT 0001.

3. *iiii* must be a register address. These positions are referred to as the *I* (instruction) address, because they usually specify the location of the next instruction to be executed.

The inclusion of the (next) instruction address as part of the instruction makes possible the statement of a sequence of instructions that can be automatically located and automatically executed by the computer. A set of instructions that directs the computer in the solution of a problem is referred to variously as a *program*, a *routine*, or a *subroutine*. The person who formulates a program is referred to as a *programmer*.

The sequence of instructions in Example 3.13 will suffice to calculate $(B + C)E/F$, rounded to two decimal places. It is assumed here that B, C, E, and F are integers stored in locations 0050 through 0053 respectively in the form 00 0000 0XXX. The first instruction is placed arbitrarily in location 0000, and the locations of succeeding instructions follow sequentially.

Example 3.13

Step	Instruction location	Operation symbol	Code Number	Data address	Instruction address	U	L	D
1	0000	RAU	60	0050	0001	B		B
2	0001	AUP	10	0051	0002	$B + C$		C
3	0002	MPY	19	0052	0003		$(B + C)E$	E
4	0003	SLT	35	0003	0004			E
5	0004	DVR	64	0053	0005		$(B + C)E/F$	F
6	0005	SRD	31	0001	NEXT		$(B + C)E/F$	F

The steps could be verbally described as follows:

1. Reset the A register, add the contents of register 0050 to the U register, then execute the instruction in register 0001.

---

[1] The STORAGE ENTRY switches are addressed at 8000.

[2] In the "IBM 650 Manual of Operating Instructions," these positions are referred to as the *D* (data) address.

2. Add C to the contents of the U register, then execute the instruction in register 0002.

3. Multiply E by the contents of the U register, then execute the instruction in register 0003.

4. Shift the contents of A register to the left three positions, then execute the instruction in register 0004.

5. Divide the contents of the A register by F, then execute the instruction in register 0005.

6. Shift the contents of the A register one position to the right and round the result. The symbolic instruction address NEXT simply implies that the location of the next instruction has not yet been determined.

As defined above, a 650 instruction specifies an operation to be performed, the location of the operand, and the location of the next instruction. The execution of an instruction can therefore be considered as a two-phase cycle. One phase of the instruction execution cycle will be referred to as the *operation phase*, because it is in this phase that the specified operation is executed. The other phase will be referred to as the *fetch phase*.[1]

3.25 Interpretation of an Instruction in the 650 Control Unit. A single 650 instruction is interpreted and executed in an instruction

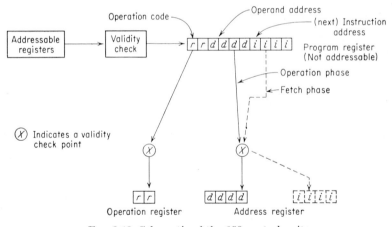

FIG. 3.13. Schematic of the 650 control unit.

cycle. The interpretation takes place in the control unit, which is illustrated schematically in Fig. 3.13. The contents of any addressable register (0000 through 1999 or 8000 through 8003) may be transferred

[1] In the "IBM 650 Manual of Operating Instructions," the operation phase is referred to as the D (data) half-cycle and the fetch phase is referred to as the I (instruction) half-cycle.

to the program register. However, the instruction cycle will not be successfully completed unless the 10-digit number meets the limitations specified (in Sec. 3.24) for an instruction.[1] The operation code is interpreted in the operation register and the addresses are interpreted separately in the address register.

If either an operation code or an address does not satisfy the restrictions specified in Sec. 3.24 or if an invalid character code is encountered as data pass through any one of the validity check points, the computer will stop automatically and no further instruction cycles can be executed until the error condition is manually corrected. Such a stop is referred to alternatively as an *error stop* or as a *machine stop*.[2]

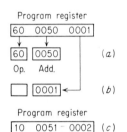

Program register

FIG. 3.14. Control unit phases. (*a*) Operation phase. (*b*) Fetch phase. (*c*) Next instruction.

We shall now discuss the operation and fetch phases of the instruction cycle in greater detail. The first instruction of Example 3.13 will be used to illustrate the discussion.

The operation phase starts when the control unit receives a signal that a 10-digit number (presumably an instruction) has been transferred to the program register.[3,4] When the signal is received, the two-digit operation code is transferred to the operation register and the four-digit operand address is transferred to the address register (see Fig. 3.14*a*).

The operation code is analyzed in the operation register. Unless it is one of the operation codes defined in Table 3.2, the computer halts immediately, because it can interpret only those two-digit codes which are defined in the table. If it is a permissible operation code, switching is initiated to execute the operation, subject to the condition that the operand address can be interpreted.

The operand address is interpreted in the address register. This interpretation depends upon the operation code. However, computer addresses (i.e., 0000 through 1999 or 8000 through 8003) are the only

---

[1] A 10-digit number that is intended as data will be executed as an instruction if it satisfies the specified limitations and is transferred to the program register. A 10-digit number that is intended as an instruction will not be executed unless it properly satisfies the specified limitations.

[2] Identification of a machine stop and subsequent restart procedures are discussed in Chap. 5.

[3] The signal is received only if the character codes for the 10 digit positions and the sign position are all valid; otherwise a validity error will be signaled and the computer will stop.

[4] Note that the path to the program register is one way.

permissible operand addresses, regardless of the operation code. In addition, for certain codes the operand address must be that of a memory register (0000 through 1999). If the operand address is not permissible, the machine stops and signals a storage selection error automatically. If both the operand address and the operation code are permissible, the operation is executed.

At an appropriate time in the operation phase, the control unit receives a signal that the fetch phase may be initiated. When this signal is received, the operation register is cleared and the address of the next instruction[1] to be executed is transferred to the address register for interpretation (see Fig. 3.14b). All machine addresses (0000 through 1999 and 8000 through 8003) are permissible as next instruction addresses. If an unpermitted address is transferred to the address register, the machine stops and signals a storage selection error automatically. Otherwise, the next instruction is located and copied into the program register (see Fig. 3.14c). The completion of the fetch phase is signaled, and the instruction cycle just outlined is repeated. By successive repetitions of the instruction cycle, the computer steps through a sequence of instructions to perform the operations specified by the programmer.

The actual time required to execute an instruction cycle is variable, since it depends upon the operation code, the location of the operand, and the location of the next instruction. The time required to complete a multiplication depends upon two things: (1) the waiting time for the memory register containing the operand to pass under its READ head so that it can be copied into the D register; (2) the number of additions that are required in the multiplication process. In the fetch phase there may be an additional waiting time, since the next instruction can be copied into the program register only as its memory register passes under its READ head.

The waiting time may be reduced by carefully selecting the address of the operand and of the next instruction so that the corresponding registers are at the READ head just at the time they are to be copied. Selecting locations to reduce waiting time is discussed in Secs. 4.10 and 4.11.

3.26 Three Classes of Operations. The operations defined for the 650 may be divided into three classes. One class comprises the *arithmetic operations*, described in the discussion of the arithmetic unit. A second class comprises the *logical* or *branch* operations. The third class comprises the *data-transmission* or *data-transfer* operations.

---

[1] The *I* address of the instruction being executed is the address of the next instruction for all operations except the branch operations, to be discussed later.

The branch operations permit the programming of simple logical decisions in the solution of a problem. The decision is basically a choice between one of two sequences of instructions available for execution and is based on the status of a specified register. For example, the instruction NZU *dddd iiii* provides for the next instruction to be copied into the program register from either *iiii* or *dddd*, depending respectively upon whether the contents of the U register are or are not 0. When the alternative next instruction address *dddd* is selected, a branch is said to have occurred.

The branch operations provided in the 650 are:

1. NZU *dddd iiii*: Branch to address *dddd* for the next instruction if the U register is nonzero. Otherwise, copy the next instruction from *iiii*.
2. NZE *dddd iiii*: Branch to address *dddd* if the A register is nonzero. Otherwise, copy the next instruction from *iiii*.
3. BMI *dddd iiii*: Branch to *dddd* if the sign of the A register is minus. Otherwise, copy the next instruction from *iiii*.
4. BOV *dddd iiii*: Branch to *dddd* if an accumulator or shift-and-count overflow has been sensed. An overflow can be sensed only if the OVERFLOW switch (see Chap. 6) is set at SENSE. Execution of the BOV operation erases the record that an overflow was sensed.
5. BDx *dddd iiii*: Branch to *dddd* if the digit 8 appears in digit position x (1, 2, 3, . . . , 9, 0) of the D register. Continue to *iiii* if the digit 9 appears in digit position x of the D register. Halt execution if a digit other than 8 or 9 appears in digit position x of the D register.

The data-transmission operations include card reading and card punching, copying into (loading) the D register, and copying from (storing) the D, L, or U register. Card reading and card punching will be discussed later in the sections devoted to the input and output units, respectively.

1. LDD *dddd*: Copy the contents of register *dddd* into the D register; symbolically, $C(dddd) \rightarrow$ D. This may be referred to as *load the D register*.
2. STD *dddd*: Copy the contents of the D register into register *dddd*; symbolically, $C(D) \rightarrow dddd$. This may be referred to as *store the D register*.
3. STL *dddd*: Copy the contents of the L register into the D register, then copy the contents of the D register into register

dddd; symbolically, $C(\text{L}) \rightarrow \text{D}$; $C(\text{D}) \rightarrow dddd$. The appropriate sign is copied from the A register.

4. STU *dddd*: This is analogous to STL; symbolically, $C(\text{U}) \rightarrow \text{D}$; $C(\text{D}) \rightarrow dddd$.

5. SDA *dddd*: This is a partial word operation that is useful in the modification of instructions. A use thereof is illustrated in Table 4.1, A Block Zeroing Subroutine. When this operation is executed, positions 5 through 8 of the L register are copied into positions 5 through 8 of the D register; then the D register is copied into register *dddd*. Positions 1 through 4, positions 9 and 10, and the sign position of the D register are not changed when positions 5 through 8 are copied from the L register. The contents of the A register are not affected by this operation.

6. SIA *dddd*: This operation is similar to SDA *dddd*, except that positions 1 through 4 of the L register are copied into the D register; then the D register is copied into register *dddd*.

Except for the operation LDD, the data-transmission operations just defined require that the operand address *dddd* be that of a memory register (0000 through 1999). If this restriction is not satisfied, a storage selection error will be detected when the address is analyzed in the address register.

There are three operations that do not fit into the above classifications. These are the no-operation, the halt, and the table lookup operation.

1. NOP *dddd iiii*:
Perform no operation; just copy next instruction from *iiii*.

2. HLT *dddd iiii*:
Halt execution until the PROGRAM START key (see Chap. 5) is depressed; then copy next instruction from *iiii*. This operation is treated as a NOP when the PROGRAMMED switch (see Chap. 5) is set at RUN.

3. TLU *dddd iiii*:
Execution of the table lookup (TLU) operation causes the computer to compare the magnitude of the integer in the D register with the magnitude of the integer in the first register in the band of memory registers that contains *dddd*. If the magnitude of the integer in the D register exceeds the magnitude of the integer in the memory register with which it is compared, the computer automatically moves to the next memory register and repeats the comparison. When the outcome of a comparison shows that the magnitude

of the integer in the D register is not greater than the magnitude of the integer in the memory register with which it is compared, the comparison cycle is automatically halted and a four-digit integer is copied into positions 5 through 8 of the L register. The integer is equal to the operand address *dddd* of the TLU operation plus the number n_p of registers passed before the comparison cycle is halted; i.e., the number is $dddd + n_p$. For example, let *dddd* be 0000 and let the comparison cycle be halted at the fifth register in the band. Four registers have been passed, so the number 0004 is copied into positions 5 through 8 of the L register, i.e., L $= XX\,0004\,XXXX$. Neither the D register nor the remaining positions of the A register are affected when the number is copied into the L register.

The comparison cycle always starts with the first register in a band. If the comparison cycle is not halted automatically at or before the forty-eighth memory register ($XX47$ or $XX97$) of a band, the last two registers in the band are passed without comparison and the next comparison is made between the D register and the first register in the next band. If the comparison cycle is not halted automatically at or before register 1997, an error is signaled and program execution is halted automatically.

A use of the TLU operation is illustrated in Table 4.12, An Accounts Receivable Posting Routine.

Except for the input and output operations, the basic operations available in a 650 have been defined. The complete set of operations is summarized in Table 3.2.

3.27 Differences among Computers in Automatic Operations Provided. The examples of Chap. 4 will illustrate the use of sequences of operations to perform useful functions. At that time the student will become aware that the programming of certain functions could be facilitated if the 650 provided additional automatic operations. On the other hand, some of the operations that are provided by the 650 could be deleted and the functions provided thereby could be programmed. For example, the TLU, MPY, DIV, and DVR operations could all be programmed.

The decision to include or exclude a given automatic operation involves economic considerations other than programming facility. If, at the time the computer is designed, a decision is made to forego an automatic operation that can be programmed, there may be a reduction in the first cost of the computer. Offsetting this saving, there may be added costs when the computer is used. These may include costs associated with programming the operation, the use of storage registers to store the additional instructions required, and the additional machine time required to perform the operation.

Consideration must be given to these economic factors as well as many others if there is a specific problem to solve and one computer must be chosen from a group. This is an interesting and important problem, but no attempt will be made to deal with it in this book. Instead, we shall assume that the computer has been selected and that the reader is faced with the job of adapting it to the solution of his problem. We shall continue to use the basic 650 for illustrative purposes.

THE INPUT AND OUTPUT UNITS

3.28 The Input Operation. The input or card-reading operation is performed in the IBM 533 Read-Punch unit under the control of the 650. The operation of the 533 unit is discussed further in Chap. 6. To discuss the read operation, it will be necessary to define the term *storage entry register*. These are memory registers, but they serve the additional function of accepting data from the input synchronizer.

Each of the 40 bands of memory registers contains a band of storage entry registers.[1] Registers 0001 through 0010 are the storage entry registers for the first band of memory registers, 0000 through 0049. Registers 0051 through 0060 are the storage entry registers for the second band of memory registers, 0050 through 0099. Similarly, each of the remaining bands of storage entry registers is located an integer multiple of 50 registers from the first set of storage entry registers, 0001 through 0010. For example, $0001 + (39 \times 50) = 1951$ defines the location of the first storage entry register in the last band of memory registers, 1950 through 1999. Similarly, $0010 + (39 \times 50) = 1960$ defines the location of the tenth storage entry register in the last band of memory registers. In short, each set of registers numbered $XX01$ through $XX10$, and each set numbered $XX51$ through $XX60$, is a set of storage entry registers.

The operand address of an instruction specifying the read operation (RCD *dddd iiii*) selects a band of memory registers, and the execution of the read operation causes the contents of the input synchronizer to be copied into the corresponding band of storage entry registers. For example, if *dddd* were one of the numbers 0500 through 0549, the contents of the input synchronizer would be copied into the band of storage entry registers with addresses 0501 through 0510.

[1] In some computers, all memory registers are storage entry registers.

The data from each of the 10 input synchronizer registers are copied into the corresponding register of the band of 10 storage entry registers, as illustrated in Fig. 3.15.

The copying requires approximately 30 milliseconds in the 650; then the input-synchronizer-register positions are all erased (each bit position in each register position is set to the zero state), after which the data from the next punched card in the input unit are translated and copied into the input synchronizer registers, as illustrated in Fig. 3.15. The computer can perform operations (other than a read operation) during the time (approximately 270 milliseconds) that is required for punched-card translation.

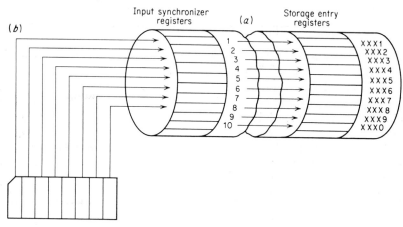

FIG. 3.15. Schematic of the sequence of events in the 650 read operation. (a) First the input synchronizer registers are copied into the selected band of storage entry registers. This transfer is always one for one as shown. (b) Next the input synchronizer registers are cleared and the data from the punched card are translated and stored in the input synchronizer registers. The relationship between card columns and register positions is controlled by plug-board wiring (see Sec. 6.3). This illustration implies 80-80 wiring.

The channeling of data from card columns to synchronizer-register positions is controlled by the wiring of a *plug board* or *control panel* (see Sec. 6.3) that is inserted in the IBM 533 Read-Punch unit, the input-output device of the 650. Plug-board wiring is discussed in Chap. 6, but we shall define 80-80 wiring now, in order that we may complete the discussion of the read operation with an illustration of a method for entering an arbitrary 10-digit number into an arbitrary memory register.

With 80-80 wiring, card columns are channeled to input-synchronizer-register positions as follows. The number in card columns 1 to 10 is channeled to input synchronizer register 1. The number reads from left to right in the register exactly as it does in the card columns. The number is considered to be negative if there is an 11 punch in column 10; otherwise it is considered to be positive. Similarly, the number in card columns 11 to 20 is channeled to input synchronizer register 2, . . . , and the number in card columns 71 to 80 is channeled to input synchronizer register 8. Registers 9 and 10 are not utilized in 80-80 wiring.

It should be noted that 80-80 wiring provides for reading 80 columns of numeric data. No provision is made therein for reading alphanumeric data. In particular, the 12 punch is ignored, and the 11 punch is recognized only as a sign indicator and then only in columns 10, 20, 30, . . . , 80. A column that contains no digit punch (0 to 9) or more than one digit punch will cause an invalid code to be channeled to the corresponding storage-entry-register position. Provision for reading alphanumeric data will be discussed in Chap. 6.

The validity check of character codes copied from the input synchronizer into the storage entry register may be made inactive by 533 plug-board wiring (see Fig. 6.25). On an 80-80 board, this check is inactive, and invalid character codes may be transferred to storage entry registers. The presence of such invalid character codes will be detected only if the register containing them is copied.

Data cannot be read directly into registers other than the 40 sets of storage entry registers. It is possible, however, to transfer a valid word from a storage entry register to any other memory register. In particular, the operation LDD, load the D register, can be used to transfer the word from the storage entry register to the D register; then the operation STD, store the D register, can be used to transfer the word to the desired memory register.

3.29 Loading Instructions or Data to Memory. The *one-word memory load*[1] *card* offers one standard procedure for loading a sequence of instructions to an arbitrary set of memory locations. The format of a one-word memory load card is illustrated in Table 3.3. Columns 1 to 10 contain the instruction LDD 1954 1953. Columns 21 to 30 contain the instruction STD XXXX 8000, where XXXX is the address of the memory register in which the contents of columns 31 to 40 are to be stored and 8000 is the address of the STORAGE ENTRY SWITCHES. The card thus contains an arbitrary 10-digit word, columns 31 to 40, and a pair of instructions for transferring the arbitrary word from

---

[1] The term *load card* is also applied to a card that is punched to impulse the LOAD hub on the 533 panel. The consequence of impulsing the LOAD hub is discussed in Sec. 6.6.

the storage entry register 1954 to the memory register XXXX, specified in columns 23 to 26. The set of six cards defined in Table 3.3 provides for loading the six instructions of Example 3.13 to memory registers 0000 through 0005.

Table 3.3   A Set of One-word Memory Load Cards for Example 3.13

Card number	Columns 1–10	Columns 21–30	Columns 31–40*
1	69 1954 1953	24 0000 8000	60 0050 0001
2	69 1954 1953	24 0001 8000	10 0051 0002
3	69 1954 1953	24 0002 8000	19 0052 0003
4	69 1954 1953	24 0003 8000	35 0003 0004
5	69 1954 1953	24 0004 8000	64 0053 0005
6	69 1954 1953	24 0005 8000	31 0001 0006

* Note that a minus sign can be indicated by an 11 punch in column 40.

If the first of the six cards is read 80-80 into the set of storage entry registers 1951 through 1960, using the instruction RCD 1951 1951, columns 1 to 10 are channeled to 1951, columns 21 to 30 are channeled to 1953, and columns 31 to 40 are channeled to 1954; then the contents of 1951 are transferred to the program register. This leads to the one-word memory load sequence of instructions shown in Example 3.14. In this and later tabulations, the abbreviation DA (data address) will be used to indicate the operand address, the abbreviation IA will be used to indicate the instruction address, and the abbreviation OP will be used to indicate the operation code.

Example 3.14

Location	Operation		DA	IA
	Symbolic	Numeric		
8000	RCD	70	1951	1951
1951	LDD	69	1954	1953
1953	STD	24	0000	8000
1954		60	0050	0001

Let us observe the operation of the sequence of instructions from the one-word memory load card. First, note that the sequence forms a closed loop as indicated by the arrow. The read operation is executed, the load and store operations are executed, and then the sequence is repeated. Second, as successive cards are read, the operand-address positions of 1953 and the contents of 1954 vary; but the remaining positions contain the same numbers each time the sequence is executed. The one-word memory load sequence could therefore be written in the following general form:

Location	OP	DA	IA
8000	7 0	1 9 5 1	1 9 5 1
1951	6 9	1 9 5 4	1 9 5 3
1953	2 4	XXXX	8 0 0 0
1954	YY	$YYYY$	$YYYY \pm$

Once the sequence is started, an arbitrary number of cards can be read automatically and a corresponding number of words stored in arbitrarily selected memory registers. Methods of breaking the loop will be discussed in Chap. 4.

The register addressed at 8000 is referred to as the STORAGE ENTRY SWITCHES, because there are 11 dial switches on the console of the 650 (see Fig. 5.1) that permit manual entry of a 10-digit number and a sign into this register. Furthermore, depressing in succession the COMPUTER RESET and the PROGRAM START keys on the console causes control to be transferred to 8000.

From time to time we shall refer to a *general-purpose* 533 board. For our purposes, this implies that the board is wired to read and punch 80-80. A general-purpose 533 board is usually available at any 650 computer installation.

3.30 The Output Operation. The output or card-punching operation PCH *dddd* is performed in the 533 Read-Punch unit under control of the 650. It is essentially the inverse of the input operation. Data may be punched only from *storage exit registers*. These are memory registers, but in addition the data therefrom can be copied into the output synchronizer registers.

Each of the 40 bands of memory registers contains 10 storage exit registers. Registers 0027 through 0036 are the storage exit registers for the first band of memory registers; and, as in the case of the storage entry registers, each of the remaining sets of storage exit registers is located an integer multiple of 50 registers from the set in the first band.

As with the read operation, the operand address of an instruction containing the punch operation code, e.g., PCH *dddd iiii*, selects a band of storage exit registers. When the instruction is executed, the selected storage exit registers are copied into the output synchronizer registers, from which they are translated to punched-card code by the output device.

A plug board that is wired to punch 80-80 channels the contents of output synchronizer register 1 to the first 10 card columns, with a negative sign being indicated by an 11 punch in column 10; the contents of output synchronizer register 2 are channeled to card columns 11 to 20; etc. One important difference from the read operation is that the storage exit registers are not reset in the punch operation—the data remain therein, unchanged.

Another important difference is that, except for machine errors, each storage-exit-register position must contain a valid 650 code. Since data cannot be read into a storage exit register directly, it follows that the contents thereof have passed a validity check point in the process of being copied therein. Thus, barring faulty plug-board wiring or machine error, each column of a card punched via a general-purpose board should contain one and only one digit punch.

3.31 The Counter and the Indexing Accumulator. It will be seen in the examples of Chap. 4 that it is frequently desirable to repeat the execution of a sequence of instructions a specified number of times. For example, a^n might be calculated as follows:

$$p_1 = a$$
$$p_2 = ap_1 = a^2$$
$$p_3 = ap_2 = a^3$$
$$.$$
$$.$$
$$.$$
$$p_n = ap_{n-1} = a^n$$

This amounts to setting $p_1 = a$ and then performing $n - 1$ repetitions of the computation $p_i = ap_{i-1}$. This can be accomplished in the computer either by executing $n - 1$ successive instructions containing the MPY operation code (and the appropriate operand address) or by executing a single instruction containing the MPY operation code (and the appropriate operand address) $n - 1$ times.

If the first procedure is used, the programmer specifies the number of successive multiplications that are to be performed by the number of successive MPY operations that he writes. In the second procedure, the programmer writes only one MPY operation; but he writes, in addition, a sequence of instructions that will enable the computer to count the number of times that the MPY operation is performed and to stop after $n - 1$ executions. The programming of the alternative procedures is left as an exercise for the reader.

The term *counter* is frequently used to refer to a register or accumulator in which a count is maintained. The counter may be added to the operand address of an instruction to index the repeated performance of an operation on a sequence of registers, as described in Sec. 4.3. A counter used for this purpose is frequently referred to as an *indexing* accumulator.[1]

3.32 A Caution to the Reader. The reader who plans to program the 650 should become thoroughly familiar with certain facts about it. He needs to be familiar with addressing systems for registers and the specialized functions of certain registers, i.e., 8000 through 8003, the storage entry registers, and the storage exit registers. He needs to be familiar with the symbolic operation codes and the computer operations implied by each. He needs to be familiar with the format of an instruction, the function of the operand address as it varies with operation codes, and the function of the next instruction address. Finally, he should be able to visualize the transfer of the data from a punched card to a set of storage entry registers when the read operation is executed and from storage exit registers to a punched card when the punch operation is executed (assuming 80-80 wiring in each operation).

Unfortunately, this requires a certain amount of memory work; but it is necessary, because the computer is a very meticulous machine. If given precise instructions, the machine executes them exactly, but when the instructions do not follow the rules set forth, the machine refuses to execute them.

In Chap. 4, examples of simple programs will be presented and the reader will be asked to program certain exercises in order to gain some facility in programming. He will soon become aware that ingenuity as well as logic plays a part in programming.

REFERENCES

1. "IBM 650 Data Processing Bulletin—Basic Operation Codes, Program Optimizing, Program Loading," G24-5002, pp. 1–22, International Business Machines Corporation, New York, 1955.
2. "IBM 650 Manual of Additional Features," pp. 6–13, International Business Machines Corporation, New York, 1955.
3. Phister, Montgomery: "Logical Design of Digital Computers," John Wiley & Sons, Inc., New York, 1958.

[1] Automatic indexing accumulators can be added to the 650 as an optional feature. Their presence simplifies the programming of operations that are to be executed repetitively, because the number of instructions required for counting and indexing may be reduced appreciably.

4. Richards, R. K.: "Arithmetic Operations in Digital Computers," D. Van Nostrand Company, Inc., Princeton, N.J., 1955.

PROBLEMS

3.1. *a.* Write a sequence of instructions that will cause the 650 to compute $A + B$, round the result to two decimal places, and store it in register 0127. Assign a memory-register address to each instruction, using registers in the band 1500 through 1549 for this purpose. Display the contents of the u, l, and d registers after each instruction is completed. To make this display specific, let

$$A = C(0174) = 001234.5678+$$
$$B = C(0175) = 0000111.333+$$

b. Same as (*a*), except that the value to be computed is $A - B$.

c. Same as (*a*), except that the value to be computed is $A - 2B + C$. For the specific display, let

$$C = C(0176) = 432.0123333+$$

Do not use the multiply operation; calculate $2B$ by repeated addition or $-2B$ by repeated subtraction.

d. Same as (*a*), except that the value to be computed is $B \times A$.

e. Same as (*a*), except that the value to be computed is B/A. The quotient is to be rounded to five decimal places.

3.2. Describe an addition procedure (for three-digit numbers) in which negative numbers are represented by their tens complement. The tens complement of $N = 10^3 - N$, where N is a three-digit number.

3.3. In a diagram, show the configuration of a core memory register capable of storing a 10-digit decimal number in the five-bit binary code described in Sec. 2.13.

3.4. Simulate graphically the operation of the control unit as $A + B$ is computed in Prob. 3.1.

3.5. Specify the layout and content of a set of one-word memory load cards for the sequence of instructions specified to compute $A + B$ in Prob. 3.1.

3.6. Write a sequence of instructions to compute $[A + (B - C)/D]E$; the result is to be rounded to two decimal places.

$$A = C(0175) = 00000X.XXXX$$
$$B = C(0176) = 000XX.XX000$$
$$C = C(0177) = 0000000X.XX$$
$$D = C(0178) = 00XX.XX00000$$
$$E = C(0179) = 0000000X.XX$$

Display the status of d, l, and u registers after each instruction is executed.

3.7. Devise a scheme for modifying the wheel-type accumulator displayed in Fig. 3.12 so that it will be direct-reading.

3.8. Perform (manually) the following arithmetic problems using the nines complement:

a. $92875 - 123456$

b. $-92875 + 123456$

3.9. Write a sequence of instructions that will perform the function performed automatically in the 650 by the TLU operation.

3.10. Write a sequence of instructions that will cause the computer to generate the sequence of numbers 00 0001 0000, 00 0002 0000, . . . , 10^{20}. An overflow stop will occur when the sequence reaches 10^{20}. Approximately how long would it take the 650 to generate this sequence? [*Hint:* Assume that a constant is stored in memory. $C(0125) = 00\ 0001\ 0000$. Generate the sequence by successive additions of $C(0125)$ to $C(\text{L})$.]

3.11. Write a sequence of instructions that will cause the computer to generate the sequence of numbers 00 0001 0000, 00 0002 0000, . . . , 00 0049 0000. [*Hint:* Make use of the sequence of Prob. 3.10, and assume that $C(0126) = 00\ 0049\ 0000$.]

3.12. Write a sequence of instructions that will cause the computer to generate the sequence of numbers 60 0033 0075, 60 0034 0075, . . . , 60 0275 0075. Store the number generated, 60 0XXX 0075, in register 0065. [*Hint:* Assume that $C(0125) = 00\ 0001\ 0000$, $C(0126) = 60\ 0032\ 0075$, and $C(0127) = 60\ 0275\ 0075$.]

3.13. The accuracy of results can be drastically affected by rounding or truncating intermediate results. Both the following sequences of instructions cause the computer to perform the formal operations involved in the computation of $B \cdot C/E$, rounded to the nearest integer.

Let
$$B = C(0100) = 00000XXXXX \pm$$
$$C = C(0101) = 000000000X \pm$$
$$E = C(0102) = 000000000X \pm$$

Sequence A		Sequence B	
Location	Instruction	Location	Instruction
0050	RAU 0100 0051	0050	RAL 0101 0051
0051	MPY 0101 0052	0051	SLT 0001 0052
0052	SLT 0001 0053	0052	DIV 0102 0053
0053	DVR 0102 0054	0053	RAU 8002 0054
0054	SRD 0001 0055	0054	MPY 0100 0055
		0055	SRD 0001 0056

a. Compare the accuracy of the answers computed by the two sequences when $B = 100$, $C = 2$, and $E = 3$. Assume that the values B, C, and E are exact.

b. Show two different ways that sequence B can be modified to yield results that are comparable in accuracy to that of sequence A.

3.14. Assume that, for the purposes of comparison and storage, it is desired to convert the information portion of the coded messages of Prob. 2.10 into octal numbers. Write a sequence of 650 instructions that would accomplish this for a single message. Display the contents of the U, L, and D registers after each instruction is executed. Assume the message is stored in drum register 0101 with the information bits in the high-order (left-most) positions followed by zeros (any transmission check bits having been discarded) and that the sign is plus. Punch the translated message (octal equivalent) in the low-order positions of the fourth word field (columns 31 to 40) of a card. Assume 80-80 wiring. In writing your sequence of instructions, select locations for instructions and constants arbitrarily from the band 0900 through 0949.

3.15. Write a sequence of instructions that would cause the 650 to compute the octal equivalent of a three-digit decimal integer and punch the result into columns 31 to 40 of a card (with the units position in column 40 and leading zeros to the left of the first significant digit). Assume 80-80 wiring. Assume the decimal integer is stored in register 0101 in the form $0000000XXX+$. Display the contents of the U, L, and D registers after each instruction is executed.

3.16. Draw a flow (block) diagram of the operations performed automatically in the 650 when the instruction MPY is executed.

4

PREPARATION OF A COMPUTER PROGRAM

The concept of a computer program as a sequence of instructions written in machine language was introduced in Chap. 3. The examples were simple enough for the logical sequence of the instructions to be determined and retained in the programmer's memory until their writing was complete. However, the solution of a complex data-processing problem requires so many instructions that their logical sequence can no longer be kept in mind. For such problems, it is recommended that the programmer develop a systematic procedure for the preparation of the computer program.

It is suggested that this procedure be divided into five phases:

1. The definition of the problem to be solved
2. The analysis of the problem
3. The translation of the analysis to a computer program
4. The testing of the computer program
5. The preparation of a set of instructions for the machine operator

The rigor with which the five-phase procedure outlined above is adhered to will depend upon many things. If the problem is simple, the first three phases may be telescoped. If the programmer is also the customer (the person for whom the problem is being solved), the first two phases may be telescoped when the problem is not too complex. The following discussions will assume that the customer and the programmer are not the same person, but that the analyst and the programmer either are the same person or work as a team. If the problem is quite complex, it is desirable that the customer or his qualified representative be a member of the team and that the five-phase procedure be adhered to rigorously.

The first phase deals with the definition of the problem to be solved. In this phase an agreement should be reached between the customer, on the one hand, and the analyst and programmer, on the other hand, as to the results or information expected from the data-processing procedures that are to be developed. The agreement should specify in detail such things as the information to be produced, the format in which the information is to be presented, the limits of accuracy required, the descriptive information to be associated with numeric information, and any other restrictions that are pertinent to the specific problem.

It is important that there be complete understanding between the customer, the analyst, and the programmer as to the definition of the problem. It is recommended, therefore, that the definition be written in considerable detail and adequately discussed before the next phase is started.

The second phase deals with the analysis of the problem defined in the first phase. In this phase the analyst and programmer develop a procedure that will satisfy the information requirements of the problem. The product of this phase should be an orderly description of the data-transmission, arithmetic, and logical operations required to transform raw (input) data into the specified output information. The sources and format of input data should be identified. The mathematical formulas to be used in the transformation of the input data should be specified. Logical decision rules should be specified. The problem analysis may call for knowledge in one or more specialized fields, e.g., accounting, statistics, numeric analysis, or others. Consultants should be called in when necessary. It is important that the problem analysis be consistent with the customer's requirements. If there is a chance for ambiguity or misunderstanding, the analyst and programmer should prepare a set of results by longhand methods and discuss the interpretation of these results with the customer.

Up to a certain point the analysis can be developed without consideration of the data-processing equipment that may be used. For example, the preliminary analysis of an accounting problem may be stated in terms of accounting procedures and logical decisions that are consistent with good accounting principles. The accounting procedures specified may then be replaced by mathematical formulas. As the analysis becomes more detailed and specific data-transmission and arithmetic operations are considered, the analysis probably will be influenced by the data-processing equipment that is being considered to implement the analysis.

The *flow diagram* or *block diagram* has proved to be a useful method of recording the results of the analytical phase. The flow diagram performs a function for the programmer similar to the function that an outline performs for an author or that a schematic diagram performs for an engineer. The flow diagram indicates the logical sequence of data flow and of operations to be performed. As in an outline, the amount of detail that will be included in a flow diagram will vary with the situation and the individual. In general, a detailed flow diagram will reduce the time required to translate the analysis to a computer program. In addition, a detailed flow diagram will often reduce the chance for misunderstanding between the customer, the analyst, and the programmer.

The notation and format used in flow diagramming varies among individuals and with the complexity of the problem. The statements in Chap. 3 of the steps executed by the 650 in the multiplication or the division operations represent an acceptable form of flow diagramming. In the examples in this chapter, the components of the flow diagram will be enclosed in rectangular frames (or blocks), hence the term block diagram. This practice is illustrated in Fig. 4.1. The function of the arrow and the relationship of the blocks in Fig. 4.1 will be discussed later.

Phase 3 deals with the translation of the analysis to a computer program. In this chapter we shall first illustrate the translation of the analysis to basic machine language. The term *basic-machine-language programming* implies that the programmer writes an instruction in machine language for each operation that the machine is to execute. Later in the chapter we shall introduce symbolic programming, wherein the programmer uses mnemonic symbols in lieu of basic machine language. In Chap. 7, we shall discuss an abbreviated programming system. Such a system permits the programmer to describe a computational process in terms of abbreviated statements that conform to specified rules. A compiler program or system of compiler programs is then provided that will interpret the abbreviated statements and compile a sequence of basic-machine-language instructions that constitute the desired program.

Phases 4 and 5 of program development deal with the testing of computer programs and the preparation of instructions for the data-processing-system operator. These subjects are dealt with in Chap. 5.

The examples that have been programmed for the 650 in this chapter have been chosen to satisfy several objectives. Some were chosen to illustrate certain programming principles, e.g., the looping sequence, the exit from a looping sequence, and address modification. Other examples illustrate functions that are performed frequently in data-processing programs, e.g., a block zeroing routine, a general-purpose card-punching routine, etc. Other examples are components of a data-processing program to be prepared by the student as a problem. Still other examples are components of a program test supervisory routine, discussed in Chap. 5, that will be used in testing programs.

EXAMPLES OF BASIC-MACHINE-LANGUAGE PROGRAMMING

4.1 A Looping Sequence. A sequence of instructions that provides for automatic repetition or iteration is called a *looping* sequence. The looping sequence is a typical element of a computer program. If the set of instructions required for the solution of a problem included no looping sequences and if the problem were to be solved only once, there would be no justification for writing a computer program. The problem could be solved more economically on a desk calculator or by some other longhand method. On the other hand, a programmed solution may be justified for a problem that must be computed by an iterative procedure (e.g., by successive approximations) or must be repeated periodically (e.g., a payroll).

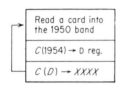

Fig. 4.1. A flow diagram for Example 3.14.

The instructions in the one-word memory load routine of Example 3.14 form a looping sequence. The operations performed in a single cycle of the loop are indicated in flow-diagram form in Fig. 4.1. A card is read via 80-80 wiring into the storage entry registers 1951 through 1958. The word just read into register 1954 is copied into the D register; then the contents of the D register are copied into a memory register that is identified by the value assigned to XXXX in columns 23 to 26 of the card just read. The loop is closed by returning to the read operation each time a cycle of operations is completed.

As is typical in looping operations, the data operated on and/or the registers operated on vary from cycle to cycle of the loop. In this example, the variation in the data and the register operated on is controlled by the punches in the cards read in successive cycles of the loop, as illustrated by the set of one-word memory load cards in Table 3.3. The contents of columns 1 to 10, 21, 22, and 27 to 30 are the same for all cards in the set, but the contents of columns 23 to 26 and 31 to 40 vary from card to card. Thus the contents of 1954 and the operand address of the instruction in 1953 vary from cycle to cycle, whereas the contents of 1951 and the operation code and the instruction address in 1953 are constant from cycle to cycle.

4.2 An Exit From a Loop. In the flow diagram of Fig. 4.1 no provision is indicated for breaking the loop of operations. To be useful, a looping sequence must provide an *exit* or a branch from the loop when specified conditions have been satisfied. This requirement can be satisfied in this example by adding a transfer card after the last one-word memory load card. The transfer card could contain the exit instruction in columns 1 to 10, e.g., 00 0000 *aaaa*, where the symbol *aaaa* is used to indicate the location of a register that contains the first instruction to be executed after a deck of cards has been read. When

Flow diagram	Location	Instructions OP	Instructions DA	Instructions IA	Step No.
Read → 1950 band	8000	70	1951	1951	1
Execute instruction in 1951	1951	rr	dddd	iiii	2
V1 Exit from loop	1951	00	0000	aaaa	2A
V2 Stay in loop	1951	69	1954	1953	2B
C(D reg.) → XXXX	1953	24	XXXX	8000	3
Start new sequence, e.g.,	aaaa	69	1225	0128	4
etc.					

FIG. 4.2. A flow diagram of a one-word-per-card memory load routine with exit.

the transfer card is read, the instruction 69 1954 1953 in register 1951 is replaced by the instruction 00 0000 *aaaa*, and the loop is broken by the subsequent execution of the latter instruction. The effect of the above modification on the flow diagram and the corresponding sequence of instructions are illustrated in detail in Fig. 4.2.

The sequence of instructions shown in Fig. 4.2 would be verbally interpreted as follows:

Step 1. 8000: 70 1951 1951
Read a card into the storage entry registers associated with the operand address 1951; then copy the contents of register 1951 into the program register. This may be abbreviated to the statement, *read a card into* 1951–60 *and go to* 1951. In this example the card will be either a one-word memory load card (see Example 3.14) or a transfer card. In either case the card is read 80-80; hence the data from columns 1 to 10 of the card will be copied into the program register during the fetch phase of the read instruction cycle.

Step 2.   1951: *rr dddd iiii*

The instruction executed in this step will vary accordingly as a transfer card or a one-word memory load card is read. The alternatives are indicated by steps 2*A* and 2*B*, respectively.

Step 2*A*.   1951: 00 0000 *aaaa*

Perform no operation; then copy the contents of register *aaaa* into the program register. This may be abbreviated to *no-op and go to aaaa* (e.g., 0063). The symbol *aaaa* is used, in lieu of a four-digit number, to indicate that the transfer address may be specified arbitrarily. When this instruction is executed, the card-reading loop is broken, which accounts for the arrow leading to the block containing *aaaa*.

Step 2*B*.   1951: 69 1954 1953

Copy the contents of register 1954 into the D register; then copy the contents of register 1953 into the program register. When this instruction is executed, the card-reading loop is continued.

Step 3.   1953: 24 *XXXX* 8000

Copy the contents of the D register into register *XXXX* (e.g., 0257); then copy the contents of register 8000 into the program register. The symbol *XXXX* is used to indicate that the operand address may vary each time the instruction is executed.

The reader is urged to form the habit of interpreting instructions in the manner indicated above. If he does so, he will find that he will soon be reading machine-language statements without difficulty. To facilitate the reading of instructions, the symbolic operation codes will be used for the most part in future examples. The reader should also form the habit of referring to the flow diagram when he has difficulty in following the sequence of the instructions.

There are actually two *variable* instructions in the one-word-per-card memory load routine. The operand address of the instruction in step 3, location 1953, is different each time the instruction is executed; however, the *I* address remains constant, so the variation in the instruction does not affect the continuity of the loop. The continuity is broken, in this example, by varying the *I* address of step 2 when the loading of memory is completed. The modification of the operation code and operand address is justified, because no operation is required in the transfer of control to *aaaa*.

In the foregoing example, the modification of the variable instruction was effected by reading in new information to replace the old. An instruction can also be modified by arithmetic operations. Since an instruction is a signed 10-digit number stored in a memory register, the operation code, the operand address, the I address, or any combination thereof can be changed from a known value to any other specified value by the addition or subtraction of an appropriate constant.

4.3 Address Modification by Arithmetic Operations. The block zeroing routine discussed below illustrates the use of the arithmetic unit for modifying the operand address of an instruction. The problem (in this example) is to write a set of instructions that will cause minus zero (00 0000 0000 −) to be copied into each register of a specified block, e.g., registers 0001 through 1549. The zeroing routine serves a function for the computer memory that corresponds to the function of an eraser for a blackboard. Therefore, a zeroing routine appears at least once in almost every large program.

A set of one-word memory load cards could be used to load each of the registers 0001 through 1549 with minus zero; but this would be very inefficient, since the 1549 cards required would be read at the rate

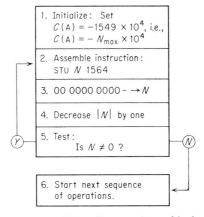

Fig. 4.3. Flow diagram for a block zeroing routine.

of 200 per minute. Instead, we shall use a more efficient looping sequence of instructions wherein an indexing accumulator is used to identify the register operated on in each cycle.

In this example, the L register will be used as the indexing accumulator and the U register will be used as the source of the minus zero to be copied into the successive registers identified by the index number. This is possible because modification of the index is the only arithmetic operation required in this particular looping sequence.

The analysis of the problem is shown in the flow diagram (Fig. 4.3). Note that the locations are zeroed in descending order—1549 first and 0001 last. The letter N is used here to denote the variable index.

The term *initialize* in the first block is used to indicate the operations that are required to set the variables in the routine to their appropriate initial value. In this case, the U and L registers are set to the appropriate initial values by entering $(-N \text{ max}) \times 10^4 = -1549 \times 10^4$ in the A register before the loop is entered.

The sequence of instructions shown in Table 4.1 will accomplish the desired objective. In addition to the sequence of instructions, the table displays the contents of the D, L, and U registers after each specified operation has been executed. The instructions are cross-referenced to the blocks in the flow diagram of Fig. 4.3. The reader should interpret Table 4.1 to determine the solution to the problem.

Table 4.1 A Block Zeroing Subroutine

Block			Instructions			Arithmetic unit	
	Loca- tion	Opera- tion code	DA	IA	U register	L register	D register
1	1561	RSL	1566	1562	00 0000 0000	00 1549 0000 −	00 1549 0000 +
2	1562	LDD	1567	1563	00 0000 0000	00 1549 0000 −	21 XXXX 1564 +
	1563	SDA	1567	8001	00 0000 0000	00 1549 0000 −	21 1549 1564 +
3	8001	STU	N	1564	00 0000 0000	00 1549 0000 −	00 0000 0000 −
4	1564	ALO	1568	1565	00 0000 0000	00 1548 0000 −	00 0001 0000 +
5	1565	NZE	1562	1600	00 0000 0000	00 1548 0000 −	00 0001 0000 +
6	1600	rr	dddd	iiii			

		Constants					
	1566	00	1549	0000 +			
	1567	21	XXXX*	1564 +			
	1568	00	0001	0000 +			

* It is apparent that only the operation code and the I address of the contents of 1567 remain constant, as indicated by the statement 21 XXXX 1564. Nevertheless, the word is referred to as a constant, because its D address has no bearing on the functioning of the routine. It may also be observed that the sign of 1567 could just as well have been negative, because the sign has no effect on the assembly of the instruction in this example.

In the interpretation, he should visualize the functioning of the control unit and the arithmetic unit as successive instruction cycles are executed.

Each time block 4 is executed, the magnitude of N, in the L register, is decreased by 1. The values shown in the L register correspond to the first cycle. In the second cycle, 1548 replaces 1549 and 1547 replaces 1548. After 1549 cycles of the loop, N is decreased to 0, and the outcome of the logical test of the contents of the A register results in an exit from the loop, i.e., a transfer of control to block 6 instead of block 2.

It should be noted that the constants specified in locations 1566 through 1568 are essential to the program and, like instructions, must be stored in memory. Instructions and constants are 10-digit numbers specified by the programmer. The difference between a constant and an instruction is that the location of a constant is not referred to as a next instruction address, whereas the location of an instruction is referred to as a next instruction address by some other instruction in the program. In other words, program constants are not intended to be fetched directly to the program register.

In this example, the L register serves as both a *counter* and an *index register*. As a counter, it counts (down) the number of iterations of the variable instruction 21 N 1564. As an index register, positions 5 to 8 of the L register are entered as the data address N of that instruction to indicate the location into which the contents of the U register are to be copied in a given cycle.

4.4 A $C(A_i) + C(B_i) \to B_i$ Routine (Vector Addition). Assume that 15 independent quantities are stored in memory registers 0016 through 0030 and that another 15 independent quantities are stored in registers 0031 through 0045. The location of the ith register in the first set may be designated as A_i, while that of the second set may be designated as B_i; then i can be considered as an index that assumes the values 1, 2, 3, . . . , 14, 15. Thus, A_1 is equal to 0016 and A_{15} is equal to 0030.

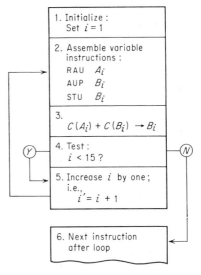

Fig. 4.4. Flow diagram for a $C(A_i) + C(B_i) \to B_i$ routine.

The A table might be a distribution by commodity of the current-month sales revenue, and the B table might be the distribution by commodity of the year-to-date sales revenue, in which case the $C(A_i) + C(B_i) \to B_i$ routine could be used to close the current-month sales distribution into the year-to-date sales distribution. (The mathematician might refer to this as vector addition.) The problem is to write a sequence of instructions that will accomplish this function.

The analysis of the problem is illustrated by the flow diagram (Fig. 4.4) and is elaborated below.

Table 4.2   A $C(A_i) + C(B_i) \to B_i$ Routine

		Instructions			Arithmetic unit		
Block	Location	Operation code	DA	IA	U register	L register	D register
1	0100	RAL	0117	0101	00 0000 0000	00 0001 0000+	00 0001 0000+
2	0101	STL	0120	0102	00 0000 0000	00 0001 0000+	00 0001 0000+
	0102	ALO	0118	0103	00 0000 0000	60 0016 0110+	60 0015 0110+
	0103	STL	0109	0104	00 0000 0000	60 0016 0110+	60 0016 0110+
	0104	ALO	0119	0105	00 0000 0000	60 0031 0110+	00 0015 0000+
	0105	LDD	0110	0106	00 0000 0000	60 0031 0110+	10 0045 0111+
	0106	SDA	0110	0107	00 0000 0000	60 0031 0110+	10 0031 0111+
	0107	LDD	0111	0108	00 0000 0000	60 0031 0110+	21 0045 0112+
	0108	SDA	0111	0109	00 0000 0000	60 0031 0110+	21 0031 0112+
3	0109	RAU	A_i	0110	XX XXXX XXXX	00 0000 0000	XX XXXX XXXX
	0110	AUP	B_i	0111	ZZ ZZZZ ZZZZ	00 0000 0000	YY YYYY YYYY
	0111	STU	B_i	0112	ZZ ZZZZ ZZZZ	00 0000 0000	ZZ ZZZZ ZZZZ
4	0112	RAL	0120	0113	00 0000 0000	00 0001 0000+	00 0001 0000+
	0113	SLO	0119	0114	00 0000 0000	00 0014 0000−	00 0015 0000+
	0114	BMI	0115	aaaa	00 0000 0000	00 0014 0000−	00 0015 0000+
5	0115	ALO	8001	0116	00 0000 0000	00 0001 0000+	00 0015 0000+
	0116	ALO	0117	0101	00 0000 0000	00 0002 0000+	00 0001 0000+
6	aaaa	rr	dddd	iiii			

Constants

Location	Operation code	DA	IA
0117	00	0001	0000+
0118	60	0015	0110+
0119	00	0015	0000+

Cycle counter and index register

Location		DA	IA
0120	00	i	0000+

1. Set the memory register that serves as a cycle counter and index accumulator to 00 0001 0000+. In this example, the index is stored in a memory register between modifications, because the A register must be cleared each cycle before $C(A_i) + C(B_i)$ is calculated.

2. Three instructions with variable D address are implied by the relationship $C(A_i) + C(B_i) \to B_i$. The data address of each vari-

able instruction is a function of the setting of the index register, e.g.,

$$A_i = 15 + i \qquad B_i = 30 + i$$

3. Execute the variable instructions assembled in block 2.
4. If $i < 15$, at least one more cycle is required. Go to block 5. If $i = 15$, no more cycles are required. Go to block 6.
5. Add 00 0001 0000 to the contents of the indexing accumulator, store the result in the indexing accumulator, and recycle.
6. Start a new sequence of instructions.

The sequence of instructions shown in Table 4.2 will accomplish the objective of forming and storing the fifteen sums, $C(A_i) + C(B_i) \rightarrow B_i$. The function of each instruction in the routine can best be understood by studying the step-by-step status of the arithmetic unit as related to the requirements specified in the discussion of the flow diagram. The table displays the status of the D, L, and U registers after each operation has been executed.

A DATA-PROCESSING PROBLEM

At this point let us digress from the discussion of programming examples to present a problem that has many of the characteristics of a full-scale data-processing problem. The problem is chosen from the field of accounting; the terms used are simple, and it is assumed that they are familiar to the reader. The problem has been simplified arbitrarily so that it can be solved in a reasonable length of time by the student. In addition, some of the examples of this chapter can be included as components of the program developed by the student.

The original statement of the problem, as received by the data processor, might be as follows:

It is requested that a procedure be developed to process sales tickets, return-sales tickets and credit memos, and cash-receipt or payment-on-account tickets for the purpose of updating the accounts receivable ledger; to prepare statements for customers; to prepare a distribution by commodity of sales revenue; and to update the inventory record on each commodity.

The statement of the problem indicates that the solution will involve sequences of arithmetic operations and that the same sequences will be used repetitively. It is appropriate therefore to consider, as one alternative, the use of an electronic computer for this data-processing function. The choice among alternative ways of performing the required data-processing operation should involve economic[1] as well as data-processing considerations. We shall simplify our problem by specifying that the 650 shall be used, thus avoiding consideration of the relative costs of alternative procedures.

4.5 Specific Requirements. The first step in the solution of the problem will be the preparation of a detailed description of the information content and format of the records to be maintained and the reports to be produced. It is important that there be complete understanding between the responsible persons in accounting and data processing as to the specific requirements. As a procedure is developed, it may become necessary to modify these requirements to satisfy limitations imposed by the equipment that will be used, but at all times in the development of the procedure there should be complete understanding among the responsible parties as to the objectives.

To simplify the problem, it will be agreed that the 650 program shall produce the following output cards:

1. A statement card for each customer with a nonzero balance shall be punched in the format defined in Table 4.3. Each card shall contain a card code 30, the date that the statement card was computed, and the customer's name, number, and balance.
2. The current-period sales distribution, the year-to-date sales distribution, the accounts receivable table, and the inventory table shall be punched in the format illustrated in Table 4.9. Let N equal 5.
3. An exception card shall be punched for each exceptional input card encountered. The following exceptions are to be recognized, and the corresponding exception card shall be identified by modifying the units digit of the input card code as indicated below. The location of the exceptional card in the input deck shall be indicated by punching in field 8 a count of cards read.

   a. $X2$ The input card contained a character code that was invalid.

   b. $X3$ The input card contained an undefined card code.

   c. $X4$ The input card contained an undefined commodity code.

   d. $X5$ The input card contained an undefined customer number.

   The X indicates the first digit of the input card code.

   Aside from the modifications indicated above, each exception card shall duplicate, in so far as is possible, the information contained in the corresponding input card.

---

[1] For a complete discussion of the principles involved in making choices among alternatives, see E. L. Grant, "Principles of Engineering Economy," 4th ed., The Ronald Press Company, New York, 1960.

The format in which the sales distributions, the accounts receivable record, and the inventory record are punched is convenient for reloading purposes but not for interpretation by interested parties. The latter requirement has been ignored for the sake of simplifying the problem.

4.6 The Input and Output Format.   The output-data requirements determine the content of the input data, but they do not determine the format of the input cards. In some problems, the programmer is free to specify the format of the input cards, in which case he may determine a convenient format as he programs the solution to the problem. In other problems, the format of the input card may be fixed by constraints within the data-processing system. Again, we

Table 4.3   Input and Output Card Format for the Data-processing Problem

Field	A/N^*	Card column	Sign	Format of contents	Storage entry address	Storage exit address
(1) Card code	N	1–2		$cc00dddddd$	0101	0077
(2) Date	N	5–10				
(3) Customer's name	A	11–20		$xxxxxxxxxx$	0102 and 0103†	0078 and 0079†
(4) Customer's number	N	31–55		$xxxxx00000$	0104	0080
(5) Commodity code	N	41–45		$xxxxx00000$	0105	0081
(6) Number of items	N	56–60	60	$00000xxxxx \pm$	0106	0082
(7) Money charged or credited	N	63–70	70	$00xxxxxx.xx \pm$	0107	0083
(8) Customer's balance	N	73–80	80	$00xxxxxx.xx \pm$	0108	0084

* A indicates alphanumeric data. N indicates numeric data.
† Two registers are required for 10 alphanumeric characters (see Sec. 2.11).

shall simplify the present problem by specifying a common card format (see Table 4.3) for all types of input cards. The common card format simplifies the problem of plug-board wiring (see Fig. 6.25), and specification of the format permits the use of a single plug board for all student programs to be tested.

The card type can be identified by the card code found in columns 1 and 2. The following card codes are defined:

Card code	Card type
10	Sales card
20	Sales-return or credit-memo card
30	Payment-on-account card
40	End-of-file card

The end-of-file card is used to indicate that all the input cards have been processed. The card code is the only pertinent information on this card, but it will be required that the remaining fields contain zero punches. (This requirement is added to simplify plug-board wiring.)

The other types of cards will all have the first four fields punched. Sales tickets and credit memos will have fields 5, 6, and 7 punched, but not field 8. All quantities on the sales card will be positive, but credit-memo cards will contain 11 punches in columns 60 and 70 to indicate negative amounts. Payment-on-account cards will have field 7 punched as a negative amount (an 11 punch in column 70), while field 8 may be either a positive or a negative amount; fields 5 and 6 will not be punched. Statement cards will have field 8 punched, but not fields 5, 6, and 7.

4.7 Allocation of Memory. Next we shall define the tables that must be available in memory for reference or modification as the input

Table 4.4

Region	Location	Description
A	0000–0010	Table of commodity codes ($xxxxx00000$) in ascending order. $C(0009) = 0$; $C(0010) = 99\ 9999\ 9999$.
B	0011–0020	Current-period sales distribution. $C(0020) = $ total sales.
C	0021–0030	Year-to-date sales distribution. $C(0030) = $ total sales.
D	0031–0040	Inventory table.
E	0050–0055	Table of customer numbers ($xxxxx00000$) in ascending order. $C(0055) = 99\ 9999\ 9999$.
F	0056–0060	Table of accounts receivable for customers identified in Table E.
G	0061–0070	Table of names of customers identified in Table E. There are two consecutive registers per name.
P	0077–0086	Punch band. It is required that $C(0086) = 80\ 0000\ 0000$ to control alphanumeric punching.
R	0101–0110	Read band.

cards are processed and the output cards are produced. The upper limit on the number of entries in each table must be determined, because the demand for memory registers may prove to be a controlling factor in the development of the processing procedure. In this problem, the tables have been artificially shortened to reduce the number of memory registers that need be punched after each program is tested on the computer.

The allocation of memory registers for the tables, the read band, and the punch band are specified in Table 4.4 in terms of memory regions. The registers in these regions may not be used by the programmer to store instructions or constants.

4.8   Library Routines Available without Programming.   In programming this problem, the reader can take advantage of some of the routines that are presented as examples in this chapter.   The programmer may assume that the following routines are available (in a

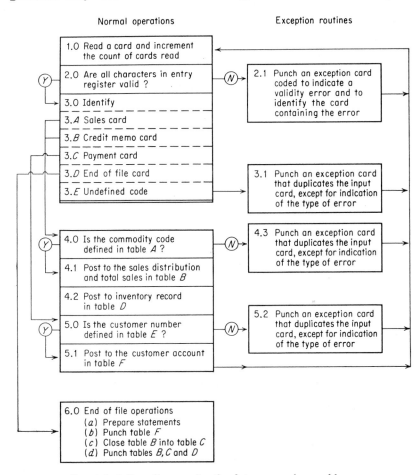

Fig. 4.5. A flow diagram for the data-processing problem.

subroutine library) in N-per-card format for loading into the appropriate memory registers.   The following restrictions on entry to a routine must be strictly adhered to, if the routine is to perform its function properly.

1. General-purpose block zeroing routine

Enter at location 1000 with 00 *FFFF LLLL* + in the L register, zero in the U register, and *rr dddd iiii* in the D register.   *FFFF* <

LLLL defines the sequence of registers to be zeroed, and *rr dddd iiii* defines the instruction to be executed upon exit from the routine.

2. *N*-per-card read routine

Enter at location 1001. This routine reads cards of the form described in Sec. 4.13 and stores the words in the appropriate register. Exit via a transfer card.

3. *N*-per-card punch routine

Enter at location 1002 with *ON FFFF LLLL* + in the L register, zero in the U register, and the exit instruction *rr dddd iiii* in the D register. This routine punches the sequence of locations *FFFF* to *LLLL* at the rate of *N* per card of the form specified in Table 4.9.

4. $C(B_i) + C(C_i) \rightarrow C_i$ routine

Enter at location 1003 with the exit instruction *rr dddd iiii* in the D register. This routine is designed specifically for the *B* and *C* tables of this problem.

4.9 General Solution of the Problem. A general solution for the problem is displayed in flow diagram form (Fig. 4.5). Blocks 2.0, 5.0, and 5.1 thereof will be programmed in detail to illustrate the error-sensing and the TLU operations, respectively. The preparation of a detailed flow diagram and a complete program will be left as an exercise for the reader.

SYMBOLIC PROGRAMMING AND OPTIMAL ASSEMBLY

Let us next discuss the meaning and justification of symbolic programming and formulate a set of rules for writing a class of symbolic programs for the 650.

In the preceding examples, e.g., Table 4.2, we have for the most part used symbolic operation codes and numeric addresses. Notable exceptions have been the numeric specification of the operation-code positions in constants and the literal expression of variable or undefined addresses, e.g., A_i, B_i, and *aaaa* in Table 4.2.

Furthermore, successive instructions have been located, for the most part, in consecutive registers except where the continuity of the program has precluded this practice. Branch operations or references to registers 8000 through 8003 as the location of the next instruction require a break in the consecutive location addresses.

There are advantages and disadvantages that can be associated with the foregoing programming practices. During the discussion of the advantages and disadvantages of programming procedures the reader should bear in mind that writing a sequence of instructions is only one phase in the preparation of a useful computer program. After the program is written, the instructions and constants must be transferred to punched cards (e.g., one-word memory load cards) for loading to specified memory registers as signed 10-digit numbers. The reader should also bear in mind that the cost of a specific data-processing operation includes the cost of computer time required to execute a program as well as the cost of preparing the program.

With these considerations in mind, let us look at some advantages and disadvantages of the foregoing programming practices.

The primary advantage has been that of convenience. Most programmers find it more convenient to work with symbolic operation codes than with their numeric equivalents. They also find it convenient to locate successive instructions in consecutive memory registers.

The use of symbolic operation codes has the disadvantage that each must be translated to its numeric equivalent before the instruction can be loaded to memory. This could be done manually, but it is a tedious job and a potential source of clerical errors. Alternatively, a program could be written that would enable the computer to perform the translation. Either alternative adds to the cost of preparing the program. If this were the only disadvantage of the foregoing programming practices, it could be overcome readily by using numeric operation codes in the initial writing of the program.

However, the location of successive instructions in consecutive memory registers, sequential programming, has serious disadvantages when the computer does not have a truly random-access memory, as is the case with the 650. It will be recalled that in the 650 a memory register can be copied from or into only as it passes under its READ-WRITE head; and when the computer is ready to copy from or into a register specified by the operand (or the instruction) address, it must wait until that register passes under its READ-WRITE head. This waiting time can be minimized by careful selection of the operand and instruction addresses. A programming procedure that selects operand and instruction addresses to minimize the waiting time is referred to as optimal or optimized programming.[1]

An optimized equivalent of the $C(A_i) + C(B_i) \rightarrow B_i$ routine is presented in Table 4.5. The rules by which the addresses were chosen are

[1] For a complete discussion of optimal programming for the 650, the student is referred to "IBM 650 Data Processing Bulletin—Basic Operation Codes, Program Optimizing, Program Loading," G24-5002, pp. 1–22, International Business Machines Corporation, New York, 1955. If memory is truly random access, optimal programming can be ignored.

not discussed here, because the symbolic programming rules to be formulated will permit delegation of this task to the computer.

If the optimized program is compared with the sequential program in Table 4.2, the disadvantages to the programmer of optimal programming become readily apparent. One is the time required to select the optimal addresses. A second one, and the more serious, is the problem of keeping track of the memory-register addresses that have been used (to store instructions, constants, or data) and hence are *unavailable* for

Table 4.5 The $C(A_i) + C(B_i) \rightarrow B_i$ Routine with Optimized Addresses

Location	Operation	DA	IA
0100	RAL 65	0103	0107
0107	STL 20	0111	0114
0114	ALO 15	0117	0121
0121	STL 20	0125	0128
0128	ALO 15	0131	0135
0135	LDD 69	0138	0141
0141	SDA 22	0138	0142
0142	LDD 69	0145	0148
0148	SDA 22	0145	0125
0125	RAU 60	0030	0138
0138	AUP 10	0045	0145
0145	STU 21	0045	0101
0101	RAL 65	0111	0115
0115	SLO 16	0131	0136
0136	BMI 46	0139	0140
0139	ALO 15	8001	0146
0146	ALO 15	0103	0107

	Constants		
0117	60	0015	0138
0131	00	0015	0000
0103	00	0001	0000

assignment and of the remaining addresses that are *available* for assignment. A third is the lack of an index for referring back to instructions that have been written. A fourth is the potential source of errors implied by the foregoing disadvantages.

These disadvantages were sufficient to justify the writing of a program that could perform the function of assigning optimal addresses and of keeping track of available addresses. This program is referred to as SOAP II[1] (symbolic optimal assembly program). It will assem-

[1] The reader is referred to Ref. 2 for a complete discussion of this program.

ble (translate) each instruction of a sequence written in the form illustrated in Table 4.6 to a basic-machine-language instruction with addresses optimally chosen. Each assembled instruction and its location will be punched out in the one-word memory load card form illustrated in Table 4.8. If the programmer wishes to take advantage of SOAP II, he must conform to the following restrictions when writing instructions. The restrictions specify the form of symbolic and numeric operation codes and the form of symbolic and numeric

Table 4.6 $C(A_i) + C(B_i) \rightarrow B_i$ **Routine in SOAP II**

IBM   650 SOAP PROGRAM SHEET

| 41 | 42 | 43 | 44- -47 | 48 | 49,50 | 51 | 52- -55 | 56 | 57- -60 | 61- | -72 | SOAP I COL |
| 41 | 42 | 43 | 44- -47 | 48 | 49,50 | 51 | 52- -55 | 56 | 57 | 58- -61 | 62 | 63- -72 | SOAP II COL |

T P	S N	LOCATION	OPER. CODE	DATA ADDRESS	A G	INSTR. ADDRESS	I G	REMARKS	ACCUMULATOR UPPER 8003	LOWER 8002	DISTRIBUTOR 8001
		$A_1A_2A_3A_4A_5$	$R_1R_2R_3$	$A_1A_2A_3A_4A_5$		$A_1A_2A_3A_4A_5$					
Blk.			Instructions								
1.		A IPBI	R AL	C ØNE		L ØØP		Initialize the			
2.		L ØØP	S TL	I REG			←	Index Register			
			A LØ	C VI				Assemble the			
			S TL	V I				Variable			
			A LØ	C 15				Instructions			
			L DD	V 2							
			S DA	V 2							
			L DD	V 3							
			S DA	V 3		V I					
3.		V I	R AU	0030		V 2					
		V 2	A UP	00 45		V 3		$[A_i] + [B_i] \rightarrow B_i$			
		V 3	S TU	00 45							
4.			R AL	I REG				Test for the			
			S LØ	C 15				completion of			
			B MI			EXIT		the last cycle.			
5.			A LØ	8001							
			A LØ	C ØNE		L ØØP →		Recycle			
		Constants									
		C VI		60		0015		V 2			
		C 15		00		0015		0000			
		C ØNE		00		0001		0000			

addresses. The specified form must be followed rigorously if the SOAP II program is to perform its assembly function properly.

4.10 Rules for Specifying Symbolic Operation Codes. The rules for specifying operation codes are defined first. Three positions are provided for specifying the operation code. These positions are referred to as $R_1 R_2 R_3$ as indicated in the column headed Operation Code in Table 4.6. The programmer may specify a two-digit integer that is to be entered in the operation-code positions of the assembled instruction, or he may specify a symbolic operation code that can be translated to a two-digit integer.

1. To specify an arbitrary two-digit integer for the operation-code positions of the assembled instruction:

Leave position R_1 blank and write the desired two-digit number in positions R_2 R_3. Thus any number 00 through 99 may be specified for entry into the operation-code positions of the assembled instruction (see the last three lines of Table 4.6).

2. To specify a symbolic operation code:
Write the appropriate three-letter symbolic operation code specified in Table 3.2 in positions R_1 R_2 R_3 (see the first 17 instructions in Table 4.6). The two-digit equivalent thereof will be located in the operation-code table and placed in the operation-code positions of the assembled instruction.

4.11 Rules for Specifying Symbolic Addresses. A symbolic address may be thought of as a "name" used in lieu of an address, and it is used only when required for reference purposes. The following rules for specifying addresses apply equally to the location (L), the operand (D), and the instruction (I) addresses. Five positions A_1 A_2 A_3 A_4 A_5 are provided for specifying an address. Position A_1 is referred to as the symbolizer position. The SOAP II program recognizes four different address forms: numeric, symbolic, blank, and regional address forms. The rules by which each of the forms is specified are defined below.

1. To specify a four-digit integer:
Leave position A_1, the symbolizer, blank and write a four-digit number in the positions A_2 A_3 A_4 A_5 (see the D addresses in the last three lines of Table 4.6). The specified number will appear in the assembled instruction; i.e., it will appear in the L, D, or I address position, whichever has been specified. No other action is performed by the assembly program in the translation of a numeric address.

2. To specify a symbolic address:
A symbolic address is used when the programmer wishes to identify a location for future reference but does not want to specify a numeric address (see Table 4.6). A letter or a number is written in position A_1. An arbitrary combination of letters, numbers, or blanks is written in positions A_2 A_3 A_4 A_5, except that the combination must not be a four-digit number. The combination of a nonblank symbolizer with a four-digit number is reserved for the regional address.

When a symbolic address is encountered by the assembly program, it searches its file of symbolic addresses. If not contained therein, the symbolic address is added to the file. A memory-register address is selected optimally from the table of register addresses that remain available. This register address is then deleted from the table of available addresses. The selected address becomes the numeric equivalent of the symbolic address and is stored in a file of numeric equivalents, to which the symbolic address file is indexed. Thus the symbolic address is translated to a four-digit memory-register address which appears in the assembled instruction.

If the file contains the symbolic address, its numeric equivalent is obtained by reference to the file of numeric equivalents. Thus a numeric equivalent is assigned to an arbitrary symbolic address the first time it is encountered, and the same numeric equivalent is assigned each time that symbolic address is encountered thereafter in the assembly of a particular program.

The symbolic-address file and the numeric-equivalent file are automatically erased at the start of the assembly of the program. Thus the entries to the symbolic-address file are determined by the programmer while the numeric equivalents are determined by the assembly program. The symbolic-address file has a capacity of 300 entries.

The programmer may place restrictions on the memory-register addresses that are available for selection as numeric equivalents. The method by which this restriction is effected will be discussed in a later section devoted to program assembly.

3. To specify the blank (symbolic) address:

The blank address can be used for a D or I address when the programmer need not identify the location for later reference, the only other reference being as an L address for the succeeding instruction. The blank address is actually a special case of the symbolic address. It is used only when a memory register is referred to in the D and/or I address of an instruction and is referred to again as the L address of the instruction of the next line in the program but is *not* referred to otherwise in the program.

The blank address is specified by leaving all five positions $A_1 A_2 A_3 A_4 A_5$ blank (see all instructions in blocks 2, 4, and 5 of Table 4.6). When a blank D or a blank I address is encountered by the assembly program, it selects optimally the address of a register from the table of available registers and assigns it as the numeric equivalent of this particular blank address. The address selected is deleted from the availability table and is saved for assignment to the blank L address that should appear on the next line of the program, but no entry is made to the symbolic-address file.   When the D and I addresses are both blank, the only difference in the procedure is that the same memory-register address is assigned to both blanks.

When a blank L address is encountered, it is assigned the same memory-register address that was assigned to the blank D and/or I address on the preceding line.   If the L address is blank and neither the D nor the I address was blank on the preceding line, the assembly program arbitrarily assigns, as the numeric equivalent, the preceding I address equivalent.   The result in the latter case is the assignment of a single address for two different functions.

The blank addresses are used by the programmer only as pairs or, in rare cases, triplets (blank D and I followed by blank L) on succeeding lines.   They are used if and only if the programmer wants an optimal address to be chosen for the register referred to by the pair (or triplet) of blanks but will not make another reference to the register elsewhere in the program.   The following are examples of the three legitimate uses of blank addresses:

a. A blank D followed by a blank L is illustrated in the third and fourth instructions of block 4 in Table 4.6.

b. A blank I followed by a blank L is illustrated in the first and second instructions of block 2 in Table 4.6.

c. Blank D and I followed by blank L is used only rarely and is not illustrated.

Any other use of the blank address will lead to erroneous assembly. Fortunately, such technical errors can be detected mechanically. The method of detection is discussed in a later section devoted to program assembly.

4. To specify the regional address:

The regional address is used when the programmer wishes to identify registers by their relative location in a consecutive sequence.   It is another special case of the symbolic address.   A region is a block of memory registers that is defined by the programmer. The definition is effected by inserting a regional specification pseudo instruction at an appropriate place in the program, usually at the start.   The pseudo instruction is of the form REG X $FFFF$ LLLL, and the L address is blank (see line 1 of Table 4.10).   REG is a pseudo operation code that is interpreted by the assembly program. X may be replaced by an arbitrary alphabetic character that becomes the symbolizer for the region and for all regional addresses associated therewith. $FFFF$ represents a four-digit number that specifies the address of the first register in the block comprising the region. LLLL represents a four-digit number that specifies the address of the last register in the block comprising the region. When the assembly program identifies the pseudo operation code REG, it associates the four-digit number $FFFF$ with the symbolizer letter in its table of regional specifications and it removes the addresses $FFFF$ to LLLL from its table of registers available for assignment.

The D address R0001 in the second line of Table 4.10 is a regional address. It is specified by writing the symbolizer, e.g., R, of the region in position A_1 of the address and by writing a four-digit number, e.g., 0001, in positions $A_2 A_3 A_4 A_5$. When the assembly program recognizes a regional address, say R0002, it assigns the address of the second register in region R as the numeric equivalent of R0002. In general, the numeric equivalent of the regional address $X\ nnnn$ is calculated to be $FFFF + nnnn - 1$, where $FFFF$ is the address of the first register in region (REG) X, and $nnnn$ is any four-digit integer.

If a regional address is specified in the program and the region has not been previously defined by a regional specification, the assembly program leaves that address blank in the assembled instruction.

This completes the rules for writing instructions in symbolic form for assembly by the SOAP II program. Additional useful provisions of the program will be discussed later in the chapter.

At first, symbolic programming will seem awkward. But it does not take long to become accustomed to the procedures. Then it is found that symbolic programming goes quite rapidly. The bookkeeping requirements placed on the programmer are considerably less in symbolic programming than in machine-language programming. He must keep a log of the symbolic addresses used and the functions of the registers so identified. Offsetting this, he will find that blank addresses can be specified for a large proportion of I and L addresses. Symbolic (nonblank) or numeric addresses need be used only for registers that must be identified for later reference. It will be noted (see Table 4.6) in the following examples that D addresses are predominantly symbolic addresses and that I and L addresses are predominantly blank. It will also be noted that the addresses and operation codes are aligned on the programming form so that the symbolizer positions A_1 and R_1 are readily identified. This facilitates accuracy in subsequent key-punching operations.

With this introduction to symbolic programming, we shall return to further programming examples.

EXAMPLES OF SYMBOLIC PROGRAMMING

4.12 A Table Punch Routine. A routine for *punching out* or *unloading* the contents of a sequence of memory registers is a common requirement in a data-processing program. It could be required, for instance, that the A and B tables of the example in Sec. 4.4 be punched out after the A table has been closed into the B table.

In particular, let it be required that the contents of memory registers 0016 through 0045 be punched out at the rate of five registers per card (80-80 format). Let it further be required that each card shall be identified by the address of the first register of the sequence of five registers whose data are contained in that card. The format of an output card and its relationship to the storage exit (punch band) words are defined, in terms of the requirement, in Table 4.7.

Table 4.7

Card columns	Description of card field	Storage exit register from which data are punched
1–10	The address (00 0000 XXXX) of the first of five registers	1
11–20	The contents of the first of five registers	2
21–30	The contents of the second of five registers	3
31–40	The contents of the third of five registers	4
41–50	The contents of the fourth of five registers	5
51–60	The contents of the fifth of five registers	6
61–80	Zeros	7 and 8

The analysis of the problem is illustrated in Fig. 4.6, a flow diagram for a table punch routine. The solution involves two indices. The letter i ($i = 1, 2, 3, \ldots , 30$) is used to represent the index on the registers in the table to be punched. The letter j ($j = 1, 2, 3, 4, 5$) is used as an index on the five storage exit registers to which the table words are transferred for punching. The band of storage exit registers starting at 0127 was chosen arbitrarily. The symbolic addresses used in the program (Table 4.8) were chosen to facilitate cross-referencing to the blocks in the flow diagram.

In this example, the organization of the flow diagram is presented somewhat differently than in the earlier examples. Previously, a flow diagram and the associated program were presented in the order that the computer executed blocks of instructions. In this example, the flow diagram is presented in the order that the problem was actually solved. First, a decision was made as to the method of indexing the transfer of the ith table word to the jth storage exit word. The decision was to include the i index in the variable data address associated with a load D register (LDD $15 + i$) operation and to include the j index in the variable data address associated with a store D register operation (STD $0127 + j$).

Once this decision has been made, the portion of the problem related to the index j could be solved. The index j is included in

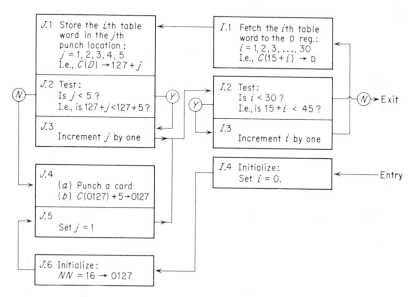

FIG. 4.6. A flow diagram for a table punch routine.

the operand address ($0127 + j$) of the instruction located at the symbolic address J1V of Table 4.8. The execution of this instruction is indicated by block J.1 of the flow diagram. Block J.2 is then entered and a test ($j < 5$?) is made to determine whether the index j has reached its limit. Whenever j is less than 5, the limit on j has not been reached; block J.3 is entered, where j is incremented by 1; then block I.2 is entered.

Whenever j equals 5, the limit on j has been reached; block J.4 is entered; a card is punched; and the address (00 0000 XXXX) contained in register 0127 is increased by 5 to identify the first of the next five registers to be transferred. Block J.5 is entered, j is reset to 1, and block I.2 is entered.

Table 4.8   A Table Punch Routine as Assembled by SOAP II

Symbolic program					Assembled program				
Location	Operation code	Data address	Instruction address	Remarks	Location	Operation code	Data address	Instruction address	Sequence number
	*BLR	0000	0099						1
	*BLR	0127	0134						2
	*BLR	0150	1999						3
I1V	LDD	0045	J1V	BLK I1	100	69	45	148	4
I2	RAL	I1V		BLK I2	101	65	100	105	5
	SLO	IC1			105	16	108	113	6
	BMI		EXIT	BLK I3	113	46	116	117	7
	ALO	IC2			116	15	119	123	8
	STL	I1V	8001		123	20	100	8001	9
I4†	LDD	IC3		BLK I4	102	69	106	109	10
	STD	I1V	J6		109	24	100	103	11
CONSTANTS									12
IC1	LDD	0045	J1V		108	69	45	148	13
IC2	LDD	0046	J1V		119	69	46	148	14
IC3	LDD	0015	J1V		106	69	15	148	15

* These instructions cause the assembly program (SOAP II) to make the specified blocks of addresses unavailable for assignment as numeric equivalents to symbolic addresses (see Sec. 4.19).

† Execution of program starts with this instruction.

Table 4.8 A Table Punch Routine as Assembled by Soap II (Continued)

	Symbolic program				Assembled program				
Location	Operation code	Data address	Instruction address	Remarks	Location	Operation code	Data address	Instruction address	Sequence number
J1V	STD	0132	J2	BLK J1	148	24	132	135	16
J2	RAL	J1V		BLK J2	135	65	148	104	17
	SLO	JC1			104	16	107	111	18
	BMI		J4		111	46	114	115	19
	ALO	JC2			114	15	118	124	20
	STL	J1V	I2		124	20	148	101	21
J4	PCH	0127		BLK J3	115	71	127	136	22
	RAL	0127		BLK J4	136	65	127	137	23
	ALO	JC3			137	15	140	145	24
	STL	0127	J5		145	20	127	138	25
J5	LDD	JC4		BLK J5	138	69	141	144	26
	STD	J1V	I2		144	24	148	101	27
J6	LDD	JC5		BLK J6	103	69	110	120	28
	STD	0127	J5		120	24	127	138	29
CONSTANTS									30
JC1	STD	0132	J2		107	24	132	135	31
JC2	STD	0133	J2		118	24	133	135	32
JC3	00	0000	0005		140			5	33
JC4	STD	0128	J2		141	24	128	135	34
JC5	00	0000	J0016		110			16	35

119

In block I.2 the index i is tested ($i < 30$?) to determine whether or not it has reached its limit. If i is 30, the punch-out of the table is complete and an exit is made from the routine, i.e., control is transferred to the next instruction to be executed. It is worth noting that special provision for punching the last card would be necessary if the registers in the table were not an even multiple of the registers punched out per card and if the card were not punched before execution of the test on index i. In short, the ranges of the indices were chosen to simplify the solution of the example.

Whenever the index i has not reached its limit ($i < 30$), at least one more table word remains to be transferred to the punch band. Block I.3 is entered and the index i is incremented by 1. Block I.1 is entered and the next table register is copied into the D register by execution of the instruction located at I1V in Table 4.8. The index i is included in the operand address of this instruction. Then block J.1 is entered, and the cycle is repeated.

The initialization of the variables in the program was determined after completion of the foregoing analysis. The routine is entered at block I.4 where i is set equal to 0. Then block J.6 is entered where the address (0016) of the first register in the table is stored in the storage exit register located at 0127. Finally, block J.5 is utilized to set j equal to 1. Note that i is tested and incremented to 1 before it is used for the first time. The initialization makes possible two or more uses of the routine in a single execution of a program containing it.

The foregoing routine is designed for a special purpose, namely, that of punching out the consecutive registers 0016 through 0045 at the rate of five registers per card. The routine could be modified so it would serve a more general purpose, namely, that of punching out an arbitrarily specified sequence of consecutive registers at an arbitrarily specified rate of N (not greater than seven) registers per card and then exiting to execute an arbitrarily specified instruction. The general-purpose N-(register)-per card punch routine should provide for indicating the value of N, as well as the address of the first of the N registers, on each card punched. Provision should be made for calculating the appropriate value of N' for the last card, so that the number of registers in the table need not be an even multiple of N. The development of an N-per-card punch routine is left as an exercise for the reader.

The N-per-card punch routine will prove quite useful for punching pertinent information when programs are being tested (see item 3 in Table 5.2). It will also be useful for punching out programs and tables that are to be reloaded to memory at some later time. A program for loading such cards to memory is presented in the next example.

4.13 An N-word-per-card Read Routine. The N-word-per-card read routine presented here is designed to read cards punched by the N-per-card punch routine discussed above and to store the N words in consecutive registers starting with the address specified in columns 7 to 10 of the card.

In particular, it is assumed that a card of the following form will be read 80-80 into the storage entry registers 1951 through 1958. The N words will then be transferred to the appropriate memory registers.

The number N indicates the number of 10-digit words that are contained in the card (in the form shown in Table 4.9) and that are to be stored in consecutive memory registers starting at $FFFF$. N

Table 4.9 N-word-per-card Format

Card columns	Contents	Input synchronizer register number*
1–10	$00\ 000N\ FFFF\ +$	1
11–20	$XX\ XXXX\ XXXX\ \pm$	2
21–30	$XX\ XXXX\ XXXX\ \pm$	3
.		
.		
.		
71–80	$XX\ XXXX\ XXXX\ \pm$	8

* 80-80 wiring is assumed.

may assume the value 0, 1, 2, . . . , 7. If N is 0, the card is treated as a transfer card and control is transferred to location $FFFF$. For all values of N, the card must contain valid numeric characters in the first $10(N + 1)$ card columns. The remaining card columns, if any, may be blank or may be punched as required by the programmer, because the data from the latter columns are ignored by the program. A negative sign is indicated by an 11 punch over the units position of a card field, i.e., columns 20, 30, 40, 50, 60, 70, or 80.

The flow diagram of Fig. 4.7 presents a solution of the problem in the order that the machine executes the blocks of instructions. First a card is read. A test is made to determine whether or not a transfer card has been read. If so, the transfer instruction is executed. If not, the index $j = 0, 1, 2, . . . , N - 1$ is set to 0. In this case, the index is the same for fetching and storing the word to be transferred. Again, the index has been included in the D addresses of the variable instructions, i.e., $1952 + j$ and $FFFF + j$, respectively. After a transfer is executed, the j index is incremented (in both D addresses); then a test is made to determine whether N transfers have been executed. If not, another transfer is executed. If so, another read is executed. The exit from the routine is effected eventually by a transfer card, i.e., a card with N equal to 0 and $FFFF$ equal to the address of the next instruction to be executed.

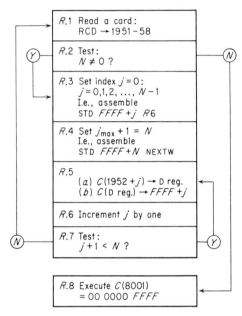

Fig. 4.7. Flow diagram for the N-per-card read routine.

An N-per-card read routine, cross-indexed to the blocks in the flow diagram, is shown in Table 4.10. Note that the band of storage entry registers, 1951 through 1960, has been specified as a region and that registers therein are referred to by regional addresses. The advantage of this procedure is that the routine can be readily relocated in memory. The subject of locating a routine in memory will be discussed in a later section on program assembly.

4.14 An Invalid-character Sensing Routine. The ERROR switch on the 650 console (Fig. 5.1) can be set at either STOP or SENSE. If an invalid character code is detected at a validity check point when the ERROR switch is set at STOP, the computer stops at the end of the instruction phase with the address register lights indicating the register containing the error.   Manual intervention is required to restart program execution.

If an invalid character is detected when the ERROR switch is set at SENSE, the contents of the D, U, L, and program registers are auto-

Table 4.10   *N*-per-card Read Routine

Block	Location	Operation code	*D* address	*I* address
		REG	R 1 9 5 1	1960
R.1	R1	RCD	R 0 0 0 1	
R.2		RAU	R 0 0 0 1	
		SRT	0 0 0 4	
		NZU		8001
R.3		SRT	0 0 0 2	
		LDD	TJMAX	
		SDA	TEMP	
R.4		SRT	0 0 0 8	
		SLT	0 0 0 4	
		ALO	8 0 0 1	
		STL	TJMAX	
		RAU	TEMP	
		ALO		8002
		LDD	R 0 0 0 2	8003
R.5	8002	LDD	R 0 0 0 2	8003
	8003	STD	*FFFF*	R6
R.6	R6	AUP	CONE	
		ALO	8 0 0 1	
R.7		SUP	TJMAX	
		BMI		R1
		AUP	8 0 0 1	8002

Constant				
CONE	00	0 0 0 1	0000

Assembled constant				
TJMAX	STD	0 0 0 0	R6

Temporary storage				
TEMP	STD	*FFFF*	R6

matically reset with zeros and control is transferred to the STORAGE ENTRY SWITCHES, 8000.   The instruction stored in 8000 can be the entry to a routine designed by the programmer to punch an exception card or to otherwise indicate the detection of an invalid character and then transfer control back to the main program to continue processing. Such a procedure is particularly useful in programs that are designed, as in this example, to process a large number of input cards, with the possibility that an invalid character may occur in any card.

The flow diagram of Fig. 4.8 and the program of Table 4.11 are an expansion of block 2.0 of Fig. 4.5. They show a validity-error sensing routine that would be practical for the foregoing problem. It assumes that a count is kept of the number of cards read, i.e., the number of executions of the read instruction in block 1.0 of

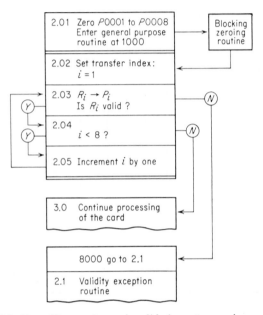

FIG. 4.8. Flow diagram for an invalid-character sensing routine.

Fig. 4.5. It further assumes that storage entry words R0001 through R0008 should all contain valid characters only for each card read. After each card is read and the card counter is incremented, the storage exit locations P0001 through P0008 are zeroed. Next, successive attempts are made to transfer storage entry words R0001 through R0008 to storage exit locations P0001 through P0008, respectively.

In the event an invalid code is sensed (block 2.0 of Fig. 4.5), the validity exception routine causes a card to be punched that identifies the input card being processed and the card field containing the error. If a validity error results from a random machine error elsewhere in the program, this event can be identified if both the transfer index and the card count have been copied into P0008. Note that the question (in block 2.03 of Fig. 4.8) "Is R_i valid?" is executed automatically; hence it does not appear in the program.

Table 4.11 An Invalid-character Sensing Routine

Location	Operation code	Data address	Instruction address
201	RAL	20C1	
	LDD	202	1000*
202	RAU	20C2	
	ALO	20C3	8003
8003	LDD	R0001	8002
8002	STD	P0001	204
204	SUP	20C4	
	BMI		EXIT
	AUP	8001	
	STU	P0008	
	AUP	CONE	
	ALO	8001	8003
Constants			
20C1	00	P0001	P0008
20C2	LDD	R0001	8002
20C3	STD	P0001	204
20C4	LDD	R0008	8002
CONE	00	0001	0000

* 1000 is the location of the entry to the block zeroing routine, from which the return to symbolic location 202 is automatic.

4.15 An Accounts Receivable Posting Routine. This example is included to illustrate the TLU (table lookup) operation code. It is assumed that the customer numbers in Table E are unique and are a strictly increasing function of memory-register address; i.e., if $N_1 > N_2$, then the address in which N_1 is stored is greater than the address in which N_2 is stored. It is further assumed that the offset between the customer's number (Table E) and his account (Table F) is the same for all customers.

As illustrated in Fig. 4.9 and Table 4.12, the first requirement is to determine whether the customer number N is in Table E. To accomplish this, N is entered as the search argument in the D register. Then the TLU (84) operation code is specified with a D address of E0001.

The computer then automatically compares the magnitude of the

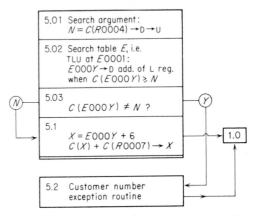

Fig. 4.9. Flow diagram for an accounts receivable posting routine.

Table 4.12   An Accounts Receivable Posting Routine

Location	Operation code	Data address	Instruction address
501	RAU	R 0 0 0 4	
	TLU	E 0 0 0 1	
	STL	TEMP	503
503	ALO	5 0 C 1	8002
8002	SUP	E 0 0 0 Y	5031
5031	NZU	5 2	
	RAL	TEMP	
	ALO	5 0 C 2	
	LDD	5 1 0 2 V	
	SDA	5 1 0 2 V	8002
8002	RAU	F 0 0 0 Y	5101
5101	AUP	R 0 0 0 7	5102V
5102V	STU	F 0 0 0 Y	10
52	Entry to exception routine		
	Constants		
50C1	SUP	0000	5031
50C2	RAU	0006	5101

contents of the D register with the magnitude of the contents of the first register in the band containing the D address E0001. In this case E0001 equals 0050 and is the first register in its band. If $|C(\text{D})| > |C(\text{E0001})|$, the comparison is repeated for the next register in the band. The comparison cycle is repeated until a register is found, say

E000Y, such that $|C(\text{D})| \leq |C(\text{E000Y})|$. When such a register is found, its address is entered in the D address positions of the L register, e.g., XX E000Y XXXX.

There are two exceptions that should be noted. The first is that no comparison is made between the D register and either of the last two registers in a memory band; i.e., a search would jump from $XX47$ to $XX50$. The second is that if the data address associated with the TLU code is not the first register in the band but is instead the kth register, then $k - 1$ is added to the address of the register at which the search stops, and this number is inserted in the D address positions of the L register.

Returning to the routine, if the contents of E000Y is the customer's number N, his balance, located at E000Y + 6, is incremented by the amount contained in R0007. If the contents of E000Y are not N, the customer number exception routine is entered.

4.16 A Trace Routine. A trace routine follows the step-by-step execution of the program. It makes available to the programmer a

Table 4.13

Columns	Description	Storage exit word
1–6	Sequence number of the traced instructions	P0001
7–10	Location of the instruction	
11–20	The instruction	P0002
21–30	The U register after execution	P0003
31–40	The L register after execution	P0004
41–50	The D register after execution	P0005

sequential record of the instructions as executed, the location thereof, and the contents of the D, L, and U registers after the instruction is executed. The routine is useful in program testing and error isolation (the subject of Chap. 5). In particular, it collects the data for punching cards of the format shown in Table 4.13. Trace cards are listed as item 5 of Table 5.2

Before the trace routine illustrated in Fig. 4.10 and programmed in Table 4.14 is entered, the location $iiii$ of the first instruction to be traced must be stored in P0002 in the form 00 0000 $iiii$. Then control is transferred to T1 (Table 4.14), at which point the trace routine assumes control of instruction execution.

The sequence number is incremented by 1, the location of the next instruction is updated, and both are stored in P0001. The instruction itself is fetched and stored in P0002. The operation code is tested

Table 4.14 Trace Program Assembled in Registers 0100 to 0149

	Symbolic program				Assembled program				
Location	Operation code	D address	I address	Location	Operation code	D address	I address	Sequence number	Error*
	BLR	0 0 0 0	00 99					1	1
	BLR	0 1 5 0	19 99					2	1
	REG	P 0 1 2 7	01 3 4					3	1
	SYN	T1	01 0 0					4	1
T1	RAM	P 0 0 0 2	T2	100	67	128	135	5	
T2	AUP	P 0 0 0 1		135	10	127	136	6	
	AUP	TC1		136	10	139	143	7	
	LDD	8 0 0 3		143	69	8003	101	8	
	SIA	P 0 0 0 1		101	23	127	137	9	
	SLT	0 0 0 4		137	35	4	147	10	
	LDD	T2 DV		147	69	102	105	11	
	SDA	T2 DV		105	22	102	106	12	
	RAU	P 0 0 0 3		106	60	129	138	13	
	ALO	P 0 0 0 4		138	15	130	140	14	
	LDD	P 0 0 0 5	T2DV	140	69	131	102	15	
T2 DV	RAM	1 1 1 1†	T2D1	102	67	9999†	103	16	
T2 D1	STD	P 0 0 0 2		103	24	128	141	17	
	SRT	0 0 0 9		141	30	9	111	18	
	ALO	TC1		111	15	139	144	19	
	DIV	TC2		144	14	148	108	20	
	NZ U		T4A	108	44	112	113	21	
	RAL	TC3		112	65	115	119	22	
	LDD	P 0 0 0 2	T4	119	69	128	142	23	

	Op							
T4	S I A	T6 V		142	23	145	149	24
	R A U	P0 0 0 3		149	60	129	146	25
	A L O	P0 0 0 4		146	15	130	104	26
T7	L D D	P0 0 0 5	T6V	104	69	131	145	27
	S T D	P0 0 0 5		107	24	131	109	28
	S T L	P0 0 0 4		109	20	130	110	29
	S T U	P0 0 0 3		110	21	129	114	30
	R A L	8 0 0 0		114	65	8000	121	31
	B M I	P0 0 0 2		121	46	124	125	32
	R A L	T10	T10	124	65	128	116	33
	B M I	P0 0 0 1		116	46	125	100	34
T10	P C H	P0 0 0 1	T1	125	71	127	100	35
T10 A	P C H	P0 0 0 2	T1	117	71	127	118	36
	R A M	0 0 0 4		118	67	128	120	37
	S R T	TC4	T2	120	30	4	135	38
T4 A	R A L	P0 0 0 2		113	65	122	123	39
	L D D	T6 V		123	69	128	126	40
	S D A	0 0 0 1	T4	126	22	145	142	41
TC1	0 0	0 0 0 0	00 01	139		1	1	42
TC2	0 0	0 0 0 0	00 05	148			5	43
TC3	0 0	T10 A	T7	115			107	44
TC4	0 0		T10	122		117	125	45

* The IBM 402 plug board is wired to indicate inconsistencies between card format and SOAP II symbolic programming rules.
The one (1) indicates a blank location preceded by a nonblank D and I.
† Note the translation of IIII, when position A_1 is blank.

to distinguish between branch and nonbranch operations.   The former class requires that both the D address and the I address be modified in the instruction to be executed under control of the trace routine, while the latter class requires that only the I address be modified in that instruction.

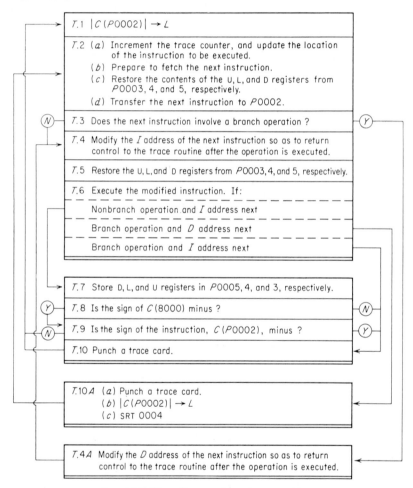

Fɪɢ. 4.10. Flow diagram for a trace routine.

The contents of P0003, P0004, and P0005 are then transferred to u, l, and d registers, respectively; the modified instruction is executed; then the contents of d, l, and u registers are stored in P0005, P0004, and P0003, respectively.   The data for punching the trace card are thus assembled.

A provision is made for limiting the number of cards punched at the discretion of the programmer. If the sign of 8000 is plus, a card is punched for each instruction executed. If the sign of 8000 is minus, a card is punched for each branch operation executed or for each instruction that is stored in memory with a minus sign.

There are certain limitations built into the routine. If the routine is entered in the manner described above, the first instruction to be traced cannot depend upon the contents of the u, l, or d registers, because their contents are destroyed before execution of the first instruction to be traced. A safe general rule, then, is to enter only with an instruction that resets the a register, e.g., RAU, RSU, etc. An alternative procedure is to store the contents of the u, l, and d registers in P0003, P0004, and P0005, respectively, before entering the routine, in which case any operation can be executed in the first instruction traced.

A second limitation involves the DIV (divide without reset) operation. If the remainder and quotient have opposite signs, an underflow will occur inevitably when the u and l registers are restored for execution of the next instruction.

The final limitation is that no provision is made for automatically breaking the trace once it is started. An entry to the trace routine can be programmed, but an exit must be effected by manual intervention.

The above limitations are not serious, and could be reduced by adding the appropriate instructions to the routine. A trace routine incorporated in the program test supervisory routine, discussed in Chap. 5, has been designed to remove these limitations.

PREPARATION FOR STORING THE PROGRAM IN MEMORY

After the program is written, it must be translated to punched-card coding for loading to the 650 memory. The translation procedure to be used will depend upon whether the program has been written numerically or symbolically.

If the program has been written numerically, the instructions and constants may be key-punched in one-word memory load card format or N-per-card memory load format. If the program has been written symbolically (for assembly by SOAP II), the punched-card format to be used is specified in the second line of the programming sheet (see Table 4.6).

4.17 Program Written in Basic Machine Language. If the program is written in basic machine language and successive location addresses on the programming sheet are (for the most part) consecutively numbered, there is some advantage in using the N-per-card memory load format. The data to be stored in as many as seven consecutive registers can be contained in one card; the number of cards to be key-punched and also the computer time required to load the program to memory are thus reduced.

If the successive location addresses are not consecutively numbered, there is little choice between the one-word and the N-per-card ($N = 1$) memory load format. The number of cards in the *program deck*, the deck of cards containing the instructions and constants, may be reduced later by punching out a program deck in N-per-card format after the one-per-card deck has been loaded to memory.

The following technical restrictions should be kept in mind when programs written numerically are key-punched regardless of the choice of format:

1. A memory load card must not specify loading of data to a location other than 0000 through 1999, i.e., a memory register.
2. Each instruction or constant to be loaded must be key-punched as a 10-digit number.
3. If a negative sign is required, it must be indicated by an 11 punch over the units position of the 10-digit number.
4. When the N-per-card format is used, the value of N can vary from card to card; but it must correctly specify the number of words from that card that are to be stored in successive registers.

4.18 Program Written Symbolically. If the program has been written symbolically, it must be assembled (see Table 4.14) before it can be loaded to memory. A card should be key-punched for each line in the symbolic program. The format of the card is specified by line 2 of the programming sheet (see Table 4.6). Note that a minus sign is indicated by an M in column 42. SOAP II translates a symbolic program to a numeric program, one card at a time. Immediately after a line is translated, a card is punched that contains both the symbolic data and their numeric translation. The deck thus produced contains the *object program* in one-word memory load format ready for loading to memory. The object program is not stored in memory as it is assembled. When the object deck is loaded to memory, cards will be automatically bypassed if they correspond to lines (in the written program) that are not to be loaded to memory, e.g., locations 8000 through 8003.

4.19 Allocation of Memory for Symbolic Programs. The regional specification, pseudo operation code REG, provides the programmer with a facility for locating tables within memory. He may wish to place further restrictions on the allocation of memory. For example, he may wish to restrict the assembled program to an arbitrary set of memory registers, e.g., 0000 through 0999. The symbolic pseudo code BLR (block reserve) provides the programmer with this facility.

The BLR code is used in Table 4.14 to restrict the assembly of the trace routine within the band of memory registers ranging from 0100 through 0149. The pseudo instruction BLR *FFFF LLLL* (*FFFF* ≤ *LLLL*) specifies that the block of registers *FFFF* to *LLLL* are to be made unavailable for assignment by the assembly program as numeric equivalents to symbolic or blank addresses. Note that in Table 4.14 the regional specification places a further restriction on the available addresses. Note also that it is permissible to specify a region within a set of registers that have been previously block reserved.

There are occasions when it is desirable to reserve a block of registers until a certain number of program lines have been assembled and then to make the reserved block available for the assembly of subsequent lines of the program. The pseudo operation code BLA (block availability) is provided for this purpose. When the SOAP II program encounters the pseudo instruction BLA *FFFF LLLL* (*FFFF* ≤ *LLLL*), it revises its availability table so that *FFFF* to *LLLL* are made available for assignment as numeric equivalents to symbolic or blank addresses subsequently encountered.

Either the BLR or the BLA operation code may be specified on any line of the program.[1] Particular care must be taken in the use of the BLA code. If the block of registers *FFFF* to *LLLL* contains a region or an address that must be reserved for any reason, such an address should be again reserved (with the BLR code); otherwise it may be assigned as an equivalent to a symbolic or blank address. Such a duplicating assignment would surely lead to trouble in program execution.

When a long program (in excess of 200 instructions) is to be assembled for testing, it is recommended that the component routines be assembled in independent blocks of memory registers. This can be accomplished by judicious use of BLR and BLA codes. Assume, for example, that the program to be tested comprises two major routines. Assume further that the first routine is to be assembled in locations 0000 through 0099 and the second in locations 0100 through 0249. These restrictions can be effected as shown in Table 4.15. The first block reservation BLR 0100 1999 restricts assembly of the

---

[1] Neither the BLA nor the BLR operation code affects the symbolic table or its table of numeric equivalents.

first routine to the registers 0000 through 0099. The second block reservation reserves any registers in the first block (0000 through 0099) not used in the assembly of the first routine. The block availability specification (BLA 0100 0249) makes the second block of registers available for assembly of the second routine.

Table 4.15

Location	Operation code	D	I
	BLR	0100	1999
.	First major routine		
.	BLR	0000	0099
	BLA	0100	0249
.	Second major routine		
.			

4.20 Other Pseudo Operation Codes. The following symbolic pseudo operation codes are also provided: SYN, EQU, ALF, PAT, and BOP.

The pseudo operation code SYN is used to define a synonymity between a symbolic address and a specific memory-register address and to reserve the specified address. For example, the instruction SYN T1 0100 (see item 4 in Table 4.14) will cause the SOAP II program to enter T1 in its symbol table with 0100 as its numeric equivalent and to remove 0100 from the table of available registers. If the synonymity is to function properly, it must be defined before the symbolic address is otherwise alluded to.

The pseudo operation code EQU is used to define an equivalence between two symbolic addresses. If a given register is alluded to by two different symbolic addresses, it will be convenient to equate them. This may happen when two or more programmers are collaborating on a program. The symbolic instruction EQU SYMBL SMBL, for example, would cause SOAP II to enter SYMBL in the symbol table with its numeric equivalent being that of SMBL. It is necessary that SMBL (the symbolic I address) shall have been previously alluded to (entered in the symbol table); otherwise the assembly program cannot define the equivalence, in which case a 9 will be punched in column 79 of the corresponding output card.

The pseudo operation code ALF (alphabetic) is used to specify that the five characters in the D address on that line are to be assembled as an alphanumeric word, rather than as a symbolic address. For example, the term ALF N3PB would be assembled as 7593776200. This code is used for assembling alphanumeric constants such as the names in Table G of the data-processing problem.

The pseudo operation code PAT (punch availability table) may be included at the last line of the program if the programmer wants a statement of the status of the availability table after assembly of the program has been completed. The registers that remain available after assembly may be used later for making corrections to the program if errors appear when it is tested.

The symbolic pseudo operation code BOP (beginning of program) permits independent assembly of two or more programs with a single loading of the SOAP II program deck. When the code BOP is encountered, the assembly program erases the symbolic and regional tables, makes all memory registers 0000 through 1999 available, and then proceeds with the assembly of the succeeding input cards. Thus, two sets of cards that are separated by a card containing the code BOP are assembled independently.

When programming is complete, including the foregoing pseudo instructions as required, key punching may be started. One card is punched for each line in the program. Up to 10 characters of alphanumeric data may be entered in the positions provided on the programming sheets for *remarks*.

4.21 Automatic Checking of Technical Errors. When the key punching has been completed, the cards should be listed. A plug board is specially wired for the IBM 402 or the IBM 407 Accounting Machine, whichever is used at the data-processing center for listing SOAP II input and output cards. The wiring provides for the detection of certain technical errors in symbolic programming, namely,

1. A line with a blank location address preceded by a line in which neither the D nor the I address is blank
2. A line with a nonblank location address preceded by a line in which either the D or the I address is blank

The manner in which the detected errors are indicated on the listing may vary among computation centers and will depend upon whether a 402 or a 407 is used for listing. The "ones" in the column headed Error in Table 4.14 illustrate one method of indicating actual or potential technical errors. In Table 4.14 no technical error actually exists; instead, the ones indicate potential errors.

It is advisable to proofread the listed program against the manually written copy. Typographical and technical errors that are observed during the proofreading should be corrected. The cards that contain errors should be replaced by the cards that are correctly punched.

When all observed errors have been corrected and the corrections have been checked, the deck may be assembled.

4.22 The Assembly Run. To perform the assembly of a symbolic program, the SOAP II program is loaded to memory; then the deck to be assembled follows the SOAP II program deck and is read a card at a time under control of the assembly program. The object (assembled) program deck is punched a card at a time.

The assembly program can detect technical errors in an input card and can indicate the detection of such errors as follows:

1. A regional address for an undefined region will be detected, and the corresponding address positions will be blank in the assembled instruction.
2. An undefined symbolic operation code will be detected, and the operation code positions will be blank in the assembled instruction.
3. An invalid character in an input-card column will be detected, and execution of the assembly program will halt. Remedial action must be taken by the machine operator.
4. If all addresses (that were made available) are used before assembly is completed, execution of the assembly program will halt.
5. If the symbol table is filled before all symbolic addresses have been assigned numeric equivalents, execution of the assembly program will halt.
6. If the location address, operation code, operand address, or instruction address fields of an instruction are left blank in an assembled card, columns 75 to 78, respectively, will contain an 11 punch.
7. If an EQU or SYN card has been ignored because of an undefined instruction address or because the symbol table is filled, the assembled card will contain a 9 punch in column 79.

The object program should be listed (on the 402 or 407). The plug board for listing the SOAP II format cards will normally be wired to detect 11 punches in columns 75 to 78 and a 9 punch in column 79 and to print appropriate error indicators.

Any errors observed on the listing of the object program should be corrected before a program test run is scheduled. When the corrections have been made, the object program may be loaded to memory using the assembled deck (as one-word memory load cards).

REFERENCES

1. Andree, Richard V.: "Programming the IBM 650 Magnetic Drum Computer and Data Processing Machine," Holt, Rinehart, and Winston, New York, 1958.
2. "IBM SOAP II Programmer's Reference Manual," International Business Machines Corporation, New York, 1957.
3. Wrubel, Marshal H.: "A Primer of Programming for Digital Computers," McGraw-Hill Book Company, Inc., New York, 1959.

PROBLEMS

4.1. Specify the layout and content of a self-contained two-word-per-card memory load card to be read 80-80 by an instruction stored in 8000.

4.2. Prepare a flow diagram and write in machine language a program for storing the word $01\ X\ X$ in location X, where X successively assumes the values 0100, 0101, 0102, . . . , 0149.

4.3. Prepare a flow diagram and write a program for storing minus zero $(00\ 0000\ 0000-)$ in the first 25 locations of alternate memory bands starting at location 1000 and including the band containing 1400.

4.4. Translate the I block of the table punch routine to machine language, i.e., numeric operation codes and absolute addresses. Locate successive instructions (and constants) in consecutive registers starting at 0100.

4.5. Prepare a flow diagram and write a routine in SOAP format to calculate

$$\sum_{i=0}^{n} p_i x_i = p_0 x_0 + p_1 x_1 + \cdots + p_n x_n$$

Assume that $n = 49$, that $0.000 \leq p_i \leq 1.000$, and that $000.0 \leq x_i \leq 999.9$. Exit from the routine with the answer in the L register, rounded to two decimal places.

4.6. Prepare a flow diagram and write a routine for linear interpolation in a table of discrete values of the function $y = f(x)$. Use the formula

$$y = \frac{x - x_1}{x_2 - x_1} (y_2 - y_1) + y_1$$

Assume that x_i, y_i are positive and are stored in the form $XXX\ 00\ YYYYY$, in ascending order on x_i, and that the table contains less than 49 registers. (*Hint:* Use the table lookup operation, you may assume that the value of x is known to be within the range of the table.)

4.7. Write a general-purpose N-per-card punch routine. Let the number of words per card N, the first table location $FFFF$, the last table location LLLL, and the exit instruction be contained in the L and D registers when the routine is entered.

4.8. Modify the trace routine to eliminate the restrictions noted for the trace routine illustrated in Fig. 4.10.

4.9. Assume that a program deck (one-word memory load cards) is being loaded to memory, and that the machine stops with (a) 69 1954 1953 in the program register and 64   24 1376 in the D register and (b) 24   8000 in the program register.   Identify the probable cause in each case, and indicate the corrective action.

4.10. Write a sequence of instructions that will cause the computer to find the largest number stored in the sequence of registers 1200 through 1233. Use a looping sequence.   Do not use TLU operation.

4.11. Write a sequence of instructions that will cause the computer to sort the set of numbers stored in registers 1200 through 1233.   By *sort* it is meant that the numbers should be rearranged so that the smallest number is in 1200, the largest is in 1233, and the intermediate numbers are in ascending sequence. Use a looping sequence.   Do not use TLU operation.

4.12. Write a sequence of instructions to calculate the value of the polynomial

$$a_4 x^4 + a_3 x^3 + a_2 x^2 + a_1 x + a_0 = \{[(a_4 x + a_3)x + a_2]x + a_1\}x + a_0$$

You may specify the locations in which the parameters $a_0, a_1, \ldots, a_4$ and the variable x are stored in memory.

4.13. Given the sequence of instructions

$$
\begin{array}{llll}
0050 & \text{RAL} & 0100 & 0051 \\
0051 & \text{DVR} & 0175 & 0052 \\
0052 & \text{SRD} & 0002 & 0053 \\
0053 & \text{ALO} & 0099 & 0054 \\
0054 & \text{STL} & 0099 & 0055 \\
\end{array}
$$

add the instructions that are required to cause the computer to calculate the sum

$$\frac{C(0100)}{C(0175)} + \frac{C(0101)}{C(0176)} + \frac{C(0102)}{C(0177)} + \cdots + \frac{C(0125)}{C(0200)}$$

you may assume that the resulting sum $< 10^{10}$, but do not assume that all quotients have the same sign.   (*Hint:* Use the technique developed in Prob. 3.12 to perform successive modifications of the instructions located in registers 0050 and 0051.   Do not forget to provide for initialization.)

4.14. Write a sequence of instructions that will cause the computer to calculate the sum $N_1 + N_2 + N_3 + \cdots + N_{37}$, where $N_i = C(0132 + i)$. $|\Sigma N_i| \geq 10^{10}$ is possible and the signs of the individual N_i's may be either positive or negative.

4.15. Write a sequence of instructions to calculate $x = \sqrt{a}$ by successive approximations, using the formula $x_{i+1} = (x_i + a/x_i)/2$. Iterate until $|x_{i+1} - x_i| < \delta$, say .001.   The starting value x_0 can be arbitrarily chosen, say $x_0 = 1$ or $x_0 = a/2$. The closer the starting value is to $\sqrt{a}$, the quicker the series will converge.

4.16. Write a sequence of instructions to calculate the roots of the quadratic equation $ax^2 + bx + c$. Provide for both real and complex roots. Use the formula

$$x = \frac{-b \pm \sqrt{b^2 - 4ac}}{2a}$$

4.17. Draw a block diagram of a subroutine for storing 00 0000 0000 − (minus zero) in all the storage *exit* registers on the drum. Write out the program instructions and constants, assigning locations from the bands 1000 through 1099.

4.18. Write a drum zeroing routine that will require eight words or less for both instructions and constants, hence can be contained on a single card, to accomplish the following:

a. Store   70 1901 1901   in location   0000.
b. Store   00 0001 0000   in location   0001.
c. Store   00 0000 0000   in locations   0002 through 1999.
d. Transfer control to location 0000 when the above are accomplished.

Specify the information to be punched into the 80 columns of the card and the settings of the STORAGE ENTRY SWITCHES required if this is to be used as a single-card drum zeroing routine with a board wired to read 80-80.

4.19. Devise a two-card drum zeroing routine to be used with the STORAGE ENTRY SWITCHES set to 70 1951 1951. Assume an 80-80 board is to be used. The program is to

a. Store   00 0000 8000   in location   0000.
b. Store   00 0001 0000   in location   0001.
c. Store   00 0000 0000   in locations   0002 through 1999.

Present your solution in a table specifying the information to be punched into the various columns of card 1 and card 2.

4.20. In the solution of a data-processing problem it is necessary to count the number of ones in a positive binary integer that has 10 digit positions. This summing must be performed many times in the solution of the data-processing problem.

Two different methods are suggested for performing this summing. One involves stripping off successive digit positions and accumulating the required sum. The following set of instructions is a start on this approach. Copy these instructions onto a 650 program sheet and complete the sequence.

Let X be the symbolic address of the register containing the binary integer that is to be summed. Let S be the symbolic address of the register in which the sum is to be stored. Let I be the symbolic address of the register that contains a count $(0, 1, 2, \ldots, 9)$ of the number of digit positions that have been summed.

LOC	OP	DA	IA
START	RAL	X	
	STU	S	
	STD	I	SHIFT
LOOP	RAL	X	SHIFT
SHIFT	SLT	0001	
	STL	X	
	AUP	S	
	STU	S	
	RAL	I	

4.21. Another approach to the summing specified in Prob. 4.20 is to consider the binary integer in register X as being partitioned into three addresses *aa bbbb cccc*, e.g., 10 0111 1111. Each time a sum is to be calculated, three instructions shown below (V1, V2, and V3) are modified so that their D addresses are those resulting from the partitioning of the contents of register X. In each of the registers whose addresses can thus be referred to, it will be necessary to store an integer (constant) equal to the number of ones in the address; e.g., the contents of 1111 will be 00 0000 0004.

You are requested to write a sequence of instructions that will appropriately modify the D addresses of V1, V2, and V3, so that the sum will be appropriately computed. The possible values of *cccc*, *bbbb*, or 00*aa* are 0, 1, 2, 3, and 4. Before you begin writing instructions, prepare a list showing for each of these values all the locations into which it must be loaded.

The following instructions and symbolic addresses are to be used in your program:

LOC	OP	DA	IA
V1	RAL	00*aa*	V2
V2	ALO	*bbbb*	V3
V3	ALO	*cccc*	
	STL	S	OUT
START	RAL	X	

4.22. Discuss the comparative advantages and disadvantages of the alternative methods suggested in Probs. 4.20 and 4.21. Your discussion should consider (but need not necessarily be limited to) memory requirements and speed of execution.

4.23*a*. A somewhat more efficient solution to Prob. 4.20 can be devised if the index register is eliminated and a nonzero A test is used to break the loop. Write a sequence of instructions based on these two ideas.

b. Write another sequence that is more efficient than any of the methods suggested in Probs. 4.20, 4.21, and 4.23*a*. (*Hint:* Use the suggestions in 4.23*a* together with the idea of using 8001 as temporary storage for the sum.)

4.24. Given the following instructions stored in memory registers 1901 to 1905 and assuming 80-80 read:

LOC	OP	DA	IA
1901	LDD	1951	1952
1902	LDD	1953	1954
1903	LDD	1955	1956
1904	LDD	1957	1958
1905	RCD	1951	1901

a. Define a four-word memory load card to provide for storing four 10-digit words in four arbitrarily specified memory registers. Provide for reading a sequence of such cards.

b. Define a transfer card for breaking the loop provided for in (a).

c. Define the setting of the STORAGE ENTRY SWITCHES, 8000, that will be required if we wish to read a single card to store the given instructions in 1901 through 1905 and then to continue automatically the processing of a sequence of four-word memory load cards.

4.25. Given an input deck in which each card (I card) contains a set of four integers X_1, X_2, X_3, and X_4 as specified in the table below. The described output is an S card and a P card for each I card, where the contents and format of the S and P cards are defined below.

Columns	I card		S card		P card	
	Content	Memory location	Content	Memory location	Content	Memory location
1–10	X_1	R0001	X_1	P0001	X_1X_2	P0001
11–20	X_2	R0002	X_2	P0002	X_1X_3	P0002
21–30	X_3	R0003	X_3	P0003	X_1X_4	P0003
31–40	X_4	R0004	X_4	P0004	X_2X_3	P0004
41–50	Zeros		$X_1{}^2$	P0005	X_2X_4	P0005
51–60	Zeros		$X_2{}^2$	P0006	X_3X_4	P0006
61–70	Zeros		$X_3{}^2$	P0007	Zeros	P0007
71–80	Zeros		$X_4{}^2$	P0008	99 . . . 99	P0008

where $0000000000 \leq X_i \leq 0000009999+$.

Your solution must involve the use of an index or loop in the processing of each card and must provide for initialization.

5

PROGRAM TESTING, ISOLATION OF ERRORS, AND COMPUTER OPERATION

Before a program is released by the programmer for general use, it should be tested to assure that it operates correctly. The test is successful if the program causes the computer to read input data correctly, perform the calculations implied by the analysis of the problem, and produce correct results in the proper format.

5.1 The Test Deck. The test is normally performed by loading the program to memory and then requiring that it process a specially selected set of input information, commonly referred to as a *test deck*. The input information contained in the test deck should be selected so that it tests the capability of the program to correctly process both normal and exceptional input data that are consistent with restrictions in the problem definition.

It is usually necessary to calculate manually the correct answers for the test-deck data. If so, the calculations should be performed in the order prescribed by the computer program and intermediate results should be collected that are likely to be useful in locating errors in the event the program fails to process the test deck correctly. It is assumed that the manual computations will be checked carefully to assure correct answers.

5.2 Test Results and Implication of Errors. The outcome of a program test run on the computer may be classified as successful only if the entire test deck is processed and the results produced by the computer are verified as correct. A repetition of a successful test run with no change in either the test deck or the program deck will result in the same sequence of computer operations. Hence the same results will be reproduced, unless a machine error intervenes.

Therefore it is assumed that the successfully tested program will correctly process any input deck containing data that satisfy the restrictions placed on the data contained in the test deck. If the test deck has been well designed, the programmer can release the program for general use with confidence that it will operate satisfactorily. It is not uncommon, however, for additional "bugs" to be encountered after the program has been released for general use. These "bugs" are often related to unanticipated exceptional input data.

If the outcome of the test run is unsuccessful, a problem of error isolation exists. The process of error isolation is sometimes referred to as "debugging." The failure of a test run may be attributable to an error or combination of errors located in a system comprising the following components:

1. The test deck
2. The input or the output translation, e.g., the 533 plug-board wiring
3. The analytical solution of the problem
4. The program
5. The computer mechanism

The problem in the event of an unsuccessful test run is to locate the error or errors causing the failure and make the necessary corrections. Since the computer is designed to operate according to a set of logical rules, it can be reasoned that a logical relationship exists between the error in the system and the faulty results of the test run. In other words, once the error or errors are isolated, the results of the test run can be explained thereby.

Unfortunately, the inverse logic is not always so obvious. The faulty results of a test run may not imply directly the nature and location of the error. However, with sufficient information about the correctness of intermediate results of machine operations, the errors in the system can be isolated by logical deduction. The procedure for collection and analysis of information in error isolation cannot be reduced to a formal set of logical rules. Instead, it depends to a certain extent upon the judgment and experience of the programmer. There are, however, certain guides that will be helpful to the inexperienced programmer.

5.3 Kinds of Errors. Programming errors that have been observed with rather high frequency can be classified in various ways. In this discussion, it seems reasonable to use a functional classification. In the following sections, we shall discuss errors in program flow, errors in coding or translation, errors in scaling plan, errors in file design, errors in transmission of input or output data, and machine malfunctions.

5.4 Errors in Program Flow. Errors that adversely affect the program flow are quite common with inexperienced programmers. Of these, the simplest to detect are errors that halt the sequence of operations before the program is completed. These frequently stem from the generation of an unpermissible operation code or address in the modification of an instruction by arithmetic operation; e.g., an unanticipated underflow occurs in the arithmetic operation.

Less simple to detect are errors that result in a looping sequence without an exit. A closed loop sometimes stems from an improperly designed logical test, e.g., a test that will always indicate that one more cycle of the loop is to be executed. A closed loop may also result from improper choice of a next instruction address or from improper choice of an operand address, e.g., the location in which an instruction is stored after modification by an arithmetic operation.

The last mentioned error may also cause the program to skip a sequence of instructions rather than loop. Such a skip might also result from improper selection of a next instruction address or from the improper design of a logical test, e.g., improper initialization or improper choice of index limits. Such errors may not halt the sequence of instructions, but they will surely lead to erroneous results.

An error that causes the program to skip a sequence of instructions will usually affect the flow of data that is to be operated on. The data flow may also be affected by the omission of instructions, by the improper choice of an operand address, or by improper indexing of a looping sequence.

5.5 Errors in Coding or Translation. Clerical errors in coding (writing instructions in basic machine language) or in translating the written program to punched cards (key-punching errors) are a frequent cause of an unsuccessful program test run. Such an error in an instruction will frequently result in an unpermissible operation code or address, with the result that the computer automatically halts when it analyzes the instruction. On occasion, such an error will lead to a strange and wonderful sequence of events that makes isolation of the error quite difficult.

It has been observed that symbolic programming is effective in reducing clerical errors, since much of the clerical work is delegated to the assembly program. In addition, several consistency checks are built into the assembly system so that certain unpermitted conditions will be detected automatically (see Secs. 4.21 and 4.22).

However, many possibilities for clerical errors remain, even with automatic assembly of symbolic programs. Transposition of characters in writing or key punching is not uncommon. Similarly, a programmer may intend to write AUP and inadvertently write ALO. Any such error that leads to a permissible statement will not be detected automatically by the assembly system.

5.6 Errors in the Scaling Plan. The scaling plan specifies the range of values for each variable that is to be processed by the program and for each variable in the results.

In a business data-processing problem, it is likely that the range of values for each variable to be processed will be known or else can be estimated and a safety factor applied to assure that the range provided will be adequate. If this is the case, it is likely that arithmetic operations will be fixed-point; otherwise, the programmer may choose to use floating-point arithmetic.

It is the responsibility of the programmer to calculate the range of values for each variable generated by the program. The most frequent error made by the inexperienced programmer involves the positioning of the dividend so that a quotient may exceed 10 digits for a critical combination of dividend and divisor. Of course this error will be detected automatically by the 650.

An error in scaling that causes overflow from the A register will also be detected automatically, but an error that leads to overflow from the L into the U register or an error that leads to underflow will not be detected automatically but will be detected frequently by the recipient of the erroneous results.

The programmer is responsible for the positioning of implied decimal points. Failure to properly position implied decimal points may lead to ambiguous results. Cumulative rounding errors (see Sec. 3.23) may lead to results that have less than the required degree of accuracy. A general rule is to carry as many significant figures as possible throughout the intermediate computations and then round the final results to the justifiable accuracy of representation.

If the range of values of input variables is not known in advance and cannot be estimated with confidence, the programmer can use floating-point arithmetic. This gives him considerable flexibility in his scaling plan.

5.7 Errors in File Design. The term *file* is used to denote a batch of data. For our purposes the data may be contained either in punched cards or in memory registers. The design of a file deals with the information content of the file, the coding of the information in the file, and the arrangement of the information in the file.

The information content of the file is usually determined by the purpose the file is intended to serve.

The kind and degree of coding of file information is usually a compromise between the desires for efficient use of storage space and for ease of retrieval and utilization of the information content by the principal users of the file. However, the equipment used for processing the data from a given file may be a controlling factor with respect to the coding.

In a punched-card file the arrangement of information is controlled by the format and the ordering of successive cards in the file. As indicated earlier, the card format specifies the relationship between card columns and data contained therein. In a memory-register file, the arrangement of information is controlled by word format and the ordering of words in successive registers.

The programmer is responsible for determining that the information content, the coding, and the arrangement of each file to be processed by a program are consistent with the sequence of operations in the program. Specifically, he must be particular to assure that each element of information in the file be unambiguously identified.

In the input and output files of Table 4.3, the identification was achieved by a combination of numeric coding and relative location coding. The different card types (e.g., sales, statement, etc.) were identified with a numeric code. The elements of information contained in a card were identified by their positions, i.e., field locations. The person or commodity to which the money or quantity fields related was identified with a numeric code. These in turn were related to the appropriate files in memory.

5.8 Errors in Transmission of Input or Output Data. The term *errors in transmission of input or output data* refers primarily to errors in channeling data from card columns to memory-register positions and vice versa. This is controlled in the 650 system by the wiring of a plug board that is inserted in the 533 Read-Punch unit (see Chap. 6).

The wiring of the plug board should be checked prior to the program test run. Card-read wiring can be checked by causing the program to read the test deck. After each card is read, the contents of the storage entry registers may be punched 80-80 by the N-per-card punch routine. The card-punch wiring can be checked by storing typical data in the storage exit registers and then executing a punch operation. Both sets of test output can then be analyzed to determine whether the proper relationship between card columns and register positions is provided by the board wiring.

5.9 Machine Malfunction. Although computers are designed to be highly reliable, components do wear out or get out of adjustment and machine malfunctions do occur. The 650 is designed to detect certain malfunctions automatically (see Sec. 5.24). The most common machine error is the dropping of a bit from a character code. Such an error is automatically detected.

A machine error that occurs less frequently, but is more troublesome when it does occur, is a malfunction of the punch unit, such that one or more extraneous punches occur in one or more card columns. The 650 system is not designed to detect such a malfunction automatically, and in some cases the resulting errors may be detected only by the ultimate users of the output information. Sometimes such erroneous data may appear to be reasonable when the cards are listed, but frequently it will appear to be suspect.

One note of caution is offered to the inexperienced programmer relative to machine malfunctions. It has been observed that their frequency of occurrence is much less than their frequency of suspicion by the inexperienced programmer. If you suspect a machine malfunction that you cannot verify and that is not observed by other users, it is probable that your error will be found in one of the foregoing classifications. If you wish to verify your suspicion, it is suggested that you devise an independent test for this purpose.

5.10 Programming to Facilitate Program Testing. It has been observed that the ratio of the time spent testing and isolating errors to the time spent on writing a long and complicated program may be as great as four, and is frequently as great as two. It is well worth while, therefore, to devote some time and effort in the programming phase to features that will facilitate the program testing phase.

One of the simplest and most effective ways of facilitating program testing is to divide the long program into several short programs or modules that can be tested independently before they are combined and tested as a single long program. Most long programs lend themselves readily to such modularity, and it remains for the programmer to take advantage of it. One hundred to two hundred instructions are suggested as a reasonable length for a test module. The flow diagram (Fig. 4.5) for the data-processing problem discussed in Chap. 4 indicates the natural modularity of a computer program. In that particular example, however, the entire program is short enough to be considered as a single test module.

5.11 Break Points and Intermediate Results. A *break point* is an instruction that will halt execution of the program. The *halt* operation code 01 will cause the 650 to stop if the PROGRAMMED switch (see Fig. 5.1) is set at STOP; otherwise the halt operation code is treated as a no-operation code, 00.

This feature makes it easy for the programmer to insert strategic break points in the program, e.g., at the start of each major block of the flow diagram, after the generation of important intermediate results, etc. During the program test phase, the PROGRAMMED (break-point) switch would be set at STOP, and each time program execution is halted, the machine operator would copy pertinent test information from the DISPLAY lights on the 650 console (see Fig. 5.1).

The information logged by the operator can be used by the programmer to check the general continuity or flow of the program and to check the correctness of intermediate results. Such information can be quite useful in isolating errors, if they exist, in the program. After program testing is completed, production runs can be made with the PROGRAMMED (break-point) switch set at RUN, and program execution will not be interrupted at the break points.

While this procedure is simple to program, it has certain disadvantages. There is always the possibility that the operator will make a mistake in copying data from the DISPLAY lights, thus introducing ambiguity as to what actually happened in a test run. The test information can be punched accurately much more rapidly than the operator can copy it; hence the computer is being used inefficiently in the break-point procedure. This procedure precludes the use of the programmed stop in production runs, unless the break-point instructions inserted for test purposes are deleted after testing is complete.

An alternative procedure is to add instructions to the program that will cause the computer to punch out the test information that would otherwise be copied manually at break points. This procedure will require more programming effort but will usually result in a reduction in program test time. The instructions added to produce test information are not intended to be part of the production program; hence it is important that they can be readily deleted, after testing is completed, without affecting the continuity of the program.

Accomplishing the deletion can be quite simple if the added instructions are properly considered to be an addendum to the program and hence to the program deck. The program is written as the programmer wants it to be after testing is completed, including only those programmed stops that are pertinent to a production run. He then identifies the strategic *test information points* corresponding to the break points of the preceding procedure, and the programmer introduces a digression at each of the test data points.

The mechanics of adding instructions to achieve a digression between two consecutive instructions in the program are illustrated by the

Fig. 5.1. 650 control console. (*Reprinted by permission from "IBM 650 Data Processing System Bulletin—General Information, Console Information, Operation, Special Divisions," G24-5000-0, copyright 1958 in original notice by International Business Machines Corporation.*)

following example. A digression is to be introduced between the instructions located at the symbolic addresses K50 and K51.

Location	Operation	DA	IA
K50	STL	B6	K51
K51	RAL	B7	

Assume that in the test phase, the programmer would like to punch the intermediate results, just stored in the location with the symbolic address B6, before executing the instruction located at K51. The programmer need only add the following instructions at the end of the program:

Location	Operation	DA	IA
K50	STL	B6	TDP1*
TDP1	STL	1977	
	PCH	1977	K51

* It is necessary that both the *D* address and *I* address be specified in the instruction at which the digression starts.

If we assume that the band of storage exit registers containing 1977 has been reserved for punching test data, the added instructions will achieve the desired result without interfering with the regular function of the program or the continuity from K50 to K51.

Since the revisions are added at the end of the program, they will follow the regular program through the assembly process. When the assembled program is loaded to memory, the regular instruction will be loaded to the location that has the symbolic address K50, but later the temporary instruction will be loaded to K50; this will erase the original instruction and provide for the digression. However, when program testing is completed the cards for the temporary instructions can be removed from the end of the program deck and the regular program remains.

The foregoing procedure can be modified to provide for punching tables, data indicating the entry to a major program block or a program test module, etc. To facilitate removal of the added temporary instructions after program testing is completed, it is important that the entire set of cards for loading these instructions be kept at the end of the regular program deck where they can be easily identified and removed.

5.12 Intraprogram Checks. It is generally a good idea to include some intraprogram checks in the program. In most cases these checks will be a part of the regular program because they will serve a useful function in production runs, but in some cases they may be added as temporary instructions.

In business data processing, the program should include the standard checks that are a part of good accounting practice. For example, a control figure on total accounts receivable would normally be carried and the sum of the individual accounts would be checked against the control figure. It would also be useful to count the number of input cards processed and compare this with a control figure to ascertain whether any cards have been lost from the file.

It may be possible to program a check to determine whether a datum of input is consistent with specified criteria. Data consistency checks are exemplified in the data-processing problem (Fig. 4.5) by the tests for exceptional card codes, commodity codes, and customer numbers. Similarly, a check may be used to determine whether a datum of results is consistent with specified criteria. For example, any customer balance that exceeded a specified magnitude might be suspect, and an exception card might be punched to call attention to this fact.

5.13 Collecting Test Information. The evaluation of the outcome of a program test is the responsibility of the programmer. For this reason, he should provide for the collection of potentially useful information during the test run. Two procedures for collecting program test information were suggested in Sec. 5.11. Others are discussed in the following sections.

An analogy can be made between the check bits in an error-detecting or an error-correcting code and the collection of test information. The check bits serve a useful function only in the event of an error; similarly, the test information serves a useful function only in the event the program test run is unsuccessful. The question then is, "How much redundancy is justified?" Unfortunately, there is no simple answer.

It is suggested, instead, that the approach to program testing and error isolation be considered as a process of successive approximations. In the first test run the programmer might provide only for the collection of general information about the continuity of program flow and important intermediate results. If a second test run is required, he may provide for the collection of more specific information based on the outcome of the first test run. Between successive test runs, he should evaluate the information collected, make indicated corrections to the program, and make appropriate modifications in his test information requirements.

5.14 Information That Is Automatically Displayed. Except for the location of the instruction being executed, the information pertinent to the execution thereof can be automatically displayed on the console (see Fig. 5.1) of the 650 whenever the program execution is halted. In particular, the automatic detection of an error condition is indicated when one or more of the CHECKING lights is on. The instruction-cycle-phase status is indicated by the OPERATING lights. The contents of the operation and address registers are automatically displayed by the correspondingly identified sets of lights. The contents of L, U, D, or program registers can be displayed in the DISPLAY lights by appropriately setting the DISPLAY switch.

The contents of 8000 are displayed by the setting of the STORAGE ENTRY switches and the adjacent SIGN switch. The mode of machine operation is determined by the setting of the PROGRAMMED, HALF-CYCLE, CONTROL, OVERFLOW, and ERROR switches.

The specific function of each of these switches and of the OPERATING and CHECKING lights will be discussed in later sections on machine operation. For the present, it will suffice to say that all the information automatically displayed on the console should be recorded by the machine operator whenever an unanticipated machine stop occurs. At such time, the respective contents of the L, U, D, and program registers should be displayed and recorded.

As indicated in the discussion of break points, only a prespecified portion of the above data need be collected when an anticipated machine stop occurs. If, for example, we were checking the sequence by means of break points, the pertinent data might be contained in the break-point instruction; e.g., the operand address could be a break-point sequence number.

5.15 Special Machine Modes for Collecting Test Information. The programmed stop or break-point mode of machine operation has been discussed earlier. Another special mode is the phase-by-phase mode. If the HALF-CYCLE switch is set at HALF, the computer executes a phase of an instruction cycle with each depression of the PROGRAM START key. We may thus observe the phase-by-phase change in the status of the information displaced by the console lights.

Needless to say, this is an extremely slow and, consequently, a very expensive method of collecting test information. The programmer should be loath to use it unless his information requirements have been pinpointed to one or two instructions.

If the CONTROL switch on the 650 console (Fig. 5.1) is set at ADDRESS
STOP, a halt occurs when the number in the address register equals
the number in the ADDRESS SELECTION switches on the console. The
address stop mode can be used to collect test information, but should
only be used on rare occasions.

5.16 Library Programs for Collecting Test Information. There
are two library programs that are frequently useful in collecting test
information. One is the N-per-card punch routine and the other is
the trace routine. The former is a generalization of the table punch
routine presented in Sec. 4.12, while the latter is presented in Sec. 4.16.

After each unsuccessful program test run it is a good idea to dump
(punch out) the portion of memory that contains information pertinent
to the test run. Where the success or failure of the run is not immediately discernible at its completion, the memory dump should be performed—just in case. Included in the memory dump should be all
registers containing instructions, constants, or tables, as well as the
storage entry registers and the storage exit registers that are pertinent
to the test run. A five-per-card memory dump after a program test
run of the $C(A_i) + C(B_i) \to B_i$ routine is shown as items 3 and 4 of
Table 5.2. This table will be discussed in detail in a later section.

The memory dump yields only static information, i.e., the status
of the memory registers at a given point in program execution. However, the status of the registers whose contents vary as the program is
executed will often yield clues that aid in the isolation of errors. Of
particular interest are registers that contain indices, counters, or intermediate results. One can frequently deduce from the status of these
registers whether or not the program has performed as anticipated up
to the point at which the memory dump was performed.

If the N-per-card punch routine is stored in memory during the
program test run, digressions (of the type described in Sec. 5.11)
can be programmed to punch out arbitrary blocks of memory registers
at any point in the program. The programmer should become familiar
with the punch routines that are available at his computation center
and take full advantage of them in program testing.

The trace routine is used to obtain detailed information about the
execution of individual instructions. It follows the execution, instruction by instruction. If execution is in the *full trace* mode, a card is
punched for each instruction executed. Each card contains a sequence
number, the location of the instruction being executed, the instruction itself, and the contents of the U, the L, and the D registers. If the
execution is in the *skeleton trace* mode, a card is punched only for
instructions that contain a branch operation code or that have a

negative sign. This mode is quite useful in collecting information about the continuity of program flow.

5.17 Economics of Collecting Test Information. It has been indicated that the programmer is normally interested in minimizing the total cost of preparing a program that is tested and operational. In the program test phase, he should consider the incremental costs of added program steps, of computer time to collect test information, and of the analysis of test information collected.

The procedure, suggested in Sec. 5.11, of programming digressions that are temporarily added to the regular program will obviously increase programming time. Offsetting this, however, may be savings in both computer time and analysis time attributable to more efficient and more selective procedures for collecting test information.

The memory dump after the test run requires no programming effort and little computer time, at least with the 650. There is, however, no selectivity in information collected; consequently much of it is useless and the cost of locating and analyzing the pertinent data may be relatively high.

The trace routine requires little or no programming effort, but it is very expensive in computer time. When the computer operates in the full trace mode, the rate of execution of instructions is reduced to the rate of punching cards. The 650 can punch cards at the rate of 100 per minute, whereas it can execute instructions at the rate of 12,500 to 50,000 per minute if successive D and I addresses are reasonably optimal. Even in the skeleton trade mode, the efficiency of computer operation will be less than 3 per cent. Consequently, the programmer should be very selective in the use of the trace routine.

Similarly, the manual techniques (Sec. 5.15) for collecting information are extremely inefficient with respect to computer time and should be used selectively.

5.18 Analysis of Program Test Information. The analysis of various kinds of test information will be illustrated by example. An error that is frequently made by inexperienced programmers has been intentionally introduced in the $C(A_i) + C(B_i) \rightarrow B_i$ routine of Table 4.6. A familiar routine was chosen in order that the reader could concentrate on the test information. The set of instructions to be tested is shown in assembled form as item 1 of Table 5.1.

Items 2 to 5 are instructions and constants that have been added for test purposes. They will be deleted when the testing is completed. Item 2 is an instruction that is stored in the EXIT, location 1026, to positively stop instruction execution when the test run is completed.

Items 3 and 4 are digressions that have been added after the test program was assembled for the purpose of punching the contents of IREG, the indexing accumulator, and the sum $C(A_i) + C(B_i)$. Item 5 is a short routine for storing the address of registers 0016 through 0045 in the D address positions of the respective registers. By thus storing a known set of values in the tables, the resulting sum for each value of the index is calculable in advance and can be readily compared with the results of the test run.

The test run is performed by first loading items 1 to 5 to memory and then transferring control to location 1040, the start of item 5. The transfer will be automatic if a transfer card is added to the deck of cards shown in items 1 to 5. Otherwise the transfer must be performed manually.

Fields 6 and 7 of item 2, Table 5.2, contain the test information produced as a result of the programmed digressions. The information in fields 1 to 4 of that line may be identified as instructions or constants from the test program that were stored in the band of storage exit registers used to punch the test information.

The test information thus produced indicates that only one cycle of the loop was executed. However, for this cycle of the loop the index was correctly set at 1 and the correct sum, $47 = 16 + 31$, was appropriately stored for that setting of the index. This information causes us to suspect that the error is related to the test $i < 15$, and our attention is directed to lines 17 to 24 of item 1 in Table 5.1.

A check of line 19, the instruction containing the branch operation, shows that both the D and I addresses lead to the appropriate actions for the events $i < 15$ and $i = 15$, respectively. A check of lines 18 and 23 shows that the appropriate constant is subtracted from the index.

The error is isolated by considering the instruction on line 17 (ALO IREG) in context with the status of the U register when the instruction is executed. The sum in the U register actually controls the outcome of the test. If the sum is positive, the sign of the A register will be positive after the test. If the sum is negative, the sign of the A register will be negative after the test. Only if the sum is zero will the test behave properly. The test will work properly in all three cases if the ALO operation code is changed to RAL. It can be readily observed that the suggested change will not affect any other block of instructions.

Items 3 and 4 of Table 5.2 display, respectively, the status of registers 1008 through 1049 (the instructions and constants involved in the test run) and registers 0016 through 0045 (the A and B tables) after

Table 5.1 Input Data For Test of $C(A_i) + C(B_i) \rightarrow B_i$ Routine

Item 1. Assembled Program

Label	Op	Field 1	Field 2	Loc				Item	
	BOP	0 0 0 0	1 0 0 7					1	
	BLR	1 0 3 1	1 9 9 9					2	1
	BLR	AI PBI	1 0 0 8					3	1
	SYN	EXI T	1 0 2 6					4	1
	SYN								
AIPBI	RAL	CON E	LOOP	1008	65	1011	1015	5	
LOOP	STL	I REG		1015	20	1019	1022	6	
	ALO	CV 1		1022	15	1025	1029	7	
	STL	V1		1029	20	1009	1012	8	
	ALO	C1 5		1012	15	1016	1021	9	
	LDD	V2		1021	69	1024	1027	10	
	SDA	V2		1027	22	1024	1028	11	
	LDD	V3		1028	69	1010	1013	12	
	SDA	V3		1013	22	1010	1009	13	
V1	RAU	0 0 3 0	V1	1009	60	30	1024	14	
V2	AUP	0 0 4 5	V2	1024	10	45	1010	15	
V3	STU	0 0 4 5	V3	1010	21	45	1014	16	
	ALO	I REG		1014	15	1019	1023		
	SLO	C1 5		1023	16	1016	1030	18	
	BMI	8 0 0 1	EXIT	1030	46	1017	1026	19	
	ALO	CONE		1017	15	8001	1018	20	
	ALO	0 0 1 5	LOOP	1018	15	1011	1015	21	
CV1	60	0 0 1 5	V2	1025	60	15	1024	22	
C15	00	0 0 1 5	0 0 0 0	1016	15		1016	23	
CONE	00	0 0 0 1	0 0 0 0	1011	1		1011	24	1

Item 2. Instruction Stored in EXIT to Stop Execution at Conclusion of Test Run

1026	1	9999	9999	1

Table 5.1   Input Data For Test of $C(A_i) + C(B_i) \rightarrow B_i$ Routine *(Continued)*

Item 3.   Digression to Store Index for Punching

See item 1, line 6

| 1015 | 20 | 1019 | 1037 |
| 1037 | 24 | 1032 | 1022 |

Item 4.   Digression to Store Sum, $C(A_i) + C(B_i)$, and Punch

See item 1, line 16

1010	21	45	1038
1038	24	1033	1039
1039	71	1027	1014

Item 5.   Routine to Store Initial Data in Registers 16–45

1040	65	1041	1042
1041		16	
1042	69	1043	1044
1043	20		1045
1044	22	1043	8001
1045	16	1046	1047
1046		45	
1047	46	1048	1008
1048	15	1049	1042
1049		46	

Item 6.   Modification of Item 5 to Initiate Punch of Trace in PTSR Test Run

1047	46	1048	1035
1035	55		1008
1018	15	1011	1036
1036	56		1015

Table 5.2 Information Collected in Test of $C(A_i) + C(B_i) \rightarrow B_i$ Routine

Item 1. Five-per-card Punch-out of Registers 1008–1049 Before Start of Test Run

5 1008	65 1011 1015	60 30 1024	21 45 1038	1	15 1016 1021
5 1013	22 1010 1009	15 1019 1023	20 1019 1037	15	15 8001 1018
5 1018	15 1011 1015	N	*	69 1024 1027	15 1025 1029
5 1023	16 1016 1030	10 45 1010	60 15 1024	1 9999 9999	22 1024 1028
5 1028	69 1010 1013	20 1009 1012	46 1017 1026		CR *
5 1033	N	N	N 5 1008 1049	51 1040	
5 1038	24 1033 1039	71 1027 1014	65 1041 1042	16	24 1032 1022
5 1043	20 1045	22 1043 8001	16 1046 1047	45	69 1043 1044
2 1048	15 1049 1042	46	16 1046 1047	45	46 1048 1008
					46 1048 1008

Item 2. Test Information Produced by Added Instructions (Items 3 and 4 of Table 5.1)

22 1024 1028	69 1010 1013	20 1009 1012	46 1017 1026	CR	1	47

Item 3. Five-per-card Punch-out of Registers 1008–1049 After Completion of Test Run

5 1008	65 1011 1015	60 16 1024	21 31 1038	1	15 1016 1021
5 1013	22 1010 1009	15 1019 1023	20 1019 1037	15	15 8001 1018
5 1018	15 1011 1015	1	*	69 1024 1027	15 1025 1029
5 1023	16 1016 1030	10 31 1010	60 15 1024	1 9999 9999	22 1024 1028
5 1028	69 1010 1013	20 1009 1012	46 1017 1026		CR 1
5 1033	47	N	N 5 1008 1049	51 1040	
5 1038	24 1033 1039	71 1027 1014	65 1041 1042	16	24 1032 1022
5 1043	20 45 1045	22 1043 8001	16 1046 1047	45	69 1043 1044
2 1048	15 1049 1042	46	16 1046 1047	45	46 1048 1008
					46 1048 1008

158

Table 5.2 Information Collected in Test of $C(A_i) + C(B_i) \rightarrow B_i$ Routine (Continued)

Item 4. Five-per-card Punch of Registers 0016–0045 After Completion of Test Run

5 16	16	17	18	19	20
5 21	21	22	23	24	25
5 26	26	27	28	29	30
5 31	47	32	33	34	35
5 36	36	37	38	39	40
5 41	41	42	43	44	45

Item 5. Trace of Second Test Run

1 1035	1008					45	
2 1008	65 1011 1015	1		1		1	
3 1015	20 1019 1037	1		1		1	
4 1037	24 1032 1022	1		1		1	
5 1022	15 1025 1029	60	16 1024	60	15 1024		
6 1029	20 1009 1012	60	16 1024	60	16 1024		
7 1012	15 1016 1021	60	31 1024		15		
8 1021	69 1024 1027	60	31 1024	10	45 1010		
9 1027	22 1024 1028	60	31 1024	10	31 1010		
10 1028	69 1010 1013	60	31 1024	21	45 1038		
11 1013	22 1010 1009	60	31 1024	21	31 1038		
12 1009	60 16 1024		16		16		
13 1024	10 31 1010	47			31		
14 1010	21 31 1038	47			47		
15 1038	24 1033 1039	47			47		
22 1024 1028	69 1010 1013	20 1009 1012	46 1017 1026		47	CR	47
16 1039	71 1027 1014	47		47		1	
17 1014	15 1019 1023	1		1			
18 1023	16 1016 1030	99 9986	46 9999	99 9986	15		
19 1030	46 1017 1026	99 9986	46 9999	99 9986	15		

completion of the test run.   This information was obtained by loading the N-per-card punch routine to memory and causing it to punch the specified registers at the rate of five per card by manual manipulation of the console switches.

Item 4 verifies that the appropriate values were initially stored in registers 0016 through 0045 and that the first sum was correctly stored in register 0031.   Item 3 verifies that the D addresses of the three variable instructions located at 1009, 1024, and 1010 (V1, V2, and V3, respectively) are appropriately set for the first cycle of the loop.

The information recorded from the console by the operator shows the contents of the A register to be 00 0046 9999 99 9986 0000+ and the contents of the program register to be 01 9999 9999, the instruction stored in EXIT.   This information substantiates our previous deductions.   It is worth pointing out that the appearance of a string of 9s in the A register is generally good cause for suspecting an underflow condition.

If we had not isolated the error on the basis of the information collected in the first test run, we might have specified that a trace be executed in the second test run.   In that case, it would be necessary that the trace routine be loaded to memory along with the test program and that program execution be interrupted to start tracing.

There is no need to trace the instructions of item 5 in Table 5.1 because the first test run indicated that this routine is functioning properly.   Since the trace must be started at an instruction containing a reset operation, we must choose between starting the trace at either the instruction on line 5 of Table 5.1 or that on line 14.   Since the choice involves a difference of only 11 (including the digression) trace cards ($\frac{1}{10}$ minute of computer time), we shall elect to initiate tracing at the instruction on line 5 even though we are reasonably certain that the program was functioning properly up to line 17.   If there were a large difference in the number of trace cards produced by the alternatives, our decision would be to initiate tracing at line 14.

Tracing can be initiated automatically by adding the appropriate instructions to the test program, or it can be initiated manually by halting the computer by an address stop just before the selected instruction is executed and performing the appropriate manipulations of the console switches, as specified in the operating instructions for the trace routine.   These operating instructions can be found at the computation center.

To initiate tracing automatically at line 5, the following digression would be added to item 5 of Table 5.1:

Location	Operation	DA	IA
1047	BMI 46	1048	1050
1050	LDD 69	1008	1051
1051	STD 24	1978	1900

This digression is predicated on the trace routine of Table 4.14, where T1 is 1900 and P0002 is 1978.

The information from the second test run is shown as item 5 of Table 5.2. In item 5, the lines with sequence numbers 1 through 19 are output from the trace routine, while the line that breaks the sequence (between 15 and 16) will be recognized as the test information produced by the digressions shown in items 3 and 4 of Table 5.1.

The key information in the output from the trace routine is contained in the lines with the sequence numbers 16 through 19. The preceding lines serve only to substantiate our conviction that the portion of the program prior to the test is functioning properly. In particular, number 18 shows that an underflow rather than a change in sign resulted from the execution of that instruction. Had the sum $C(A_i) + C(B_i)$ been negative, an underflow would have resulted from the execution of the preceding instruction.

5.19 Inserting Corrections. When an error is isolated, its correction will usually require the modification of one or more instructions or constants in the program. It may also require the addition or deletion of instructions or constants. The mechanics of making corrections correspond to those for inserting digressions, as illustrated in the preceding section.

It is suggested that an orderly record of the corrections be kept and that each correction be cross-indexed to the point in the main program at which it was made. A note as to the purpose of the correction will frequently prove useful.

Since the corrections are intended as a permanent part of the program, the punched cards containing them should be inserted between the original program deck and the deck containing temporary additions for test purposes. It is suggested that no attempt be made to correct or delete cards from the original program deck, but rather that a new memory load card be typed for each correction. If the new cards are appended to the original program deck, the obsolete data will be replaced by the corrections as they are loaded to memory. We may take advantage of color coding and corner cuts of the punched cards to physically distinguish between the original program deck, the corrections to the original program, and the temporary additions for test purposes.

When program testing is completed, the programmer can remove the temporary additions, load the original program and the corrections to memory, and then punch out the final program. It may be desirable to add the corrections to the original symbolic program and reassemble the final program. If so, the programmer must delete the obsolete cards from the original assembled program and insert the corrections at the correct places, then reassemble the corrected program and test it.

While the mechanics of making corrections are simple, the precise definition of the correction may not be simple. In the foregoing example, it was easy to determine that the replacement of ALO by RAL in line 19 of Table 5.1 would not adversely affect any other segment of the regular program or of the temporary additions that had been made for the collection of test information. In a more complex problem, it may be necessary to refer to the flow diagram and study the effect that a proposed change may have on other segments of the program. If this is not done, the correction of an error may create another error elsewhere. After the correction to the program has been determined, the programmer must decide whether the temporary additions require modification to accommodate the changes in the program proper.

MANUAL OPERATIONS

In some computation centers the programmer may be required to operate the computer during program testing; in others he may not be permitted to operate the computer. In the former case, he should become thoroughly familiar with the function of switches and lights on both the 650 console and the 533 Read-Punch unit. In the latter case, he need only become sufficiently familiar with the function of switches and lights on the 650 console to give instructions to the computer operator relative to switch settings and information to be collected. The following sections about manual operations are organized on a functional basis so that the reader can select the information that is pertinent to his interests.

In Secs. 5.20 to 5.23 we shall discuss the procedure for loading the program. To do this, reference must be made to the function of certain switches on the console of the 650 and to the actions required to ready the 533 unit. In Sec. 5.24 we shall discuss the function of certain lights on the console of the 650 and on the 533 unit in the identification of the immediate cause of a halt in instruction execution. In Sec. 5.25 we shall discuss the function of certain switches on the 650 console in restarting automatic execution of instructions, and in Sec. 5.26 we shall discuss procedures for restarting card feeding in the 533.

5.20 Loading the Program. To load a program to memory, the machine operator must set the switches on the 650 console to their appropriate positions, initiate automatic execution of instructions, and make the 533 unit ready to feed cards under control of the program.

5.21 Setting the Console Switches. The console switches alluded to in this section can be identified in Fig. 5.1. The programmer should be familiar with the function of each of these switches in order that he can specify their settings.

There are 10 switches identified by the words STORAGE ENTRY and one associated switch identified by the word SIGN. The setting of the 11 switches specifies the contents of the register addressed at 8000. When a program is to be loaded, the instruction that initiates card reading must be dialed into these switches.

The remaining switches on the 650 console are used to select the operating mode of the computer.

If execution is to be in the programmed stop (break-point) mode, the switch identified by the word PROGRAMMED is set at the STOP position, in which case execution is halted (in the succeeding fetch phase) when a halt (01) operation code is encountered. If this switch is set at the RUN position, a halt operation code is treated as a no-operation (00) code and automatic execution continues.

If execution is to be in the phase-by-phase mode, the switch identified by the word HALF-CYCLE is set at the HALF position, in which case a single phase of an instruction cycle is executed with each depression of the PROGRAM START switch. If the HALF-CYCLE switch is set at the RUN position, it has no effect on instruction execution.

The switch identified by the word CONTROL is used to select one of three modes. If this switch is set at the RUN position, it has no effect on the automatic execution of instructions. If it is set at the ADDRESS STOP position, execution of instructions is automatically halted whenever the number in the adjacent ADDRESS SELECTION switches is equal to the number in the address register. If the control switch is set at MANUAL, automatic execution of instructions is precluded. This setting is used to permit manual transfer of control, manual display of the contents of a memory register, or manual entry of a number into a memory register.

The switch identified by the word DISPLAY is used to select one of four registers—U, L, D, or program—for automatic display, to select the READ OUT STORAGE mode for manual display (see Sec. 5.28) of a memory register, or to select the READ IN STORAGE mode for manual entry of a number into a memory register. The contents of the register selected are displayed in the lights identified by the words DISPLAY and SIGN.

If the switch identified by the word OVERFLOW is set at STOP, program execution stops automatically at the end of the execute phase of an instruction cycle in which *any* kind of overflow occurs. If this switch is set at SENSE, program execution stops only after a quotient overflow, but any other overflow condition is sensed—i.e., an overflow circuit is set to the ON state and the overflow light is turned on—and its occurrence can be identified by a subsequent execution of a branch on overflow (47) operation. The overflow circuit is automatically reset to the OFF state when a branch on overflow operation is executed.

If the switch identified by the word ERROR is set at STOP, program execution stops automatically at the end of the phase of the instruction cycle in which an error is sensed at a validity check point or in which a clocking error is sensed. When this happens, the address of the register from which the invalid character was copied will be displayed in the lights identified by the word ADDRESS, and the register into which the invalid character was copied will be identified by the status of the CHECKING lights. If this switch is set at SENSE and a validity error or a clocking error is sensed, program execution is temporarily halted while the following actions are performed automatically. The ERROR SENSE light is turned on, a COMPUTER RESET operation is performed, the number 8000 is entered in the address register, and then program execution is resumed with the execution of the instruction stored in 8000.

The programmer is responsible for specifying the appropriate setting of each of the foregoing switches for the mode of computer operation required in each run.

5.22 Initiating the Execution of Instructions. If the program is to be loaded, the first instruction to be executed is normally located in register 8000 by manual manipulation of the switches. If such is the case, instruction execution will be initiated if the following actions are performed in the order shown:

1. Depression of the COMPUTER RESET key
2. Depression of the PROGRAM START key

All the control switches should be set to their appropriate state before execution of instructions is initiated.

If the program has been loaded to memory, instruction execution can be initiated by the *transfer of control* procedure discussed in Sec. 5.25.

5.23   Readying the 533 Unit.   The appropriate plug board must be inserted in the receptacle at the end of the 533 unit.   The card-read feed is readied by inserting the file of input cards in the read hopper (see Fig. 5.2) face down and twelve edge leading.   Feeding of cards is initiated by depressing the left (read) START key (see Fig. 5.3) on the

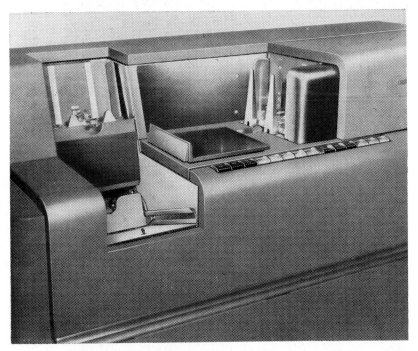

FIG. 5.2.   533 read feed (*left*) and punch feed (*right*).   (*Reprinted by permission from* "*IBM 650 Data Processing Bulletin—533 Card Read Punch, 537 Card Read Punch, 407 Accounting Machine,*" *G24-5001-0, copyright 1958 in original notice by International Business Machines Corporation.*)

533 unit.   The card-punch feed is readied by inserting a file of blank cards in the punch hopper (see Fig. 5.2) face down and twelve edge leading.   Feeding of cards is initiated by depressing the right (punch) START key (see Fig. 5.3) on the 533 unit.

5.24   Automatic Execution Halted.   Once automatic execution of instructions is initiated, it will be halted only by manual intervention of the operator, by a programmed halt, or by the automatic detection of an error condition.

FIG. 5.3. 533 control keys and indicator lights. (*Reprinted by permission from "IBM 650 Data Processing Bulletin.—533 Card Read Punch, 537 Card Read Punch, 407 Accounting Machine," G24-5001-0 copyright 1958 in original notice by International Business Machines Corporation.*)

The operator may terminate automatic execution immediately by depressing the PROGRAM STOP key (see Fig. 5.1) on the 650 console. He may cause automatic execution to stop in the execute phase of the next read (70) operation or punch (71) operation, whichever occurs first, by depressing either STOP key on the 533 unit.

When automatic execution of instructions is halted, the contents of the registers in the control unit remain constant. The contents of the operation and address registers are automatically displayed on the 650 console by the lights identified by the words OPERATION and ADDRESS (see Fig. 5.1). If the status of all these lights remains constant for as long as a second, it is probable that automatic execution is halted, although it is possible that the sequence of instructions being executed may form a very tight loop. If automatic execution is actually halted, the status of the lights on the 650 console located under the words OPERATING and CHECKING will indicate the reason for the halt. Restart procedures are discussed in later sections. The status of these lights at the end of a test run should be included in the test information collected by the operator.

If the INPUT-OUTPUT light is on, the machine is waiting for a card to be fed into either the read feed or the punch feed of the 533 unit, i.e., the read feed or punch feed is empty.

If the OVERFLOW light is on, an overflow condition has occurred. The pertinence of this light to the stop depends upon the setting of the OVERFLOW switch.

If the PROGRAM light is on, program execution was stopped manually, by a programmed stop, or by an address stop.

Either the DATA ADDRESS or the INSTRUCTION ADDRESS light will be on, depending upon the phase of the instruction cycle in which execution was halted.

If the PROGRAM REGISTER, the DISTRIBUTOR, or the ACCUMULATOR lights are on, the detection of a validity error in the corresponding register is indicated.

If the STORAGE SELECTION light is on, an invalid address has been detected in the address register.

If the CLOCKING light is on, an error has been detected in the timing circuitry.

If a stop is not indicated by the foregoing lights, the operation register must be checked for an invalid operation code. If the code is valid and not 01, the operator must depress the PROGRAM STOP key, set the HALF-CYCLE switch at HALF, and then depress the PROGRAM START key. If the status of the OPERATION and ADDRESS lights changes, there has been no error stop. Instead, a tight loop is indicated.

The CARD FEED STOP light on the 533 unit goes on when a card fails to advance from the hopper to the feed in a read feed. Program execution stops when a read operation code (70) is next transferred to the operation register.

The pair of unlabeled lights on the 533 unit is on whenever the associated START key must be depressed to activate the feed unit.

The DPBC (double-punch, blank-column) light goes on when a double-punch or blank-column error is detected by plug-board wiring.

5.25   Restarting Automatic Execution.   The action to be taken by the operator in the event of a halt in automatic execution, other than a card feed stop, may well vary depending upon the nature of the halt.

Programmed stops and address stops can be anticipated by the programmer, in which case the operator can be instructed to record certain information and then restart execution with or without transfer of control. If no transfer of control is required after the stop, a depression of the PROGRAM START key will cause automatic execution to be resumed.

If a transfer of control is required, the programmer must specify the address at which automatic execution is to be resumed. The transfer is effected in the following manner:

1. Set the ADDRESS SELECTION switches equal to the address at which automatic execution is to be resumed.
2. Set the CONTROL switch at MANUAL.
3. Depress the PROGRAM RESET key.
4. Depress the TRANSFER key. This causes the contents of the ADDRESS SELECTION switches to be transferred to the address register.
5. Set the CONTROL switch at RUN or at ADDRESS STOP. If the latter is chosen, reset the ADDRESS SELECTION switches to the appropriate address.
6. Depress the PROGRAM START key.

In the event of a halt resulting from the automatic detection of an error, it is usually specified that the operator collect certain test information—e.g., the status of the console switches and lights and a punch-out of a specified portion of memory—and then relinquish the computer.

Before automatic execution can be resumed after an error stop, the error condition must be cleared.

Depression of the PROGRAM RESET key resets the program register to zero, clears the associated error circuits, and signals the control unit that the fetch phase may be started. Its effect upon the ADDRESS REGISTER depends upon the setting of the CONTROL switch. If it is at MANUAL, the address register is cleared; if not, 8000 is entered in the address register.

Depression of the ACCUMULATOR RESET key resets the A and D registers to zeros and resets the associated error circuits.

Depression of the ERROR RESET key resets the circuits activated by a clocking error or by an overflow stop condition.

Depression of the COMPUTER RESET key is equivalent to the successive depression of each of the preceding three keys.

The ERROR SENSE RESET key is effective only if the ERROR switch is at SENSE, in which case its depression turns off the ERROR SENSE light.

5.26 Restarting Card Feeding.   In the event of card-feed stop or a validity error due to a mispunched card, it will be necessary to clear the feed and restart card feeding.

A card-feed stop can be cleared by the operator without affecting the operation of the program. He must remove the cards from the read hopper and reproduce any cards in the file (particularly the first two or three) that are damaged. He must clear the read feed by depressing the READ start key until all four cards from the feed have run out into the stacker. He then takes the last two cards from the stacker, places them in front of the file removed from the hopper, places the file in the hopper, and depresses the READ start key.

If the stop is due to punch feed, he must lift the blank cards from the hopper, remove any damaged cards from the file, depress the PUNCH start key until the feed is cleared, replace the file in the hopper, and again depress the PUNCH start key. There will be a nonpunched card in the output file at the point at which the card-feed stop occurred. The operator should identify this card and remove it from the file.

If a validity error is the cause of the stop and if the address register contains the address of a storage entry register, it is probable that the error is in the last card read. In this event, the operator proceeds as with a card-feed stop until he has run the cards out of the feed. He removes the last four cards from the stacker and places them at the front of the input file, just removed from the read hopper. The first card now in the input file is the suspected card. The operator should mark the location of the suspected card in the file, record the console data, and perform any other test information collection actions specified by the programmer.

A *card jam* occurs when cards enter the feed from the hopper but do not advance from the feed to the stacker. When this happens, the cards involved in the jam will usually be mutilated and require reproduction or replacement before processing can be resumed. *An inexperienced operator should not attempt to clear a card jam.* The programmer can provide a measure of protection against destruction of a program deck in a card jam by having a duplicate program deck in reserve.

5.27   A Machine Error.   If the address register does not contain the address of a storage entry register when an invalid character is detected, a machine error is implied.   In this event, remedial action will depend upon the specific situation.   If only a small amount of computer time is invested, it is a good idea to restart at the beginning of the program. If such machine errors persist, there is undoubtedly a faulty component in the computer.

Machine errors are usually random events.   The probability that a machine error will occur is small unless a component has failed or is marginal.   However, since machine errors are random events, they can occur at any time.   To protect against large losses of computer time in the event of a machine error, the programmer can include in his program provision for restarting at an intermediate point, e.g., production of a periodic memory dump, which is related to a specified restart procedure.

5.28   Manual Display or Modification of the Contents of a Register.   The contents of the operation and address registers are automatically displayed by their respective sets of console lights.   The contents of register 8000 are determined by the setting of the STORAGE ENTRY SWITCHES.   The contents of either the U, L, D, or program register are displayed automatically in the DISPLAY lights whenever the DISPLAY switch is set at the corresponding position.

In rare cases it is desirable to display the contents of a memory register.   In the event an invalid character is attributable to a machine error, the restart procedure may depend upon whether the contents of a memory register are valid.   To display a memory register, the operator will proceed as follows:

1. Set the CONTROL switch at manual.
2. Set the DISPLAY switch at READ OUT STORAGE.
3. Set the address of the memory register in the ADDRESS SELECTION switches.
4. Depress the PROGRAM RESET key.
5. Depress the TRANSFER key.
6. Depress the PROGRAM START key.

Note that the contents of the program register are destroyed in this procedure.   In addition, the contents of the D register are destroyed, because the contents of the memory register are copied into the D register for display.

On occasion it is desirable to store a number in a memory register without reading a card. This can be accomplished by modifying step 2 in the above procedure to read:

2a. Set the DISPLAY switch at READ IN STORAGE.
2b. Set the STORAGE ENTRY and SIGN switches equal to the number to be stored in the memory register.

5.29 End-of-file Procedure. When either the read or the punch hopper is emptied, card feeding stops until the supply of cards in the hopper is replenished and the corresponding START key is depressed.

If the input file is exhausted, there are still three cards in the feed that have not been processed. At this point the operator depresses the END OF FILE key on the 533 unit (see Fig. 5.3), and the END OF FILE light goes on and remains on until the data from the third and last card have been transferred to the storage entry registers.

5.30 Instructions for the Computer Operator. The necessity for the programmer to furnish the computer operator with an explicit set of instructions can be inferred from the foregoing discussions of the collection and analysis of test information and from the discussion of computer operation. It is recommended that a standard procedure be followed, even when the programmer is also the computer operator. A suggested form is shown as Table 5.3.

To initiate a program test run, the machine operator needs a properly organized input file, i.e., a set of input cards that are properly sequenced; and he needs the appropriate plug board to insert in the 533 unit. He needs to know the initial settings of the console switches, i.e., the STORAGE ENTRY SWITCHES, the ADDRESS SELECTION switches, and the control switches. With this information he can initiate execution of instructions.

Automatic execution of instructions, once started, will stop only if one of the following events occurs:

1. The input file is completely processed.
2. A programmed stop is executed.
3. An error condition is automatically detected.
4. The operator stops execution.

To obtain maximum benefit from the computer run, the programmer should furnish written instructions to the operator as to the action to be taken whenever the machine stops.

Table 5.3   Instructions to 650 Operator

Requested by: Date: Acct. no.

Program name: Number: Est. running time:

1. Loading sequence:

     Deck number   Deck name   Notes

     a.

     b.

     c.

     d.

     e.

2. 533 plug board   Notes

     a.

     b.

3. Control switch settings:

     Storage Entry: _____   Sign: + −

     Programmed: S   R   Half-Cycle: H   R   Addr. Sel._____

     Control: AS   R   M   Display: L   U   D   PR

     Overflow: Stop   Sense   Error: Stop   Sense

4. Trace required: Yes   No   Starting at: _____

5. Programmed stops:

         Identification   Action

6. Memory dump required after test run: Yes   No   8000 _____   +

7. Error stops:

Do or Do not record the status of the display lights.

     U _____   + −   Op. ____

     L _____   + − Addr. _____

     D _____   + −

     PR _____   + −

Show status of operating lights by circling those that are ON.

	Operating		Checking	
DA	PR	In-Out	PR	CU
Inq.	DS	Mag. Tape	SS	SU
IA	A	Oflo	D	C
			A	ES

         End of file

8. Verify settings of control switches:

     Storage Entry: _____   Sign: + −

     Programmed: S   R   Half-Cycle: H   R   Addr. Sel. _____

     Control: AS   R   M   Display: L   U   D   PR   ROS   RIS

     Overflow: Stop   Sense   Error: Stop   Sense

     533 Board

         Date: Time: Operator:

An end-of-file stop or a programmed stop is an event that is anticipated by the programmer. He should furnish the operator a list of
these events. For each event on the list he should show the means of
identifying it (i.e., specify the contents of the program register) and
the action to be taken if it occurs. The action may be a restart procedure or it may be a test information collection procedure.

The operator will recognize an error stop from the status of the
OPERATING and CHECKING lights, or he may stop the machine if a
closed loop is indicated. The programmer should specify the test
information collection procedures that the operator is to perform in
either event. If the test run is long, the operator may have to inter-
rupt execution because the estimated running time is exceeded.
Hence, it is desirable that the programmer identify one or more break
points where the operator can halt the program and dump the memory
so it can be re-stored at a later date and the processing continued from
the break point without being affected by the loss of the contents of
the A, D, or program registers. Thus the computer time invested in
the incomplete run will not be lost.

**5.31 Communication of Instructions for the Collection of Test
Information Directly to the Computer.** When instructions for the collection of test information are directed to the computer rather than to
the operator, the programmer will generally get more accurate information at less cost in computer time. If the instructions are correctly
programmed, they will be followed explicitly, usually their execution
will require less computer time than that required when the operator
must intervene, and mistakes in transcription of test information will
be eliminated.

The advantages of direct communication are offset, at least partially,
by the additional programming required. However, it has been
observed that inexperienced programmers frequently spend a great
deal more time on the program test phase than on the programming
phase. There is, therefore, potential for a saving in the programmer's
time as well as computer time.

To facilitate the automatic collection of test information and to
speed the testing of sequences of short programs (e.g., the testing of
term problems for a class), the author has developed a program that
will henceforth be referred to as the Program Test Supervisory Routine
or as PTSR. A complete set of operating instructions for the PTSR is
contained in the Appendix. The instructions should be studied in
detail by the programmer who plans to take advantage of the features
incorporated therein. The principal features of the program will be
pointed out in this section.

The PTSR includes a block zeroing routine, a card-reading routine, an N-per-card punch routine, and a trace routine.   Provision is made for programmed entry to and exit from each of these routines.[1]   Provision is made also for manual entry to each of the routines.[2]   Thus the PTSR contains the basic library routines that are used in program testing.

The program is self-loading.[3]   When the program is loaded, control is automatically transferred to the card-reading routine.   This routine can identify five different types of cards by the number entered in storage entry register 1.   A one-word memory load card is identified by 69 1954 1953, a transfer card by 00 0000 $iiii$, an N-per-card memory load card by 00 000N $iiii$ ($N \leq 7$), an STPL[4] (start test program load) by 99 9999 9998, and an STPE[5] (start test program execute) by 99 9999 9999.   Any card that is not identified or that contains invalid characters in pertinent columns will be bypassed, and an exception card will be punched automatically to indicate that it was bypassed.

The STPL card indicates that a program test is to be initiated.   In addition, it specifies the portion of memory that is to be zeroed automatically before the program is loaded, the number of registers N per card for punching the specified portion of memory if an error condition is found, the overflow mode of computer operation, and an identification number for the program.

After the "housekeeping" operations required by the STPL card have been performed, the read routine is re-entered.   If the input file is properly organized,[6] the data to be loaded to memory by the read routine will be contained in the cards that follow the STPL card and precede the STPE card.   In any event, when card reading is resumed it will be interrupted only by a transfer card, another STPL card, or an STPE card.

The STPE card indicates that the loading of memory for the program test is completed and that program execution is to be started. It contains the transfer instruction for entering the test program, the identification of the program, a specification of the validity error mode for the test run, and the transfer instruction for entering the validity exception routine, if one is contained in the program.   Since the STPE card controls the transfer to the test program, no transfer card (00 0000 $iiii$) should intervene between an STPL and an STPE card.

[1] See Secs. XIII, XI, XII, and VI, respectively, in the Appendix.

[2] *Ibid.*

[3] See Sec. II of the Appendix.

[4] See Sec. IIIA of the Appendix.

[5] See Sec. IIIC of the Appendix.

[6] See Sec. III of the Appendix.

If one does, execution of the test program will be initiated prematurely, the "housekeeping" indicated by the STPE card will not be performed, and the outcome of the test run will probably be unsuccessful.

Instructions in the test program are executed under control of the trace routine until a programmed exit is encountered. However, no trace cards are punched until a programmed entry to the trace punch mode is encountered.[1] In addition to the collection of data for trace cards, the trace routine included in the PTSR has several features not included in the trace routine shown in Table 4.14. It provides for the execution of the pseudo operation codes explicitly defined in Sec. V of the Appendix. It protects the PTSR against modification by the test program. It limits the number of trace cards that can be punched and the number of instruction cycles that can be executed in the trace mode. The latter furnishes automatic protection against unlimited repetition of a closed loop.

The trace routine analyzes each instruction and the operand if necessary. When the execution of an instruction would lead normally to a machine stop, the trace routine transfers control to the error routine, which automatically punches out the portion of memory specified by the STPL card and then reads cards until the next STPL card is encountered. Whenever an STPL card is encountered, a trace card is punched that contains the information about the last instruction executed in the preceding program.

5.32 Efficient Use of the PTSR. The PTSR is best suited for testing a sequence of programs, or modules of a long program, each of which contains 100 to 200 instructions and requires 1000 to 2000 instruction executions in a test run. Such programs will each require 3 to 6 minutes to load, to test in the trace mode, and to obtain the automatic memory dump. If the same programs were tested independently and not traced, the computer time would be approximately the same. The time saved by running the test at machine speed, rather than in the trace mode, would usually be devoted to manual collection of test information and the loading of auxiliary routines, e.g., the read-and-punch routine.

The PTSR will be efficient in testing longer programs only if the programmer takes full advantage of the provision for programmed entry to and exit from the trace mode. If this is done, the programmer can permit instruction execution to proceed at machine speed through portions of the program that are known to be free of errors; then he can use the features provided by the PTSR to collect test information about those portions of the program that may contain errors.

[1] See Sec. VI of the Appendix.

5.33 Example of Test Information Produced by the PTSR. Table 5.4 displays output from a test run of the $C(A_i) + C(B_i) \to B_i$ routine under control of the PTSR.

Item 1 indicates that the STPL card for program 51 has been identified.

Item 2 identifies each card that was bypassed while the program was being loaded. Field 8 of each specifies the relative location of that card from the STPL card. Each of the five cards called for the data to be stored in an unpermitted address, i.e., 24 8000 1604.

Item 3 indicates that the STPE card for program 51 has been identified. Field 8 indicates that it was the thirty-third card after the STPL card.

Item 4 displays a set of trace cards produced by the PTSR. (The fifth line from the end is recognized as the test information produced by instructions added to the test program.) Field 1 contains the trace sequence number of the instruction and the identification of the program. Field 2 contains the location of the instruction. Field 3 contains the instruction. Fields 4 to 6 contain the contents of the u, l, and d registers, respectively, after execution of the instruction in field 3. Field 7 contains the trace punch sequence number. Field 8 differs from field 3 only when an error condition obtains, as in item 6.

Item 5 is the punch-out of registers 1008 through 1049. The automatic punch-out was forced by the invalid addresses in the instruction stored in EXIT, 1026.

Item 6 is the trace card for the last instruction executed. It differs from the last line in item 5 only in field 8, which contains the instruction that led to the error condition.

5.34 Automatic Supervision of Computer Operations. With increased speed and memory capacity of computers and with the attendant increase in cost per unit time, it has been recognized that the inefficiency of manual intervention is intolerable. To alleviate this inefficiency, programs have been developed to automatically supervise computer operations.

Basically, such programs not only provide for but, in fact, require communications from the programmer to be made directly to the computer rather than indirectly via the machine operator. For such a supervisory program to be effective, it must provide for automatic handling of ambiguous communications and error conditions. This is usually accomplished by programming the computer to automatically write a message that indicates the nature of the error and, in some cases, other pertinent information whenever an error condition is encountered. After this has been accomplished, the supervisory

Table 5.4 Information Produced by PTSR in Test of $C(A_i) + C(B_i) \rightarrow B_i$ Routine

Item 1. STPL Card Identified

51	N	N	*	CR	*	CR

Item 2. Exception Cards for Cards Bypassed by Read Routine

51	N		8000	CR 24 8000 1604	CR	1
51	N		8000	CR 24 8000 1604	CR	2
51	N		8000	CR 24 8000 1604	CR	3
51	N		8000	CR 24 8000 1604	CR	4
51	N		8000	CR 24 8000 1604	CR	5

Item 3. STPE Card Identified

51	N 99 9999 9999		CR 24 1035 1604	CR 33

Item 4. Trace Cards Produced by PTSR

1820	51	1035	55 1008				45	55 1008
1830	51	1008	65 1011 1015		1		1	65 1011 1015
1840	51	1015	20 1019 1037		1		1	20 1019 1037
1850	51	1037	24 1032 1022		1		1	24 1032 1022
1860	51	1022	15 1025 1029	60	16 1024	60	15 1024	15 1025 1029
1870	51	1029	20 1009 1012	60	16 1024	60	16 1024	20 1009 1012
1880	51	1012	15 1016 1021	60	31 1024	60	15	15 1016 1021
1890	51	1021	69 1024 1027	60	31 1024	60	45 1010	69 1024 1027
1900	51	1027	22 1024 1028	60	31 1024	60	31 1010	22 1024 1028
1910	51	1028	69 1010 1013	60	31 1024	60	45 1038	69 1010 1013

Table 5.4 Information Produced by PTSR in Test of $C(A_i) + C(B_i) \to B_i$ Routine (Continued)

Item 4. Trace Cards Produced by PTSR (Continued)

1920	51	1013	22 1010 1009			60 31 1024	21 31 1038	11	22 1010 1009	CR
1930	51	1009	60 16 1024	16			16	12	60 16 1024	CR
1940	51	1024	10 31 1010	47			31	13	10 31 1010	CR
1950	51	1010	21 31 1038	47			47	14	21 31 1038	CR
1960	51	1038	24 1033 1039	47			47	15	24 1033 1039	CR
22 1024 1028			20 1009 1012			CR	1	47		
1970	51	1039	69 1010 1013	46 1017 1026			47	16	71 1027 1014	CR
1980	51	1014	71 1027 1014	47			1	17	15 1019 1023	CR
1990	51	1023	15 1019 1023	47		1	15	18	16 1016 1030	CR
2000	51	1030	16 1016 1030	46 9999		99 9986	15	19	46 1017 1026	CR
			46 1017 1026	46 9999		99 9986				

Item 5. Five-per-card Punch-out of Registers 1008–1049

5 1008	65 1011 1015	60 16 1024	21 31 1038	1	15 1016 1021		
5 1013	22 1010 1009	15 1019 1023	20 1019 1037	15	15 8001 1018		
5 1018	15 1011 1036	1	*	69 1024 1027	15 1025 1029		
5 1023	16 1016 1030	10 31 1010	60 15 1024	1 9999 9999	22 1024 1028		
5 1028	69 1010 1013	20 1009 1012	46 1017 1026	CR	1		
5 1033	47	N 55	N 55 1008	56 1015	24 1032 1022		
5 1038	24 1033 1039	71 1027 1014	65 1041 1042	16	69 1043 1044		
5 1043	20 45 1045	22 1043 8001	16 1046 1047	45	46 1048 1035		
2 1048	15 1049 1042	46	16 1046 1047	45	46 1048 1035		

Item 6. Trace Card for Last Instruction Executed

2000	51	1030	46 1017 1026	46 9999	99 9986	15	19	1 9999 9999

178

program will provide for automatic initiation of execution of the next in a sequence of programs that are available in the input unit.

The program test supervisory routine, described in the Appendix, was developed with this objective in mind. The conception of its operation is that once loaded to memory, it can efficiently supervise the testing of a sequence of short programs. Because of the limitations of the 650 memory, this supervisor is not particularly sophisticated; but it has proved quite effective in testing sequences of term problems for the course in which this text is used. The compiler for the BALGOL language (see Chap. 7) provides a similar function in a much more sophisticated manner. Other compiler systems such as FORTRAN also incorporate such features.

Thus, the machine operator will become more and more a specialist excluded from the channel of communications between the programmer and the computer. It is suggested that, whenever possible, the person learning to communicate with the 650 adopt the philosophy of direct communication with the computer. Such a philosophy requires better planning and more careful organization on the part of the programmer, but it will generally pay off in savings of both his time and computer time.

PROBLEMS

In solving the following problems, you may assume that the Program Test Supervisory Routine described in the Appendix is available as a library program. Alternatively, you may assume that the general-purpose read routine and the N-per-card punch routine contained in the PTSR are combined as a separate library program. This latter program can be loaded to memory by following the instructions specified for the PTSR, but it occupies only registers 1850 through 1999. Entry to the routines in the latter program are as defined in Secs. XI and XII of the Appendix.

5.1. You wish to test the block zeroing subroutine shown in Table 4.1.

a. What test information will be required to demonstrate that the subroutine is performing the desired function?

b. Can the test be organized so that the required information will be produced without manual intervention once card reading has been initiated?

c. What programs, including library programs, will be required?

d. Will any data cards be required? If so, what data will they contain?

e. In what order should the required decks of cards be fed into the read hopper of the 533 unit? Can these be organized into a single deck, to be read as required, without manual intervention once card reading is started?

f. Specify the 650 console settings required for the test run.

5.2. When a program is being tested, it is frequently desirable to observe the contents of certain registers at various times during the execution of the program. This can be done at the console by use of the ADDRESS STOP and the READ OUT STORAGE switches.   In general, this method is very inefficient.   It will usually be more efficient to modify the program temporarily, as discussed in Sec. 5.11, so that the required information can be produced automatically.

In testing the program of Table 4.2, it is required that $C(0109)$, $C(0110)$, and $C(0111)$ be punched out just prior to the execution of $C(0109)$ as an instruction.   Specify, in detail, the manner in which you would satisfy this requirement.

5.3.   While you are reading cards under control of the general-purpose read program, card feeding stops automatically.   You observe the console lights and see that none of them are twinkling, i.e., they remain in a steady state. This indicates that instruction execution has halted.

For each of the different situations described below, diagnose the problem and specify the action that you would take.   Assume that all the lights are functioning properly.   The letter E included in a number below, e.g., $1EE1$, indicates that the lights for that position display an invalid code.

a. No CHECKING lights are on.   The PROGRAM light is on.   The DISPLAY lights read 70 0150 0025.   The OPERATION and ADDRESS lights read 01 1111.

b. The DISTRIBUTOR CHECKING light is on.   The DISPLAY switch is set at DISTRIBUTOR.   The OPERATION and ADDRESS lights read 69 1954.   The DISPLAY lights read 19 $1EE1$ 0532.

c. The PROGRAM REGISTER CHECKING light is on.   The DISPLAY switch is set at PROGRAM REGISTER.   The OPERATION lights are off.   The ADDRESS lights read 1996.   The DISPLAY lights read 70 $19EE$ $19EE$.

d. No CHECKING lights are on.   The 533 CARD FEED STOP light is on.

e. No CHECKING lights are on.   The PUNCH (OPERATING) light is on.

5.4.   Prepare instructions for the 650 operator (see Table 5.3) for execution of the program test of Prob. 5.1.

5.5.   Prepare instructions for the 650 operator (see Table 5.3) for execution of the program test of Prob. 5.2.

5.6.   The program displayed in Table 4.2 is to be tested using the PTSR. It is required that the sequence of instructions contained in registers 0109, 0110, and 0111 be executed in the trace mode with punching, and the remaining instructions are to be executed at machine speed, i.e., not in the trace mode.

Specify in detail how you would modify the program (see Sec. 5.11) to accomplish the specified objective.   Prepare instructions for the 650 operator (see Table 5.3).   (Hint: See Sec. V of the Appendix, pseudo operation codes 55 to 57; see also Sec. VI.)

5.7.   Same as Prob. 5.6, except the second sentence is to be modified as follows: The entire test is to be run in the trace mode (without punching) and register 0109 is to be surveilled (see Sec. V of the Appendix, pseudo operation code 54).

6

CONTROLLING MACHINE FUNCTIONS
BY PLUG-BOARD WIRING

In the preceding chapters we have learned how to communicate with a computer, namely, the 650, by means of a set of instructions that are stored in memory to specify a sequence of machine functions. The control unit of the computer translates an operation code or an address code to electric impulses that control machine functions. The programmer indirectly controls the timing and destination of the control impulses by the content and sequencing of the instructions. However, detailed consideration of the paths and timing of impulses was limited to the discussion of copying data from one memory register into another.

In this chapter, we shall find that the functions of much of the auxiliary equipment found in a computation center are controlled by plug-board wiring. For such equipment, the programmer must be concerned directly with the path and timing of control impulses as well as data impulses. First we shall discuss the organization and control of some basic functions of auxiliary equipment; then we shall discuss the organization and control of selected equipments—the sorter, the reproducer, the collator, the interpreter, the electronic accounting machine, the multiplying punch, the statistical sorter, the key punch, and the verifier.

BASIC COMPONENTS

6.1 The Plug Board. The basic purpose of the plug board is to provide the programmer a choice in the completion of machine circuits. In this respect, the plug board is analogous to the set of switches in the electric system of a home. When a switch is turned to the off position, the circuit is broken and electric current can no longer flow.   The plug board provides the programmer with the equivalent of a set of switches for completing circuits within a machine.

Figure 6.1 illustrates the manner in which a plug board may be used to complete machine circuits by external wiring.   There are two matching boards or panels; one is a *stationary machine panel* and the other is a *removable plug board* (control panel).   For each *hub* (receptacle for the end of the wire) on the stationary panel there is a mating hub on the removable plug board.   When the plug board is fitted into place, the mating hubs are connected.   Machine wires are permanently

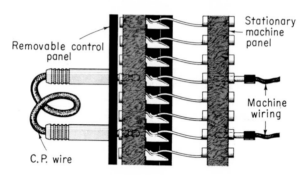

Fɪɢ. 6.1. Circuit completed by external wiring. (*Reprinted by permission from "IBM Reference Manual—Functional Wiring Principles," A24-1007-0, copyright 1956 in original notice by International Business Machines Corporation.*)

attached to the stationary panels.   A machine circuit can be completed by connecting the appropriate pair of plug-board hubs with an external wire and inserting the plug board in the machine.

A plug-board-controlled machine is thus programmed by plug-board wiring.   The wired plug board is equivalent to the computer program. The programmer must concern himself with the function of individual hubs and the timing of impulses.

6.2   Sensing Punches in a Card.   The manner in which punches are sensed in a moving card is illustrated in Fig. 6.2.   The card as shown is moving from right to left (twelve edge leading) over a roller that is connected to a source of current.[1]   The brush in the diagram is aligned with a specific card column.   When the brush contacts the roller, a circuit is completed through which current can flow.   When a card is passing over the roller, an electric impulse is available in the circuit leading from the brush whenever a punch is encountered in the

---

[1] Some equipments sense cards with twelve edge leading, while others sense cards with nine edge leading.

card column aligned with the brush.   If all 80 card columns are to be sensed simultaneously, a row of 80 brushes must be provided—one brush aligned with each card column.

A punch in a card is uniquely identified by specifying its location, i.e., a row and a column.   The row determines the value assigned to the punch and the column determines the card field to which the value belongs.   Similarly, the impulse that results from the sensing of the punch can be uniquely identified by the circuit that is impulsed (each brush is associated with a specific card column) and the relative time

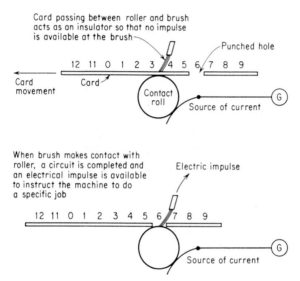

Fig. 6.2. Brush-sensing a 6 punch. (*Reprinted by permission from "IBM Reference Manual—Functional Wiring Principles," A24-1007-0, copyright 1956 in original notice by International Business Machines Corporation.*)

at which the impulse is emitted, i.e., the relative time at which a specific card row passes under the row of read brushes.

A timing chart for a twelve-edge-first card-read cycle is shown in Fig. 6.3.   The cycle starts at 288 degrees of arc on the circle, corresponding to the point in real time at which the read feed is activated. From 288 to 0 degrees, the card is accelerated from rest and moved toward the row of brushes shown in Fig. 6.2.   At 0 degrees in the cycle the card is moving at a uniform velocity and its leading (twelve) edge has reached the read brushes.   The shaded interval identified by the number 12 corresponds to that portion of the cycle (9 to 18 degrees) during which the 12 row passes under the read brushes.   This interval is frequently referred to as 12 time in the read cycle, and the associated impulse is referred to as a 12 impulse.   The 11, 0, 1, 2, . . . , 9 rows of the card pass under the read brushes at regular successive intervals thereafter.   These intervals are referred to respectively as 11, 0, 1, 2, . . . , 9 time in the read cycle.   The associated impulses are similarly identified.

Each read brush is connected permanently to a hub on the stationary control panel.   The impulses emitted during the card-read cycle are made available to the programmer for controlling machine functions by a set of READ hubs on the plug board.

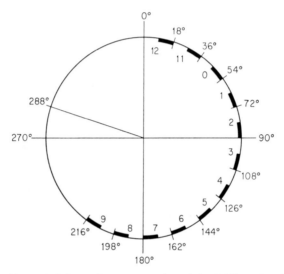

FIG. 6.3. Schematic representation of the (533) read cycle.

The plug board for the 533 unit is illustrated in Fig. 6.25.   There are three sets of READ hubs on this board that are connected in parallel to a set of 80 read brushes.   The READ CARD A hubs are located in board columns 1 to 20, rows A to D.   The hubs in row A are numbered 1 to 20, those in row B are numbered 21 to 40, those in row C are numbered 41 to 60, and those in row D are numbered 61 to 80.   The hub number identifies the card column that is sensed by the brush connected to that hub.   The second and third parallel sets of READ hubs, READ CARD B and READ CARD C, are located below the READ CARD A hubs in rows Q to T and X to AA, respectively.   The impulses from a given card column are available simultaneously at each of three correspondingly numbered hubs in sets A, B, and C.

A fourth set of READ hubs, FIRST READING, are located in board

columns 23 to 42, rows A to D.   These hubs are connected to another
set of 80 read brushes.   As indicated in Fig. 6.4, the first-reading
brushes are located one read cycle before the second-reading (READ
CARD A, B, C) brushes.   In other words, a card that passes under the
first-reading brushes during a given read cycle will pass under the
second-reading brushes during the subsequent read cycle.   Each card
is thus read twice.   Alternatively, two different cards are read synchronously during each read cycle.   One card passes under the first-
reading brushes while the preceding card passes under the second-
reading brushes.   The justification for two sets of read brushes will
become apparent in later discussions of machine functions.

**6.3 Storing Numeric and Alphanumeric Data in a Memory
Register.**   In the preceding section we discussed the conversion of card

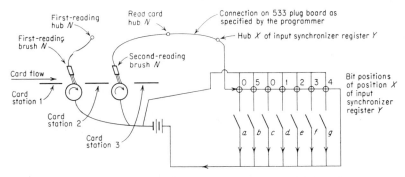

FIG. 6.4 Schematic of the translation of a digit punch.

punches to electric impulses.   In this section we shall discuss a method
for translating a digit impulse to a seven-bit binary code stored in an
input synchronizer register.

The reader will recall that there are 10 input synchronizer registers
in the 650.   Each register has 10 digit positions and a sign position.
For each position there is a STORAGE ENTRY hub on the plug board.
If a READ hub is connected to a digit-position STORAGE ENTRY hub by
external plug-board wiring, the digit impulse emitted by the READ hub
will be translated to a binary code stored in the register position that
is connected (by internal machine wiring) to the STORAGE ENTRY hub.

The translation function is schematically illustrated in Fig. 6.4.
An external connection is made between the SECOND READING hub N
($N = 1, 2, 3, \ldots$, or 80) and the STORAGE ENTRY hub X ($X = 1, 2,$
$\ldots$, or 10) of input synchronizer register Y ($Y = 1, 2, \ldots$, or 10)
to complete a circuit containing the horizontal wire (cf. Fig. 3.4)
threading the cores of that register position.

As a card passes from card station 2 to card station 3 in the read feed, it passes under the second-reading brushes. Assume that all synchronizer-register cores are reset to the 0 state prior to 0 degrees in the read cycle. A digit punch in column N will be converted to an impulse in the horizontal wire threading the cores. The appropriate vertical impulse is provided by the automatic closing and opening of switches a to g at the appropriate intervals in the read cycle. Switch a is automatically closed at 0, 1, 2, 3, and 4 times and is open during the remainder of the cycle. Switches c to g are successively closed at 0, 1, 2, 3, and 4 times, respectively. Similarly, the closing of switch b and switches c to g are synchronized with 5 through 9 times of the read cycle. Thus a card punch can be translated to a binary code. Note that two or more digit impulses will cause three or more cores to be set to the 1 state, while the absence of a punch will leave all cores at the 0 state. In either event, an invalid code will result.

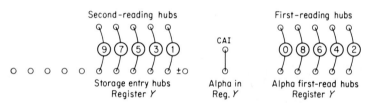

Fig. 6.5. External 533 wiring for storing alphanumeric data in memory.

If a SECOND READING hub is wired to a sign-position hub of an input synchronizer register, an 11 impulse will be translated to the binary code for a minus sign while the absence of an 11 punch will be translated to the binary code for a plus sign. The translation circuit of Fig. 6.4 ignores 12 and 11 impulses because all vertical circuits are open at these times. Therefore, a different translation circuit (not shown) is required for the sign position.

The wiring is more complicated when alphanumeric data are to be stored in a memory register. Since the two impulses must be translated to a two-digit decimal number, no more than five alphanumeric characters can be stored in a memory register. The procedure used in the 533 unit requires that the appropriate input synchronizer register be conditioned to accept alphanumeric data, that the digit impulses be channeled from SECOND READING hubs to the five low-order STORAGE ENTRY hubs of that register, and that the zone impulses be channeled from FIRST READING hubs to the ALPHABETIC FIRST READ hubs of that register.

Figure 6.5 illustrates the external 533 wiring to store five alphanumeric characters in input synchronizer register Y ($Y = 1, 2, \ldots,$ 6). The CAI hub is wired to the ALPHA IN hub of register Y to condition that register to accept alphanumeric data. The CAI hub emits an impulse from 324 to 354 degrees of each read cycle, and the ALPHA IN hub accepts impulses from 340 to 9 degrees of each read cycle. Since these periods overlap, the ALPHA IN hub is impulsed each read cycle. When the ALPHA IN hub for input synchronizer register Y is impulsed, that register is automatically conditioned to accept alphanumeric data during *that read cycle*.

The wiring from the FIRST READING hubs to the ALPHABETIC FIRST READ hubs provides for translation of each of the five zone impulses as the card passes the first-reading brushes. The numbers 2, 4, 6, 8, and 0 indicate the input-synchronizer-register positions to which the translations of the respective zone impulses are to be entered *during the succeeding read cycle*, if the appropriate ALPHA IN hub is impulsed.

The wiring from the SECOND READING hubs to the STORAGE ENTRY hubs provides for translation of each of the five digit impulses as the card passes the second-reading brushes. The numbers 1, 3, 5, 7, and 9 indicate the input-synchronizer-register positions to which the translations of the respective digit impulses are to be entered *during that read cycle*, if the appropriate ALPHA IN hub is impulsed.

The foregoing discussion describes the external 533 wiring for storing data in 650 memory. The IBM 77 and 85 Collators, the IBM 407, 408, and 409 Accounting Machines, the IBM 557 Interpreter, and the IBM 602 Calculating Punch each have a limited number of memory registers. The external wiring for storing data in the memory registers of these machines is analogous but not identical to that for the 533.

6.4 Printing Numeric and Alphanumeric Data. The impulses emitted from the READ hubs may be used to control type bars or type wheels for printing the characters. In this section we shall discuss the printing of numeric and alphabetic characters only.

The reader will recall that the punched-card alphanumeric code is readily divided into four zones: A to I, J to R, S to Z, and 0 to 9 according to whether the zone punch is respectively 12, 11, 0, or blank. If the characters on the type bar are grouped accordingly (see Fig. 6.6), the zone punch can be used to select the appropriate group of characters and the digit punch to select the character from the group. Associated with each type bar is a PRINT ENTRY hub to which impulses may be channeled to control the operation of that particular type bar. If the character from card column M is to be printed by type bar N, then SECOND READING hub M is wired to PRINT ENTRY hub N.

Some machines (e.g., the 402) have two PRINT ENTRY hubs associated with each type bar.   One will be referred to as the ZONE ENTRY hub and the other as the PRINT ENTRY hub.   The ZONE ENTRY hub accepts the zone punch during the first reading and controls the positioning of the type bar at the start of the following cycle to the selected group of characters. The PRINT ENTRY hub accepts the digit punch and controls the relative positioning of the type bar to the appropriate character within the group. If the character from card column M is to be printed by type bar N on such a machine, then the FIRST READING hub M is wired to ZONE ENTRY hub N and SECOND READING hub M is wired to PRINT ENTRY hub N.

The IBM 402, 403, 407, 408, and 409 Accounting Machines all have either type bars or type wheels and are used for printing data from punched cards. These machines are sometimes referred to as tabulating machines.   The IBM 548 and 557 Interpreters are used to print data from card columns onto the card itself.

6.5   Automatic Punching of Cards.[1]   A punch mechanism such as illustrated in Fig. 6.7 could be used to punch holes in a card.   To control the punching, it is necessary that the card be positioned as to row and column under the die and that the punch be actuated after the card is properly positioned.

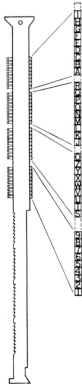

FIG. 6.6 Alphanumeric type bar. (*Reprinted by permission from "IBM Reference Manual—Functional Wiring Principles,*" A24-1007-0, *copyright* 1956 *in original notice by International Business Machines Corporation.*)

If the roller and the 80 brushes of the punch-sensing mechanism of Fig. 6.2 are replaced by a set of 80 punch mechanisms (one for each card column) and if each punch is independently actuated when row 12, 11, 0, 1, . . . , or 9 is aligned with the die and its associated PUNCH hub receives a 12, 11, 0, . . . , or 9 impulse respectively, a mechanism is provided for the automatic punching of cards.

Such card-punching mechanisms are found in the IBM 513 and 514 Reproducing Punches and in the IBM 521, 533, and 537 Read-Punch units.

6.6   Switching the Paths of Impulses.   Switches with which the programmer can vary the paths of impulses are available in several forms.   The reader will recall that in the data-processing problem of Chap. 4 the opera-

[1] The IBM 26 Key Punch is discussed in Sec. 6.22.

tions to be performed varied with the type of card.   In the 650 program for this problem, the variation in operations was provided by different routines.   In plug-board programming, variation is provided by switching the paths of impulses.

The DIGIT SELECTOR is essentially a distributor (see Fig. 6.8) that enables the programmer to select or isolate individual impulses from the set 12, 11, 0, 1, . . . , 9.   The COMMON hub of the DIGIT SELECTOR is connected to a rotor.   The rotation of the rotor is synchronized with the card cycle so that the COMMON hub is successively connected to

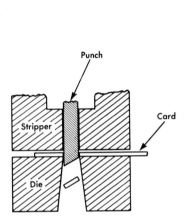

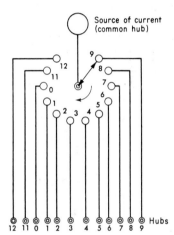

FIG. 6.7. Punch and die. (*Reprinted by permission from "IBM Reference Manual—Functional Wiring Principles," A24-1007-0, copyright 1956 in original notice by International Business Machines Corporation.*)

FIG. 6.8. Schematic of a digit selector. (*Reprinted by permission from "IBM Reference Manual—Functional Wiring Principles," A24-1007-0, copyright 1956 in original notice by International Business Machines Corporation.*)

each of the digit hubs (12, 11, 0, 1, . . . , 9) at the corresponding impulse times in the card cycle.   If the READ hub for column M is connected to the COMMON hub of the DIGIT SELECTOR, a unique path is created between read brush N and digit hub X ($X = 12, 11, 0, 1,$ . . . , 9) at the corresponding impulse times of each card cycle.   Thus a distinction can be made between the presence or absence of a specific punch in column M of the card being read during a given read cycle. The direction of rotation of the rotor in Fig. 6.8 corresponds to a nine-edge-first card cycle.   For a twelve-edge-first card cycle, the direction of rotation would be reversed.

In the remainder of this section, it will be assumed that cards enter the feed with the twelve edge leading.   The reader is cautioned that he should refer to the manual of operation of a given unit for specific details about card feeding, timing, etc.

The COLUMN SPLIT is a switch that splits or partitions the digit impulses into two subsets: 12 and 11 impulses and 0 through 9 impulses (see Fig. 6.9). The COMMON hub is connected to a switch that functions automatically. The COMMON hub is connected to the 12-11 hub at 12 and 11 time of the card cycle; then the switch transfers automatically and the COMMON hub is connected to the 0-9 hub at 0 through 9 time in the card cycle.

The PILOT SELECTOR is a two-bladed switch that can be actuated by external board wiring. There are nine hubs associated with the PILOT SELECTOR illustrated schematically in Fig. 6.10. The three pickup hubs control the energization of the solenoid that switches the pair of blades simultaneously. There are three hubs associated

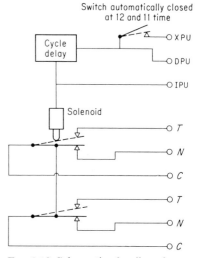

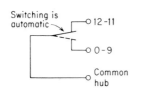

FIG. 6.9. Schematic of a column split.   FIG. 6.10. Schematic of a pilot selector.

with each blade—a COMMON (C), a NORMAL (N), and a TRANSFERRED (T) hub. Unless the solenoid is actuated, each COMMON hub is connected to its corresponding NORMAL hub.

The X pickup (XPU) hub accepts impulses only at 12 and 11 time.[1] The D pickup (DPU) hub accepts all impulses. If either of these hubs is impulsed during a card cycle, the *cycle delay* is activated. If the cycle delay is activated during a card cycle, it automatically emits an impulse prior to zero degrees of the next card cycle.[2] This impulse energizes the solenoid and is emitted at the I pickup (IPU) hub. When the solenoid is energized, both blades are simultaneously switched to the positions indicated by the dotted lines and each COMMON hub is connected to its corresponding TRANSFERRED hub.

[1] An 11 punch (impulse) is frequently referred to in IBM literature as an X punch (impulse) and a 12 punch (impulse) as a Y punch (impulse).

[2] The cycle delay impulse is emitted at 318 to 350 degrees in the 533 *read* unit. The timing of this impulse for another unit (e.g., the 533 punch unit) can be determined from the timing chart for that unit.

The IPU hub serves a dual function. As stated earlier, it emits the cycle delay[1] impulse; hence the programmer can use it as the source of a delayed impulse. In addition, it accepts any impulse[2] and energizes the solenoid immediately; this results in immediate switching of the pair of blades.

The length of time that the blades are held in the transferred position after initial energization of the solenoid varies among equipments. In some cases, the blades are automatically held in the transferred position for the duration of the card cycle in which the solenoid is energized. In other cases (e.g., the 533 unit) the blades are held in the transferred position only as long as an associated HOLD hub is continuously impulsed. Finally, the blades of some switches are *latched* upon transfer and remain transferred until an associated UNLATCH hub is impulsed. Neither of the latter hubs is indicated in Fig. 6.10.

The PILOT SELECTOR enables the programmer to use a selected impulse or set of impulses to vary the paths of flow of subsequent impulses wired to the COMMON hubs.

The COSELECTOR is a five-bladed switch. If the XPU and DPU hubs were eliminated from Fig. 6.10 and if three more blades with associated T, N, and C hubs were added in tandem to the pair of blades shown, the result would be a schematic of a COSELECTOR. As in the case of the PILOT SELECTOR, the IPU hub will accept any impulse. The solenoid is energized and all five blades are transferred immediately whenever the IPU hub receives an impulse. As in the case of the PILOT SELECTOR, the duration of transfer depends upon the particular unit. In the 533 unit the blades remain transferred only as long as an associated HOLD hub is continuously impulsed.

One or more column-split devices, PILOT SELECTOR switches, and/or COSELECTOR switches are included in almost every plug-board-controlled equipment. The names applied to these devices may vary from unit to unit and the details of operation may vary, but the basic function is usually that described above. Digit selectors are present with less frequency.

Some units provide externally controllable gang switching on a large scale. In the 533, for example, there are three complete sets of STORAGE ENTRY hubs—STORAGE ENTRY A, B, and C. Only one set of

---

[1] The cycle delay impulse is referred to as a couple exit impulse in the IBM literature.

[2] The IPU hub accepts impulses from 340 to 220 degrees of the *read cycle* in the 533. The number of degrees in the interval may vary from unit to unit, so the reader should refer to the timing chart of a particular unit for specific limits of the interval.

these hubs is connected by machine wiring to the input synchronizer registers at a time.   The ENTRY A and ENTRY B hubs provide for externally controlled gang switching of the complete set of storage entry circuits.   Figure 6.11 schematically illustrates the operation of a three-way switch controlled by the ENTRY A and ENTRY B hubs.

If the ENTRY B hub is impulsed during a read cycle, the cycle delay unit is activated, which in turn energizes solenoid B prior to 12 time in the next read cycle, i.e., the next time a read operation is executed. When solenoid B is energized, gang switching takes place and all the input synchronizer register circuits are simultaneously disconnected from the STORAGE ENTRY C hubs and connected to the STORAGE ENTRY B hubs, as indicated by the dotted line under solenoid B.   The diode prevents solenoid A from being energized when the ENTRY B hub is impulsed, but it permits solenoid B to be energized when the ENTRY A hub is impulsed.

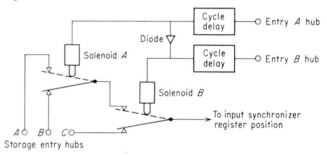

FIG. 6.11. Schematic of entry A, B, C switching.

If the ENTRY A hub is impulsed during a read cycle, both solenoids are energized prior to 12 time in the next read cycle and STORAGE ENTRY A hubs are connected to the input synchronizer register circuits.

This gang-switching feature simplifies the programmer's wiring problems when he has two or three card formats in his input deck. One card format can be wired from READ C hubs to STORAGE ENTRY C hubs, another from READ B hubs to STORAGE ENTRY B hubs, and a third from READ A hubs to STORAGE ENTRY A hubs.   A common way of distinguishing between formats is to set aside a column for a card code and to assign a different digit in this column for each format.   If this has been done, the digit selector can be used at first reading to isolate the digit impulse that is to be channeled to the ENTRY B hub.   Thus the card type is identified at first reading, and the switching is performed prior to 12 time in the following read cycle.

The PUNCH A and PUNCH B hubs on the 533 board perform an analogous function in the selection of output formats.   Their selection depends upon identifying data stored in the tenth STORAGE EXIT register and will be discussed in the section on read-out of storage.

The LOAD hub on the 533 board controls another important gang-switching function. This hub accepts impulses at 12 time only. When it is impulsed during a read cycle, gang switching takes place prior to 12 time in the next read cycle, i.e., when the next read operation is executed. This gang switching overrides entry A, B, or C and causes the card to be read 80-80 via internal wiring.[1] This internal wiring requires that columns 10, 20, . . . , 80 contain (in addition to a digit punch) either a 12 punch or an 11 punch to identify the sign as positive or negative, respectively.

When an ALPHA IN hub (Fig. 6.5) is impulsed, gang switching takes place so that the associated input synchronizer register is conditioned to accept alphanumeric input. Similarly, when an ALPHA OUT hub is impulsed, gang switching takes place so that the data from the associated output synchronizer register are punched alphanumeric.

6.7 Comparing Units. Comparing units perform a function in the plug-board-controlled machine that is comparable to a programmed

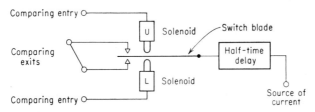

FIG. 6.12. Schematic of an equal-unequal comparing unit.

logical test in the stored-program computer. Figure 6.12 schematically illustrates a device for dynamically comparing the states of two circuits. Assume that one source of impulses, say FIRST READING hub M, is connected to the upper COMPARING ENTRY hub by external board wiring and that a second source of impulses, say SECOND READING hub M, is connected to the lower COMPARING ENTRY hub by external board wiring. If the upper COMPARING ENTRY hub receives an impulse, solenoid U is energized. If the lower COMPARING ENTRY hub is impulsed, solenoid L is energized. If both solenoids are impulsed simultaneously, the forces counterbalance and the blade does not move. If either solenoid is impulsed independently, the blade transfers and latches. The half-time delay is introduced to allow for small differences in the timing of input impulses and differences in the rates at

[1] Furthermore, the control unit automatically branches to the data address when the first read operation is executed following the impulsing of the LOAD hub.

which the two solenoids operate. The half-time delay emits impulses between punch impulse times—say 19 through 26, 37 through 44, . . . , 199 through 206, and 217 through 224 degrees of the read cycle illustrated in Fig. 6.3.

If the switch blade is held in the transferred position until the end of the half-time impulse before it is returned to its normal position, the COMPARING EXIT will emit an impulse if and only if one of the solenoids is energized independently. In other words, an impulse will be emitted from a COMPARING EXIT hub if and only if the source impulses at the two COMPARING ENTRY hubs are not identical; e.g., if the punches in column M of the cards at the first- and second-reading stations are not identical.

If we wish to compare a card field, say columns A, B, and C, in a card passing the first-reading brushes with the corresponding card field in the card passing the second-reading brushes, we need only wire corresponding FIRST and SECOND READING hubs to corresponding pairs of COMPARING ENTRY hubs and connect their COMPARING EXIT hubs, as illustrated in Fig. 6.13. If identical sets of impulses are not received by the two sets of COMPARING ENTRY hubs, then at least one impulse will be emitted from the string of COMPARING EXIT hubs and this impulse can be used to control certain machine functions, e.g., to cause a sum to be printed whenever a change in index number is identified.

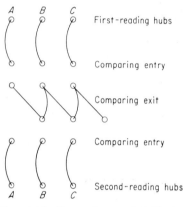

FIG. 6.13. Comparing card fields for inequality.

The unit described above will be referred to as an equal-unequal type of comparing unit. It is found in the IBM 402, 403, 407, 408, and 409 Accounting Machines and in the IBM 513 and 514 Reproducing Punches. In the latter, however, there are no external COMPARING EXIT hubs; instead, each COMPARING EXIT hub is internally wired to control a corresponding latch (see Sec. 6.15).

The unit schematically illustrated in Fig. 6.14 provides for comparison of two integers A and B to determine when $A > B$, $A = B$, or $A < B$. The unit shown provides for comparison of two-digit numbers only. However, the same principles can be extended to an arbitrary number of digit positions. The tens position of A would be externally wired into hub A_2, and the units position into A_1; while the tens position of B would be externally wired into B_2, and the units position into B_1.

The inequalities shown assume that the timing of digit impulses follows the sequence illustrated in Fig. 6.15.[1] It is common practice to ignore zero punches in comparing devices, with the consequence that no distinction is made between a zero punch and the absence of a digit punch.

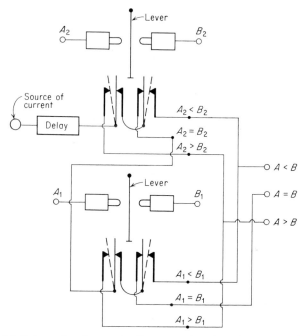

FIG. 6.14. Schematic of a greater-than, equal, or less-than comparing unit.

The unit operates as follows. If hub A_2 is impulsed and hub B_2 is not, the solenoid actuates the lever and a circuit is completed between the source of current and the external hub $A > B$. If we assume that once the lever is actuated it is latched in that position until an impulse is emitted from the delay after the last digit impulse time, then the completion of the circuit $A > B$ implies that hub A_2 received an impulse before hub B_2 and A is in fact greater than B. If hub B_2 is impulsed before hub A_2, then a circuit is completed appropriately between the source of current and the external hub $A < B$. If both A_2 and B_2 are impulsed simultaneously, then a circuit is completed

[1] This corresponds to a read cycle in which the nine edge of the card leads. If the order of digit impulses is reversed, i.e., twelve edge first, then the inequalities must be reversed at the external hubs.

between the source of current and the internal hub $A_2 = B_2$, which in turn serves as a source of current for the units position comparing circuit.

The comparison of the digits A_1 and B_1 is analogous to the comparison of digits A_2 and B_2, and, in fact, both comparisons are performed in a single cycle. It should be noted, however, that the internal $A_1 = B_1$ hub is connected to the external $A = B$ hub.

An impulse is emitted from the delay at an appropriate time after comparing is completed and a circuit is established between the delay and the appropriate external hub $A < B$, $A = B$, or $A > B$. The

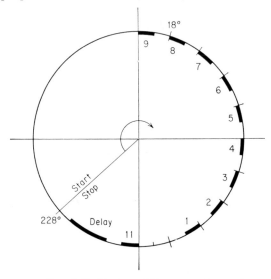

Fig. 6.15. Timing of the comparing cycle.

impulses from these hubs can be used to control certain machine functions, e.g., the routing of cards to different stackers in a collator, as discussed in the next section.

This type of comparing unit is found in the IBM 77 and 85 Collators.

6.8   Switching the Paths of Cards.   In the earlier discussion of card feeding, it was assumed that there is a single path that a card can follow from the feed hopper to the stacker.   In the *card-sorting* operation it is necessary to provide paths to 13 different stackers from a single feed hopper and to provide impulse-controlled switching to choose the appropriate path for each card.   In the *card-collating* operation, paths are provided to four stackers from two feed hoppers, and impulse-controlled switching is provided to choose the appropriate path for each card.

The mechanics of switching card paths are illustrated in Fig. 6.16. In the card sorter, the leading edge of the card forces its way under the chute blades until a punch (e.g., 4) is sensed, at which time the magnet coils are energized. The magnets draw plate E and the blades that are still touching it down; this permits the card to enter the chute between adjacent blades. The card is conveyed along the chute by a series of rollers and is finally guided into the appropriate stacker (e.g., 4) by the curved (left) end of the blade above it. If no punch is

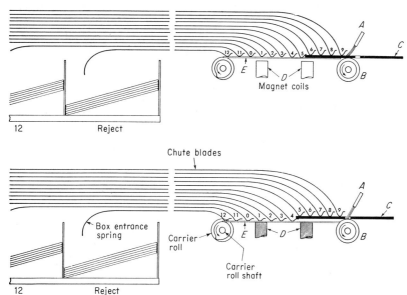

Fig. 6.16. Schematic of a card sorter. (*Reprinted by permission from "IBM Electric Punched Card Accounting Machines—Principles of operations, Sorters,"* 22-3177-3, *copyright* 1949 *in original notice by International Business Machines Corporation.*)

sensed, the card forces its way under all blades and is guided into the reject stacker.

The foregoing system whereby the selection of the stacker to which a card is to be conveyed is determined by the *first* punch sensed in a selected column is used in IBM 75, 80, and 82 Sorters. The same principle for guiding cards to stackers is used in the IBM 101 Sorter; however, stacker selection in the latter can be controlled by board wiring and may involve punches in more than one column. In the IBM 77 and 85 Collators the selection of the path of a card is determined by externally wiring control impulses (e.g., $A > B$, $A = B$, $A < B$) to hubs that control the switching of the chute blades.

6.9   Adding and Subtracting.   The addition and subtraction operations for the 650 have been described previously.   In this section we shall discuss control of the addition and subtraction operations in the IBM accounting machines.   To simplify the discussion, we shall consider an accumulator[1] with only two digit positions; however, several independent accumulators with up to eight positions are available in these machines, and if more than eight positions are required, two accumulators can be coupled.   No attempt will be made to discuss the internal wiring or the physical operation of the accumulators; instead, we shall discuss the external wiring only.

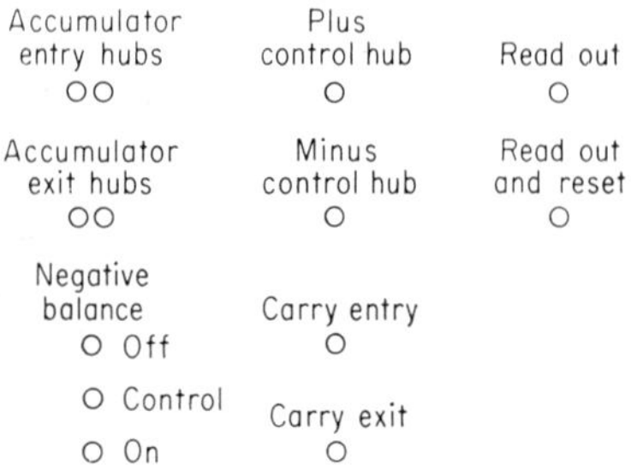

Accumulator entry hubs	Plus control hub	Read out
O O	O	O
Accumulator exit hubs	Minus control hub	Read out and reset
O O	O	O
Negative balance	Carry entry	
O Off	O	
O Control	Carry exit	
O On	O	

Fig.   6.17.   Accumulator   Entry, Exit, and Control hubs.

The set of hubs shown in Fig. 6.17 is associated with a particular accumulator.   Each other accumulator has its own corresponding set of hubs.   Input data (e.g., from second-reading brushes) are wired externally to the ACCUMULATOR ENTRY hubs.   However, the data are added to or subtracted from the accumulator only during a cycle in which the appropriate PLUS CONTROL hub or MINUS CONTROL hub is impulsed.   The PLUS CONTROL hub is impulsed during each cycle in which the data received by the ENTRY hubs are to be added into the accumulator, and, alternatively, the MINUS CONTROL hub is impulsed when the data are to be subtracted from the accumulator.   If the data to be added to or subtracted from the accumulator are read from a card,[2] an impulse[3] that is automatically emitted each card cycle is wired to the appropriate control hub.

If the operation to be performed varies from card to card, the programmer must provide for varying the paths of either the control impulses, the data impulses, or both.   For example, a minus quantity will normally be identified by an 11 punch in a specified column and a positive quantity by the absence of both an 11 and a 12 punch in that column.   The programmer can use the 11 punch to control a pilot selector, as discussed in Sec. 6.6, to switch the path of the control impulse from the plus control hub to the minus control hub.

The quantity in the accumulator is emitted at its EXIT hubs during

---

[1] Accumulators are commonly referred to as *counters* in the IBM literature on accounting machines.

[2] Addition of an accumulator to or subtraction of an accumulator from another is possible, but control of these operations will not be discussed.

[3] See card cycles impulse in Sec. 6.12.

a cycle in which either its READ OUT or its READ OUT AND RESET hub is impulsed.   In the latter case, the accumulator is reset with nines after read-out, e.g., 99 in a two-digit accumulator.

The negative-balance hubs are necessary because the accumulators are not direct-reading; i.e., the nines complement of a negative sum or one less than a positive sum appears in the accumulator.   An impulse is emitted from the NEGATIVE BALANCE ON hub (see 407 timing chart, Fig. 6.20) in each cycle that a 9 appears in the high-order position of an accumulator.   When an accumulator sum can be either positive or negative, its NEGATIVE BALANCE ON hub should be wired to its NEGATIVE BALANCE CONTROL hub.   If the latter hub is impulsed in a cycle in which the READ OUT hub is impulsed, the nines complement of the integer in the accumulator will be emitted at the EXIT hubs.   When an accumulator sum can only be positive, its NEGATIVE BALANCE OFF hub should be wired to its NEGATIVE BALANCE CONTROL hub so that the correct sum will be printed rather than one less than the sum.   If two accumulators are coupled, the CARRY EXIT hub of the low-order accumulator should be wired to the CARRY ENTRY hub of the high-order accumulator in order that an overflow from the lower accumulator will be properly added into the high-order accumulator.   Similarly, the CARRY EXIT hub from the high-order accumulator should be wired to the CARRY ENTRY hub of the low-order accumulator.   In addition, the CONTROL hubs should also be coupled, with NEGATIVE BALANCE ON (OFF) wired only for the high-order accumulator.

The CARRY EXIT and CARRY ENTRY hubs play a part in the conversion of accumulator sums to their correct magnitudes and should be wired together.

6.10   Read Out Storage.   Reading data out of storage is essentially the inverse operation to that of storing data in a memory register, as discussed in Sec. 6.3.   The code stored in each register position must be translated to the appropriate digit impulse, which is channeled to a STORAGE EXIT hub by internal wiring.   Read out storage is initiated in the 650 by execution of the punch operation and in other machines by appropriately impulsing the STORAGE OUT control hub associated with a specific storage register.

In the 533 punch unit, there are three sets of STORAGE EXIT hubs— A, B, and C—and three sets of PUNCH hubs—A, B, and C.[1]   A set of 80 PUNCH hubs controls the actuation of the 80 punch dies in the 533 punch unit.   If there is only one format for output cards, the programmer will normally wire the STORAGE EXIT hubs of set C to the PUNCH hubs of set C so that data is channeled from storage-exit-

---

[1] The STORAGE EXIT and PUNCH hubs are shown on the right side of Fig. 6.25 symmetrically with the STORAGE ENTRY and READ hubs.

register positions to card columns as required by the card format.   If the data are strictly numeric, the wiring is strictly analogous to that for reading numeric data.

If, however, the data is alphanumeric, the ALPHA OUT hub must be impulsed prior to 12 time in the punch cycle and only the five low-order STORAGE EXIT hubs for that register are wired to PUNCH hubs. Both the digit impulse and the zone impulse for a character are transmitted to the PUNCH hub through a single wire.   An impulse emitted each punch cycle from a PUNCH HOLD[1] hub can be used to impulse the ALPHA OUT hub.

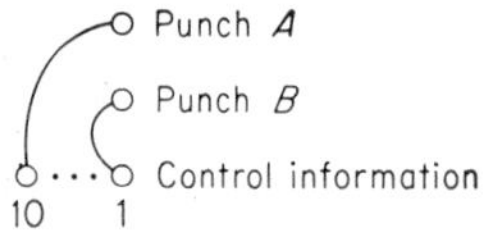

FIG. 6.18. External wiring for selection of PUNCH A and PUNCH B hubs.

If more than one output format is required, then the programmer may wire the A or B sets of PUNCH hubs.   The three sets of STORAGE EXIT hubs are all wired in parallel to the output-synchronizer-register circuits, but the three sets of PUNCH hubs are independent. External wiring for selection of the PUNCH A and PUNCH B hubs is illustrated in Fig. 6.18.

Selection of the punch format depends upon the data to be punched; hence the selection must be controlled by data stored in memory. There are 10 sets of CONTROL INFORMATION hubs on the 533 panel—columns 55 to 64 and rows AK to AM of Fig. 6.25.   An impulse is emitted prior to 12 time in a punch cycle by each of the three CONTROL INFORMATION hubs in the first set, column 64, if an $\underline{8}$ is copied into position 1 of the tenth output synchronizer register in that cycle. Thus if a CONTROL INFORMATION hub is externally wired to the PUNCH B and if an $\underline{8}$ is stored in the corresponding position of the tenth storage exit register from which the data are to be punched, then the PUNCH B hubs will control the set of punches in the 533 unit.   PUNCH A can be selected similarly, but a different digit position and CONTROL INFORMATION hub must be used.   The PUNCH C hubs control the set of punches in the 533 unit unless A or B is selected.   In Fig. 6.18, position $\underline{1}$ is used to select PUNCH B and position $\underline{10}$ is used to select PUNCH A.

In other machines the impulses from the STORAGE EXIT hubs may be wired at the discretion of the programmer (subject, of course, to the limitations of the machine) to control type bars, as input to an accumulator, as input to a comparing unit, etc.

6.11 The Timing Chart and Impulse Emission.   From the foregoing discussions it should be clear that control of a machine depends upon the channeling of the appropriate impulse to the appropriate hubs at the appropriate times in the appropriate cycles.

We can get a general idea of the operations that a given plug-board-

[1] See Fig. 6.25, columns 39 and 40 and rows R and S.

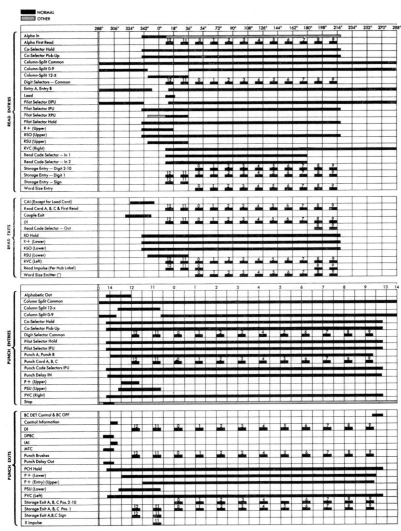

Fig. 6.19. 533 timing chart. (*Reprinted by permission from "IBM 650 Data Processing Bulletin—533 Card Read Punch, 537 Card Read Punch, 407 Accounting Machine," G24-5001-0, copyright 1958 in original notice by International Business Machines Corporation.*)

controlled machine can perform by becoming familiar with the functions of the hubs on the plug board. We have discussed several such functions in the preceding sections. To actually control the operations of a machine, we must also become familiar with the timing of impulse emission. Timing charts are shown for the 533 unit (Fig. 6.19) and the 407 Accounting Machine (Fig. 6.20).

EXITS

CONTROL PANEL HUBS		
All Cycles	AW 53-68	A
Alter. SW Exit	H 73-76	A
Asterisk Control	BI 33-34	A
Bal. Test Cycle	AU 61-64	1
CO-CC / Card Cycles	O 53-72, Q 37-40	C 2
Card Reading Impulses		CM 3
Carriage HH, HD, DH, DD, Offlow	N-O 33-40	A
Channel Entry	AV 53-68	A
Character Emitter	S-V 41-52	AS 4
CI Carry Exit	AJ 53-80	A 5
Column Split CPL	AC 51-52	AS
Comparing Exit	D-E 1-30	CM
Counter-Controlled Print (Echo Impulses)	AZ-BB 1-40	A 6
Counter Exit	AR-AY 1-42	A
Counter Punch Exits	BC-BF 1-42	A 7
Couple Control (Lower)	AB 53-80	AS
Cycle Count	AO 41-42	A
Digit Impulse	F 37-40	A
Exit 9	P 39-40	8
Filter Exit	BL 15-34	9
Final Total	AP 73-77	F
First Card (Mi, Int, Maj)	M-O 73-74	10
Half Adjust	AP-AQ 41-42	A
Immediate Exit	F 31-34	A
Last Card Skip	N 29-30	A
Last Card Total (Upper)	G 80	CF 11
List Off (Upper)	E 80	AS 11
MLR Couple	R 37-38	M
MLR Repeat CPL	E 37-40	12
Negative Bal. On-Off	AC 53-80, AF 53-80	A
Overflow Couple	AP-AT 79-80	O
Overflow Programs	AP-AT 67-68	O
Overflow Transfer	AW 69-72	O
Pilot Sel Couple Exit	C 53-72	A

FUNCTIONAL CYCLE

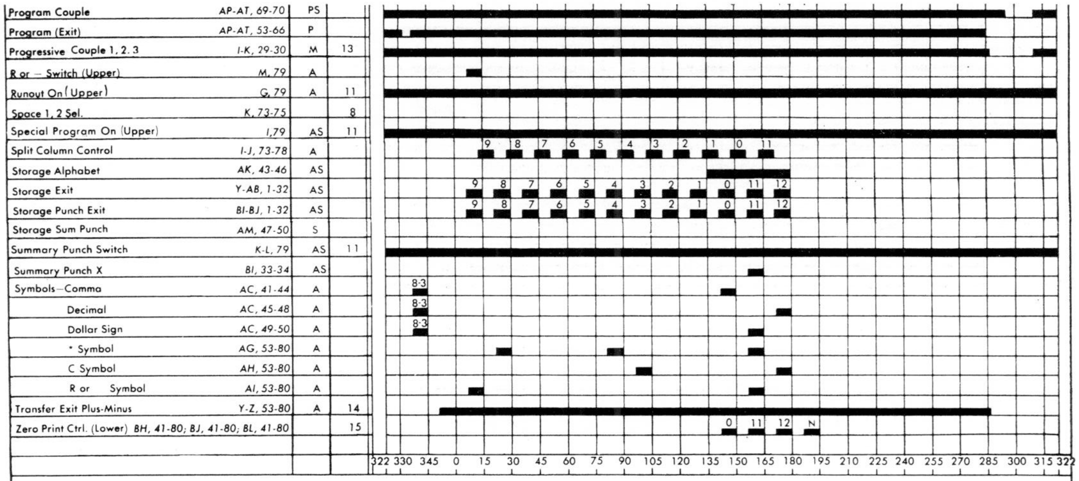

Program Couple	AP-AT, 69-70	PS
Program (Exit)	AP-AT, 53-66	P
Progressive Couple 1, 2, 3	I-K, 29-30	M	13
R or – Switch (Upper)	M, 79	A
Runout On (Upper)	G, 79	A	11
Space 1, 2 Sel.	K, 73-75	S	8
Special Program On (Upper)	I, 79	AS	11
Split Column Control	I-J, 73-78	A
Storage Alphabet	AK, 43-46	AS
Storage Exit	Y-AB, 1-32	AS
Storage Punch Exit	BI-BJ, 1-32	AS
Storage Sum Punch	AM, 47-50	S
Summary Punch Switch	K-L, 79	AS	11
Summary Punch X	BJ, 33-34	AS
Symbols – Comma	AC, 41-44	A
Decimal	AC, 45-48	A
Dollar Sign	AC, 49-50	A
* Symbol	AG, 53-80	A
C Symbol	AH, 53-80	A
R or Symbol	AI, 53-80	A
Transfer Exit Plus-Minus	Y-Z, 53-80	A	14
Zero Print Ctrl. (Lower)	BH, 41-80; BJ, 41-80; BL, 41-80	A	15

Degree scale: 322 330 345 0 15 30 45 60 75 90 105 120 135 150 165 180 195 210 225 240 255 270 285 300 315 322

MACHINE CYCLES CODE

A All machine cycles, except summary punch and long carriage
C Card cycles
F Final total cycle
M MLR cycles
O Overflow programs
P Program cycles
S Summary punch cycle, timing under control of summary punch

NOTES

1. Should not be used for counter crossfooting skip cycles
2. Q, 37.40, O, 79-80 active on all card cycles; 0, 53-72 except HC and MLR cycles
3. N not read from card, internal no-zone impulse
4. Except special program
5. Emits impulses as designated on control panel
6. All cycles if impulsed
7. Except on direct entry or direct reset
8. Under control of carriage
9. Emits whatever is entered
10. Minor also active on first body card
11. Wire only to lower hub
12. All MLR cycles after repeat is impulsed   First repeat cycle good only from 310-350°
13. Timing shown for MLR only. When used as entries, timing depends on pickup impulse
14. Only when counter is impulsed to read out and reset
15. Print cycles only
16. Immediate transfer at time impulsed
17. Minus must be impulsed not later than 35I°
18. Counter-controlled print internally common with either normal or transfer print entry on first half of cycle
19. Must be impulsed not later than 336°
20. Except when release is impulsed on the same cycle
21. Including last MLR cycle
22. Accepts 3 on line 3, 2 on line 2, 1 on line 1
23. Accepts only after overflow program start has been impulsed
24. Except overflow programs
25. Transfer time on X or D pickup
26. Com. accepts any program; Mi, Int, Maj accept when corresponding program start is impulsed; Final accepts when runout final is active
27. Except cycle preceding summary punch cycle
28. Read in effective on next card feed cycle or next MLR cycle; Read out effective on same card feed cycle if impulsed between 322 and 335°
29. Read in effective on next card feed cycle or next MLR cycle
30. Any impulse from 5 to 110 degrees including digits 9 through 3 will suppress spacing before and after printing. Any impulse on a program cycle from 135 to 260 degrees will suppress any automatic spacing that may occur after total printing

FIG. 6.20a. 407 timing chart: exits. (*Reprinted by permission from "IBM 407 Accounting Machine—Manual of Operation," 22-5765-7, copyright 1950 in original notice by International Business Machines Corporation.*)

203

ENTRIES ■ Normal / ▭ Other

FUNCTIONAL CYCLE

CONTROL PANEL HUBS		MACH CYCLE	NOTES
Alter. SW Sel (Trans)	E.G. 73.76	A	
Ampersand, Minus Entry	BK. 35.40	A	
Asterisk Entry	BJ. 35.40	A	
Auto Stop	AH. 51.52	A	
Bal Test P.U.	AU. 65.66	A	
C Carry Entry	AK. 53.80	A	
Carriage Form Skip	P. 37.38	A	
Immediate Skip	L. 31.40	A	
Short Skip	M. 33.40	A	
Skip Control	M-N. 31.32	A	
Skip D	J-K. 31.40	A	
Skip X	L. 31.40	A	
Channel Entry (Spec Prog On)	AV. 53.68	A	
Column Split 0.9	AE. 41.52	AS	
Column Split 11.12	AF. 41.52	AS	
Comparing Entry	C.F. 1.30	A	
Co-selector P.U.	A.B. 53.80, C.D. 73.76	AS	
Co-selector (Transferred)		AS	16
Counter Control Plus-Minus	S-T. 53.80, U-V. 53.80	A	17
Counter Controlled Print	AZ.BB. 1.40	A	18
Counter Entry	AG.AN. 53.80	A	
Counter Exit	AR.AY. 1.42	A	
Counter Readout & Readout Reset	AL.AO. 53.80	A	
Couple Control (Upper)	AA. 53.80	A	
Digit Selector C	A. 41.52	A	
Direct Entry or Reset	W-X. 53.80	A	19
Extra Space	K. 76.77	A	
Filter Entry	BK. 15.34	A	
First Card Selectors (Trans)	M-O. 75.77	CM	10
Head D or Head D Suppr	D. 35.36, F. 35.36	A	
Head X or Head X Suppr.	C. 35.36, E. 35.36	A	
MLR-Lines 1, 2, 3 (Progressive Sel. Trans)	J-K. 1.30	A	13

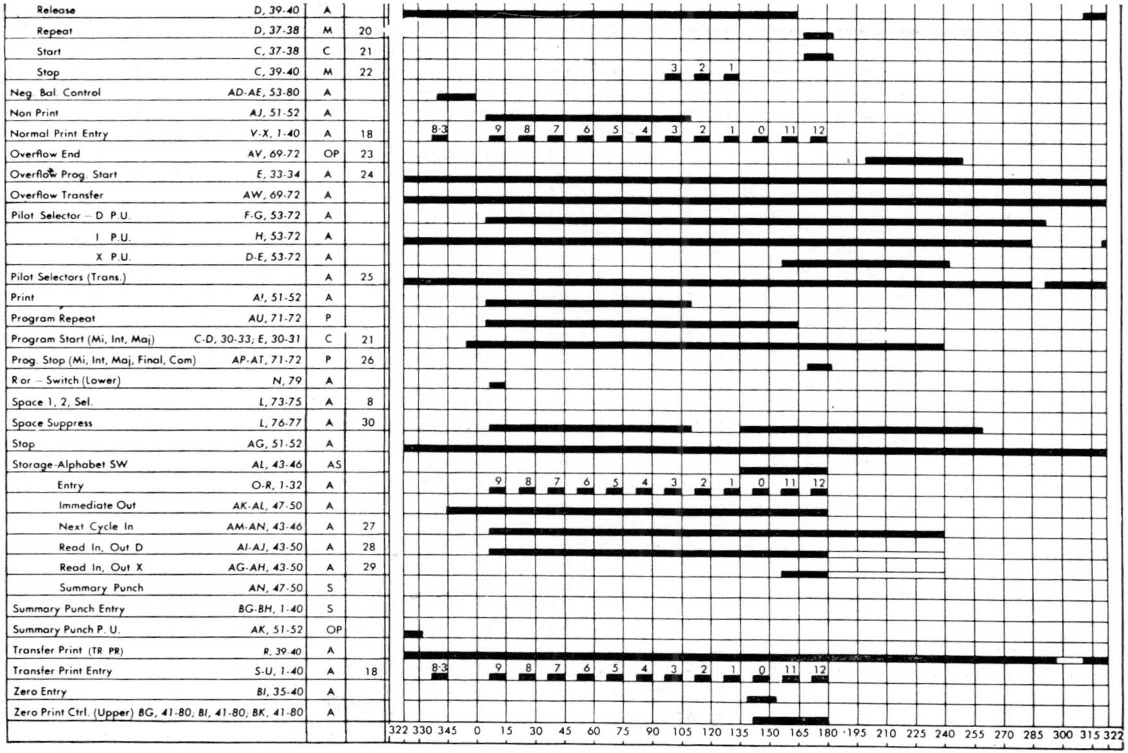

Fig. 6.20b. 407 timing chart: entries. *(Reprinted by permission from "IBM 407 Accounting Machine—Manual of Operation," 22-5765-7, copyright 1950 in original notice by International Business Machines Corporation.)*

These charts indicate when during a cycle an impulse or a sequence of impulses are emitted from exit hubs, and when during a cycle an impulse will be accepted by an entry hub. Each line on a chart is associated with a particular hub.[1] We shall not discuss all the hubs on the charts, but several will be familiar from earlier discussions.[2]

The functions of most of the hubs identified as *Read Entries* in Fig. 6.19 have been discussed; e.g., ALPHA IN, ALPHA FIRST READ, STORAGE ENTRY, DIGIT SELECTOR COMMON, etc. Among the hubs identified as *Read Exits* that have been discussed are CAI, READ (CARD) A, B, C, FIRST READ, and COUPLE EXIT (IPU of a pilot selector). It can be observed from the chart that the ALPHA IN hub can be impulsed from either the CAI, the COUPLE EXIT, or the READ HOLD hub; and that the PILOT SELECTOR DPU hub and the COSELECTOR PICKUP hub can be impulsed from any EXIT hub.

Impulses emitted from the READ hubs correspond to the punches sensed at the read brushes, and impulses emitted from the STORAGE EXIT hubs correspond to the codes in the output synchronizer registers. As indicated earlier, the COUPLE EXIT hub emits an impulse only if either the corresponding XPU or DPU hub was impulsed on the preceding read cycle. The remaining automatic Read Exit impulses are emitted each read cycle. Similarly, a CONTROL INFORMATION impulse is conditionally emitted, but the remaining automatic Punch Exit impulses are emitted each punch cycle.

Several EXIT and ENTRY hubs on the 407 timing chart (Fig. 6.20) will be recognized from the preceding discussions, e.g., CARD CYCLES, CARD (FIRST and SECOND) READING IMPULSES, COMPARING EXIT, COUNTER (ACCUMULATOR) EXIT, STORAGE EXIT, COMPARING ENTRY, COSELECTOR PICKUP, COUNTER (ACCUMULATOR) CONTROL PLUS-MINUS, COUNTER (ACCUMULATOR) ENTRY, COUNTER (ACCUMULATOR) READ OUT and READ OUT RESET, DIGIT SELECTOR COMMON, NORMAL PRINT ENTRY, PILOT SELECTOR, STORAGE ENTRY, etc.

In reviewing the list of hubs, it is noted that certain hubs transmit primarily data that are to be processed while others transmit impulses that are used almost exclusively to control machine operations. As would be expected, there are many more of the latter kind on the 407 board than on the 533 board.

Two sets of hubs that are of particular interest are the PROGRAM START entry (MI, INT, MAJ) hubs and the PROGRAM (exit) hubs (see

---

[1] There may be several hubs that perform identical functions, e.g., the READ hubs.

[2] The reader should refer to the manufacturer's operating manual for detailed information about a given machine.

Fig. 6.21). The functions of these hubs will be discussed in the next section.

6.12 Program Cycles. If one of the three PROGRAM START hubs (MI, INT, or MAJ) on the 407 panel is impulsed during a read cycle, e.g., by a COMPARING EXIT impulse, card reading is halted at the completion of the cycle and one or more program cycles are executed before card reading is resumed automatically.

If the major (MAJ) PROGRAM START hub is impulsed in a read cycle, three program cycles will intervene before card cycles are resumed automatically. In the first program cycle a PROGRAM (exit) impulse will be emitted from each STEP-1 hub on the panel (see Fig. 6.21). In the second program cycle a program impulse is emitted from each of the STEP-2 hubs. In the third program cycle a program impulse is emitted from each of the STEP-3 hubs. These impulses can be used to control machine functions, e.g., read-out of accumulators or storage registers, add one accumulator to or subtract one accumulator from another, etc.

If the intermediate (INT) PROGRAM hub is impulsed, two program cycles intervene automatically between card cycles with the corresponding emission of impulses from STEP-1 and STEP-2 hubs. If the minor (MI) PROGRAM hub is impulsed, a single program cycle intervenes automatically between card cycles and impulses are emitted from the STEP-1 hubs.

```
Program start
    MI    O
    INT   O
    MAJ   O

Program (exit)
  Step 1   O
  Step 2   O
  Step 3   O
```

FIG. 6.21. 407 PROGRAM START and PROGRAM (exit) hubs.

The principal differences between a card cycle and a program cycle are that card reading is suspended and program impulses are emitted. Many of the hubs on the panel behave the same in either cycle. There are notes on the timing chart (Fig. 6.20) that indicate the cycles during which each hub is active. The timing is the same in the 407 for both read and program cycles.

The IBM 602 and 604 Calculating Punches have program cycles and punch cycles as well as read cycles. These machines can perform multiplication and division as well as addition and subtraction.

6.13 Multiplication and Division. The multiplication and division operations have been discussed for the 650. The plug-board-controlled 602 and 604 Calculating Punches can also be used to perform multiplication, division, addition, and subtraction.

To perform a multiplication in the 602, the multiplier must be stored in a special register where it can be analyzed digit by digit. The multiplicand must be stored in either a storage or an accumulator register from which it can be repeatedly copied. The EXIT hubs from the counter (or storage) register containing the multiplicand are wired to the accumulator in which the product will be generated. A PROGRAM EXIT hub is wired in parallel to the READ OUT hub of the register containing the multiplicand, to the PLUS CONTROL hub of the accumulator in which the product will be generated, and to the MULTIPLY CONTROL hub. When the PROGRAM EXIT hub emits an impulse, an automatic multiplication operation is initiated and the product is generated by successive additions as in the 650.

Automatic division is performed in an analogous manner. The hubs for controlling such functions will be described in Sec. 6.19.

PUNCHED-CARD EQUIPMENTS

In the remaining sections we shall discuss basic punched-card equipments that include various combinations of the components discussed in the preceding sections. It is intended that from these discussions, the reader will be able to make inferences about the potential applicability of an equipment to the solution of a given data-processing problem or a portion thereof. It is assumed that the reader will study the operating manual of the particular equipment chosen before attempting to work out the details of the solution of his particular problem.

6.14 The Punched-card Sorter. A punched-card sorter provides a card feed, a single movable brush for sensing punches in an arbitrarily selected card column, and a set of chute blades to guide each card to one of 13 card stackers. The stacker to which a card is guided is determined by the first punch sensed in the column passing under the brush.

The following logic for arranging a deck of cards in ascending sequence on a numeric index can be adapted to the punched-card sorter. First, sort the deck on the units position of the index number as follows:

1. Take the card from the front of the deck.
2. Observe the digit in the specified column.
3. Place the card, face down and nine edge to the left, in the stacker for that digit.
4. Is the deck exhausted?
    a. If not, return to step 1.
    b. If so, go to step 5.
5. Reassemble the deck by collecting the cards from the stackers as follows: remove cards from stacker 0 face down, remove cards from stacker 1 face down and place on those from stacker 0, . . . , remove cards from stacker 9 face down and place on those from

stacker 8.   The bottom card from stacker 0 is now the first card in the deck.

6. Has the deck been sorted on all digit positions in the index?

    a. If not, select the column containing the next higher digit position and return to step 1.

    b. If so, sorting is finished and the cards are in ascending sequence.

The procedure described above corresponds to feeding cards face down and nine edge leading into the sorter of Fig. 6.16, with the read brush set to sense punches in the column being sorted.

If the cards are to be arranged in descending sequence on the index, we need only reverse the order in which cards are removed from the stacker in step 5.   If the index is an alphanumeric punched-card code, then the procedure is modified so that two passes through the deck are made for each column that may contain an alphabetic character.   In the first pass, the cards are sorted on the digit punches 0 through 9. On the second pass they are sorted on zone punches 0, 11, and 12 only. The second pass can be accomplished in the sorter of Fig. 6.16 by means of a switch that suppresses selection on digits 9 through 1 or by feeding the deck face up and twelve edge leading.   If the latter procedure is used, the stacking procedure after the second pass must be modified appropriately.

6.15   The Reproducing Punch.   A reproducing punch is schematically illustrated in Fig. 6.22.   It has two card feeds that will be referred

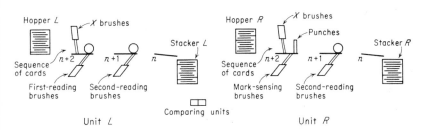

Fig. 6.22. Schematic of a reproducing punch.

to as unit *L* (left) and unit *R* (right).[1]   Unit *L* has two sets of read brushes.   Unit *R* has a set of punches in place of the first-reading brushes, and it has a set of second-reading brushes.   The reproducing punch also has a set of comparing units and one or more gang switches.

If the programmer wished to copy (reproduce) the punches from a

---

[1] The IBM terminology is different from that used here.   For example, units *L* and *R* are referred to as read and punch units, respectively.   The terminology used here is consistent with that of the preceding sections.

selected card column (say M_1) of each card from hopper L into a specified card column (say M_2) of each corresponding card from hopper R, he would wire the plug board so that first-reading brush M_1 of unit L controls punch M_2 of unit R.   The two feeds are synchronized so that the nth card from hopper L passes the first-reading brushes as the nth card from hopper R passes the punch dies.

If the programmer wished to compare the punches in column M_1 of each card from hopper L with the punches in column M_2 of the corresponding card from hopper R, he would wire second-reading brush M_1 of unit L and second-reading brush M_2 of unit R into a mating pair of COMPARING ENTRY hubs.   If the punches in the compared columns are not identical, a comparing exit impulse (see Sec. 6.7) automatically releases a latch that identifies the unit that emitted the impulse and causes card feeding to stop at the end of the cycle in which the impulse was emitted.

If the programmer wished to copy (gang punch) a specified set of punches into column M_2 of each card in the deck, he would wire the plug board so that second-reading brush M_2 of unit R would control punch M_2 (in unit R).   Thus the punches sensed in column M_2 of the nth card are copied into column M_2 of the succeeding card.   The desired set of punches would be key-punched into the first card of the deck.

Assuming that cards are fed with the twelve edge leading, the X brushes sense 11 punches only.   An impulse from an X brush is emitted early in the read cycle and can be used to control a COSELECTOR for the purpose of varying the paths of impulses.

A mark-sensing brush in unit R can sense marks on a card provided that they are made at an appropriate place on the card and that they are made with an ink or lead that will conduct current.   A mark-sensing brush may be externally wired to control any punch in unit R. Thus appropriate marks on a card may be translated automatically to corresponding punches in a specified column of that same card.

6.16 The Collator.   A collator is schematically illustrated in Fig. 6.23.   It has two feeds—a primary and a secondary.   The primary feed has two sets of reading brushes while the secondary feed has only one set of reading brushes.   The collator has two comparing units, identified as A and B.   Each comparing unit has two registers, each with 16 positions.   The collator has four card stackers.   A card from the primary feed will enter stacker 2 unless it is switched to stacker 1. A card from the secondary feed will enter stacker 2 unless it is switched to either stacker 3 or 4.

The principal control hubs for the collator of Fig. 6.23 are shown in

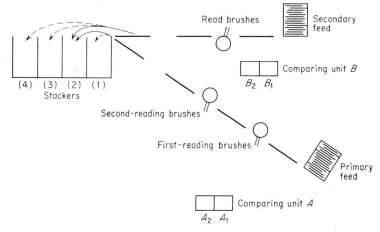

FIG. 6.23. Schematic of a collator.

Fig. 6.24.[1] The timing cycle of Fig. 6.15 applies to the collator. The CONTROL IMPULSE hub emits an impulse at delay time (see Fig. 6.15) in each cycle.   The COMPARING EXIT hubs emit at the same time, but only in a cycle in which a comparison is made and the outcome is as indicated.   In the remainder of this section the term *control impulse* will apply to an emission from any of the EXIT hubs shown.   These impulses are emitted at the end of a cycle and are used to control functions in the following cycle.

When the PRIMARY FEED hub or the SECONDARY FEED hub receives a control impulse, the cards in the respective feed advance in the following cycle.   When the PRIMARY EJECT hub receives a control impulse, the leading card in the primary feed is moved to a stacker, but the remaining cards in that feed do not advance.

[1] The collator illustrated here approximates the IBM 77 Collator.

Entry hubs	Exit hubs
O Primary feed	O Control impulse
O Primary eject	Comparing exits
O Secondary feed	
O Error stop	O $A_2 > A_1$
Stacker selection	O $A_2 = A_1$
O Primary-to-1	O $A_2 < A_1$
O Secondary-to-3	O $B_2 > B_1$
O Secondary-to-4	O $B_2 = B_1$
Restore control	O $B_2 < B_1$
O Register A_1	
O Register A_2	
O Register B_1	
O Register B_2	
Compare control	
O Unit A	
O Unit B	
Selector	
O Pickup	
O T	
O N	
O C	
Cycle delay selector	
O Pickup	
O T	
O N	
O C	
O Release	

FIG. 6.24. Collator control hubs.

When the PRIMARY-TO-1 hub receives a control impulse, the path from the primary feed is switched during the following cycle to lead to stacker 1 instead of to stacker 2.   When the SECONDARY-TO-3 or the SECONDARY-TO-4 hub receives a control impulse, the path from the secondary feed is switched to lead to the appropriate stacker during the following cycle.   If both hubs are impulsed, simultaneously, the switching results in a path leading to stacker 4.

If a control hub RESTORE register A_1, A_2, B_1, or B_2 receives a control impulse, the corresponding register is cleared and new data are copied into the register during the next cycle.   Data are normally channeled to a storage register from one of the three sets of reading brushes (see Fig. 6.23); Fig. 6.24 does not show either the READ hubs or the STORAGE ENTRY hubs.   Once data are copied into a register, they remain there until the associated RESTORE control hub is impulsed.

If a control hub COMPARE unit A or unit B receives a control impulse, the numbers in the two registers—e.g., A_1 and A_2—of the corresponding unit are compared in the following cycle and the outcome of the comparison is indicated by a control impulse emitted from the appropriate COMPARING EXIT hub, e.g., $A_2 < A_1$, $A_2 = A_1$, or $A_2 > A_1$.   The contents of a register are not destroyed by a comparison.   Furthermore, a register can be involved in a comparison in the same cycle that data are being copied into that register.

If a SELECTOR PICKUP hub receives a control impulse, the associated switch is transferred immediately (i.e., hub C is connected to hub T) and remains transferred only as long as the PICKUP hub is continuously impulsed.

If a CYCLE DELAY SELECTOR PICKUP hub receives a control impulse, the associated switch transfers at the beginning of the next cycle.   It latches on transfer and remains latched until it is released.   If the RELEASE hub receives a control impulse, the associated switch will be released (i.e., returned to its normal position) at the end of the next cycle.   If the CYCLE DELAY switch is to be transferred for a single cycle, the PICKUP hub and the RELEASE hub should be impulsed simultaneously.

The collator described above can be wired to select all cards with a specified index number from a deck of cards arranged in random order on the index number.   It can be used to check whether or not a deck of cards is arranged in ascending (descending) sequence on an index number and, if desired, to select from the deck all cards that are out of sequence.   It can be used to merge (collate) two decks that are each arranged in ascending (descending) sequence on a numeric index into a single deck that is arranged in ascending (descending) sequence on the index.

The following procedure could be used to check a deck to see if it is in descending order on an index number. It is suggested that the reader apply this procedure to the sequence 5, 2, 3, 4, 1.

1. Take a card from a deck and record its index number, say in column A_2.
2. Take the next card from the deck and record its index number in column A_1.
3. Compare the last number in column A_1 with the last number in column A_2.

   a. If $A_2 \geq A_1$, the two adjacent cards are in descending sequence. Draw a line through the last entry in each column. Place the card whose index number was in column A_2 face down in stack 2, which contains those cards that are in descending sequence. Replace the other card on top of the deck. Now return to step 1.

   b. If $A_2 < A_1$, the second card is out of sequence with respect to the first. Draw a line through the last entry in A_1. Place the card whose index number remains in column A_2 face down in stack 2. Place the card whose index number was in column A_1 face down in stack 1, which contains those cards that are out of sequence. Now return to step 2.

The collator can perform this function if its plug board is wired properly. To simplify the discussion, we will ignore the wiring required to initialize the registers when card reading is started. We would use the primary feed, because two readings of each card are required. It is suggested that the reader simulate the following wiring on a panel like that in Fig. 6.24.

The set of first-reading brushes that sense the card columns containing the index number would be wired to storage register A_1, and the corresponding set of second-reading brushes would be wired to storage register A_2 so that the index numbers in the two registers are matched position by position.

The CONTROL IMPULSE hub would be wired to the COMPARE UNIT A control hub, to the PRIMARY FEED hub, and to the RESTORE control hub of register A_1, because each of these operations is to be performed each cycle regardless of the outcome of the comparison.

The COMPARING EXIT hubs $A_2 > A_1$ and $A_2 = A_1$ would be wired to the RESTORE control hub of register A_2, because the index number

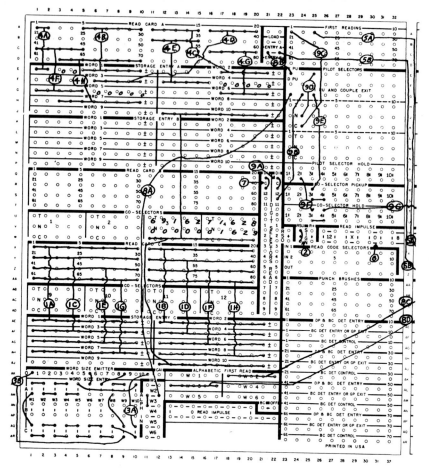

Fig. 6.25. Wiring example, 533 plug

in this register is to be erased only if the two adjacent cards are in descending sequence.

The COMPARING EXIT hub $A_2 < A_1$ would be wired to the PICKUP hub and the RELEASE hub of a cycle delay selector. The CONTROL IMPULSE hub would be wired to the C hub of the cycle delay selector and the T hub would be wired to the PRIMARY-TO-1 hub. This would cause the card whose index number was just in register A_1 to be diverted to stacker 1 after it passed the second-reading brushes, i.e., after a cycle delay. Since storage register A_2 is not reset in a cycle in which A_2 is less than A_1, cards would be successively diverted to stacker 1 until a card with an index number less than or equal to the

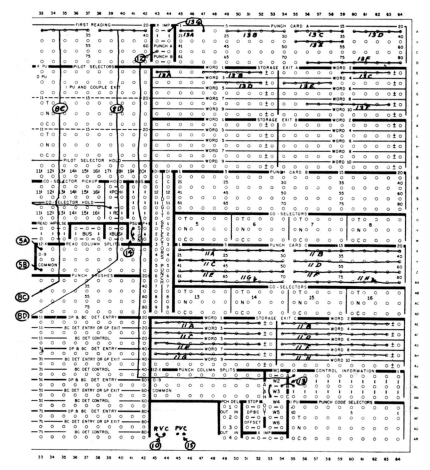

board. (*Form courtesy of IBM.*)

number in A_2 passed the first-reading brushes.   The index number of such a card would be copied into register A_2 as it passed the second-reading brushes, and the card itself would be routed to stacker 2 where it would rest face down on top of the one whose index number was just erased from register A_2.

After the complete deck had been sequence-checked, those cards that were diverted to stacker 1 could be arranged in descending sequence on the sorter.   Then the two decks could be collated (in descending sequence) by the following procedure.   We shall refer to the decks as B_1 and B_2.   It is suggested that the reader apply this procedure to the sequences $B_1 = 5, 2, 1$ and $B_2 = 4, 3$.

1. Take a card from deck B_1 and write its index number in a column headed B_1. Take a card from deck B_2 and write its index number in a column headed B_2.
2. Compare the last number in column B_1 with the last number in column B_2.
   a. If $B_2 > B_1$, go to step 3.
   b. If $B_2 = B_1$, go to step 3.
   c. If $B_2 < B_1$, go to step 4.
3. Draw a line though the last number in column B_2 and place the corresponding card face down in the stacker 2, which contains the collated deck. Take another card from deck B_2, write its index number in column B_2, and then return to step 2.
4. Substitute B_1 for B_2; otherwise, step 4 is identical to step 3.

This procedure can be readily adapted to the collator as follows. Use the primary feed for deck B_1 and the secondary feed for deck B_2. Wire the index number to storage register B_1 from the second-reading brushes of the primary feed and to storage register B_2 from the read brushes of the secondary feed.

Wire the CONTROL IMPULSE hub to the COMPARE UNIT B control hub. Wire the COMPARING EXIT hubs $B_2 > B_1$ and $B_2 = B_1$ to the SECONDARY FEED hub and to the RESTORE REGISTER B_2 control hub. Wire the COMPARING EXIT hub $B_2 < B_1$ to the PRIMARY FEED hub and to the RESTORE REGISTER B_1 control hub.

These examples illustrate the manner in which the comparing units can be used to selectively control the two feeds and to switch the paths between the card feeds and the stackers.

6.17 The 533 Read-Punch Unit. As has been indicated earlier, the functions of the 533 unit are reading data into the 650 memory from punched cards and copying data from memory into punched cards. Figure 6.25 shows a 533 plug board wired to satisfy the input and output requirements of the data-processing problem discussed in Chap. 4. An item-by-item discussion of this wiring will call attention to most of the components of the 533. Many of the components will be recognized from discussions in earlier sections. The purpose of some components, not discussed previously, will be briefly described. A few rather specialized components will not be mentioned.[1]

Item 1.   The eight sets of wires connecting READ CARD hubs to STORAGE ENTRY hubs, 10 wires to each set, provide for reading each card 80-80 unless entry A is selected. Item 1A

[1] The reader is referred to the "IBM 650 Manual of Operation" for a detailed discussion of 533 wiring.

implies that 10 wires are used to channel data from card columns 1 to 10 to input synchronizer register 1, positions 10 to 1, respectively.

Item 2.   This wire activates the RSU unit which causes the internal wires to the sign position and the units position of each input register to be connected. Thus the sign, plus or minus, of a register is determined by the absence or presence of an 11 impulse from the wire to position 1 of that register, i.e., the sign is read from the units position.

Item 3.   The WORD SIZE EMITTER and the WORD SIZE ENTRY hubs can be used to cause automatic emission of a zero impulse into unwired high-order positions of an input synchronizer register. The WORD SIZE EMITTER hub (0, 1, 2, . . . , 10) to be connected to an input synchronizer register (W_1, W_2, . . . , W_{10} of entry A, B, and C) WORD SIZE ENTRY hub is determined by the number of positions wired in that register. If WORD SIZE EMITTER hub S is wired to a WORD SIZE ENTRY hub X, then input must be wired to STORAGE ENTRY hubs 1, 2, . . . , S of register X, and zeros will be automatically entered in positions $S + 1$, $S + 2$, . . . , 10. The automatic emission of zero impulses to positions 1, 2, . . . , S is discussed in item 6.

Item 4.   STORAGE ENTRY A is used to read the data cards for the data-processing problem. The zeros in the low-order positions of words 4 and 5 indicate that these hubs are to be wired to a READ IMPULSE 0 hub (see item 6).

Item 5.   ENTRY A is selected through a column split by the presence of a 12 or an 11 punch in card column 3.

Item 6.   The READ IMPULSE hubs (12, X, 0, 8, 9) emit the indicated impulses each read cycle. The zero (0) hubs are connected to positions 1 to 5 of words 4 and 5 in entry A and to positions 7 and 8 of word 1, entry A.

Item 7.   The DI hub emits each impulse 12, 11, 0, 1, . . . , 9 in each read cycle. These impulses are fed into the C (COMMON) hub of the digit selector, thereby converting it to a digit emitter. Digit impulses from the digit emitter are wired, as indicated by the numbers by the hubs, to the T and N hubs of the adjacent coselectors. This rather specialized wiring satisfies a requirement of the Program Test Supervisory Routine.

Item 8.   Registers 2 and 3 of entry A are conditioned to accept alphanumeric input by wires 8A and B. Wires 8C and D

transmit zone impulses to the ALPHABETIC FIRST READ hubs from FIRST READING hubs.

Item 9. This DI hub emits half-time impulses, i.e., $12\frac{1}{2}$, $11\frac{1}{2}$, $\frac{1}{2}$, $1\frac{1}{2}$, . . . , $9\frac{1}{2}$. The $12\frac{1}{2}$ impulse is after 12 time but before 11 time in the read cycle. The wiring here is used to transfer coselectors 3 and 4. If a 12 punch is sensed in column 1 at first reading, the coselectors are transferred at the beginning of the next read cycle, i.e., while the card that contains the 12 punch is passing the second-reading brushes. This wiring is required by the Program Test Supervisory Routine.

Item 10. When the RVC (read validity check) hubs are wired, the validity check between the input synchronizer and storage entry registers is inactivated.

Item 11. The sets of wires connecting the STORAGE EXIT hubs to the PUNCH CARD hubs provide for punching a card 80-80 unless punch A is selected. The two sets of hubs that are to be connected pairwise, left to right, are identified by a common code, e.g., $11A$.

Item 12. A CONTROL INFORMATION impulse is used to select PUNCH A.

Item 13. This wiring is required to punch the statement cards for the data-processing problems. The CONTROL INFORMATION hub is wired to the ALPHA OUT hubs for words 2 and 3. An 11 impulse is wired to column 3.

Item 14. The PSU (punch sign from units position) hubs are analogous to the RSU hubs. The sign impulses from an output synchronizer register are transmitted through the units position hub.

Item 15. If the PVC (punch validity check) hubs are wired, the validity check point between the output synchronizer registers and the punch unit are inactivated.

6.18 The Punched-card Accounting Machine. The accounting machine processes punched cards. Its principal functions are card reading; accumulating totals; printing or listing data from cards, accumulators, or storage units; and control of a summary (reproducing) punch for punching data emitted from accumulators or storage registers.

There are many hubs on the plug board of a punched-card accounting machine, and we shall not attempt to discuss them in detail. Many of them will be recognized from the discussions in the preceding sections. In this section, we shall discuss the plug-board wiring of the

407 illustrated in Fig. 6.26.   This 407 plug board can be used to prepare the statement cards for the data-processing problem of Chap. 4 if
the following restrictions are satisfied:

1. The input file has been sorted on customer number so that all the
   cards for each customer are grouped together.
2. The first card in each customer group is a previous-balance card,
   coded 0 in column 1, from a file maintained in the data-processing
   center.   This file would be a duplicate (except for the card code) of
   the file of statement cards prepared and mailed in the previous
   accounting period.
3. No customer's balance will exceed seven digit positions.   This
   restriction could be eliminated by coupling two accumulators.

The wiring shown in Fig. 6.26 will be related to the items in the
following discussion by the item numbers.   To further facilitate the
discussion, the names of the data associated with a set of hubs for this
particular problem are identified on the diagram.

Item 1.   Card codes are distinguished at first reading by wiring FIRST
            READING hub 1 to the COMMON (C) hub of a digit selector.
            Impulses emitted from the digit hubs are used for control
            purposes.
Item 2.   The card code, the customer's name, and the customer
            number are wired to STORAGE ENTRY and to PRINT ENTRY
            hubs from the SECOND-READING hubs.   The STORAGE IN hubs
            (2A) are impulsed only when a card with code 0 is at first
            reading, and the STORAGE ENTRY hubs are active during the
            following read cycle only.   Storage units B and D are condi-
            tioned (2B) to store alphanumeric data.   Similarly, wiring
            the LIST hub to OFF (2C) inactivates the PRINT ENTRY hubs
            except for the first card of a group and for program cycles.
Item 3.   Either the previous balance or the charge (or credit) is wired
            from SECOND READING hubs to the COUNTER (ACCUMULATOR)
            ENTRY hubs via the TRANSFERRED (T) or NORMAL (N) hubs,
            respectively, of coselectors.
Item 4.   The coselectors are in the transferred state when a
            previous-balance card is passing the second-reading brushes.
            An impulse from the zero hub of the DIGIT SELECTOR activates
            the PILOT SELECTOR D PICKUP, and the resulting COUPLE EXIT
            impulse activates the COSELECTOR PICKUPS at the beginning
            of the next cycle; this causes them to transfer immediately
            and remain transferred for that cycle.

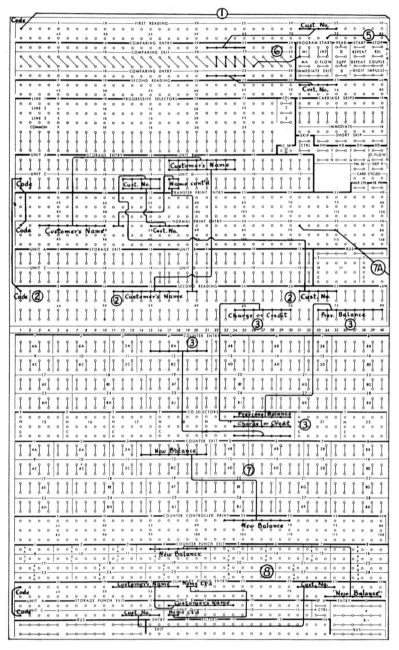

Fig. 6.26. 407 wiring example, state-

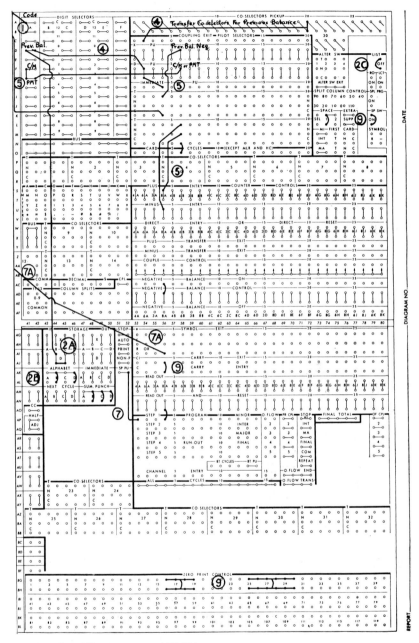

ment cards. (*Form courtesy of IBM.*)

Item 5. The counter is controlled to add if the number at the counter entry is either a charge or a positive previous balance, and it is controlled to subtract if that number is a credit, a payment, or a negative previous balance. The latter conditions are identified respectively by a code 2, a code 3, or a code 0 together with an 11 punch in column 74.[1] The PLUS and MINUS CONTROL hubs of counter 8A are connected to a CARD CYCLES hub via the NORMAL (N) and TRANSFERRED (T) hubs, respectively, of a PILOT SELECTOR. The DPU hub of the PILOT SELECTOR is connected to the digit 2 and 3 hubs of the DIGIT SELECTOR. The XPU hub of the PILOT SELECTOR is connected to column 74 after 0 time in any cycle that a code 0 card is passing the first-reading brushes. Note that 11 time follows 0 time in the 407 cycle.

Item 6. The customer number is wired from FIRST READING hubs and from SECOND READING hubs to matching sets of COMPARING ENTRY hubs. The five COMPARING EXIT hubs are linked together in a chain leading to the MINOR (MI) PROGRAM START hub. A COMPARING EXIT impulse initiates a minor program start when the last card in a group is passing the second-reading brushes and the first card in the succeeding group is passing the first-reading brushes. At the end of that cycle, card reading is suspended and a program cycle intervenes before card reading is resumed.

Item 7. During the program cycle, the counter is read out and reset, the new balance is printed, storage is read out, and a summary punch cycle is initiated. A PROGRAM STEP 1 hub is wired to the READ OUT AND RESET hub of counter 8A, another is wired to the SPPU (summary punch pickup) hub, and storage units B, C, and D are wired to read out on each summary punch cycle. The new balance is wired to COUNTER CONTROLLED PRINT hubs from counter 8A EXIT hubs. The symbol that is automatically emitted when the counter contains a negative balance is wired (7A) to normal print entry.

Item 8. In the summary punch operation, the accounting machine controls a reproducing punch to which it is connected by cable. Impulses from storage units and counters in the

[1] In punched-card accounting procedures, a negative sign is normally indicated by an 11 punch over the high-order position of a number. A positive sign is indicated by the absence of the 11 punch. This wiring requires that a positive sign be indicated by the absence of a 12 punch as well as an 11 punch.

accounting machine are transmitted via the cable to control the punch unit in the reproducing punch.   The card code, the customer's name, and his number are wired from STORAGE PUNCH EXIT hubs to the appropriate SUMMARY PUNCH ENTRY hubs.   The new balance is wired from COUNTER PUNCH EXIT hubs.

Item 9.   The CARRY EXIT hub is wired to the CARRY ENTRY hub for counter 8A.   Single spacing of the form on which the results are printed is specified by wiring a SPACE control hub to the 1 hub.   The SPSW (summary punch switch) is wired to ON to permit summary punching when the SPPU hub is impulsed.   Finally, the ZERO PRINT CONTROL hubs are wired to suppress high-order zeros in numeric fields.

The card cycle is the automatic cycle in the punched-card accounting machine.   Once card reading is started, it continues automatically unless it is interrupted by a program start, an error condition, or by emptying the read hopper.   When card reading is interrupted for program cycles, it is automatically resumed after the specified number of program cycles have intervened.

6.19   The Calculating Punch.[1]   The calculating punch has a read unit, a punch unit, storage registers, accumulators, automatic multiplication, and automatic division.   It may be controlled by plug-board wiring to read a card, perform a sequence of arithmetic and data-transmission operations, and then punch the results into the same card or into subsequent cards.

The following data-transmission operations can be performed, with the paths for impulses being provided in each case by external plug-board wiring.   A number can be copied into a storage register from the read unit, from an accumulator, or from another storage unit.   A number can be added into an accumulator from the read unit, from a storage register, or from another accumulator.   A number can be punched from specific storage registers.   A product or a quotient can be generated in an accumulator.

The manner in which a calculating punch is controlled in the execution of a sequence of operations is in some respects analogous to that of a 650.   In the latter machine, successive instruction cycles are executed automatically, with the operation performed in successive instruction cycles determined by a sequence of instructions stored in memory.   In the calculating punch, a sequence of program steps

[1] The discussion in this section is based on the fundamental components of the IBM 602 Calculating Punch.

(cycles) is initiated automatically after a read operation, and the sequence of operations performed is determined by plug-board wiring. After each program step $(1, 2, 3, \ldots, K)$, the machine proceeds automatically to the next step unless the sequence is interrupted by a read operation or by an error condition. The program steps correspond to a sequence of control impulses emitted from the successive PROGRAM STEP hubs $(1, 2, 3, \ldots, K)$ illustrated in Fig. 6.27. The operations performed in a given program step are determined by the control hubs (see Fig. 6.27) to which that PROGRAM STEP hub is wired.

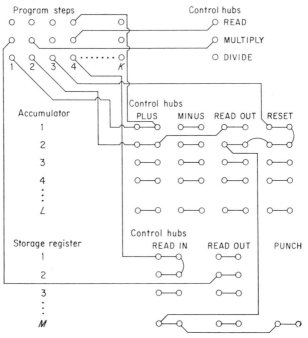

FIG. 6.27. Calculating punch control hubs wired to calculate $A(B + C)$.

The program in Table 6.1 indicates how the calculating punch of Fig. 6.27 would be externally wired to calculate $A(B + C)$ and punch the result in the card from which A, B, and C were read. The first read operation is manually executed, so successive read operations will be executed at the last program step. Assume that A is read into storage unit 1, B into accumulator 1, and C into storage unit 2; that the sum $B + C$ is generated in accumulator 1; and that the product $A(B + C)$ is generated in accumulator 2 and then transferred to storage register M for punching. After each read, the cycle automatically restarts at program step 1.

Table 6.1

| Program step | Operation | Accumulator | | Storage unit | | |
		1	2	1	2	M
First read	Read	B		A	C	
1	$B + C$	$+$			Read out	
Result		$B + C$		A	C	
2	$A(B + C)$	Read out	$+$			
Result		$B + C$	$A(B + C)$	A	C	
3	$A(B + C) \to M$ and punch	Reset	Read out and reset			Read in
Result				A	C	$A(B + C)$
4	Read	B		A	C	

The storage capacity of a calculating punch is much less than that of the 650, and the number of different program steps that can be executed between read operations is much less. It is in general a much slower machine than the computer; for example, it may process from 10 to 100 cards per minute.[1] However, a calculating punch costs only a fraction of what a computer would, so it can be a very economical machine for certain applications.

6.20   The Statistical Sorter and/or Tallier.[2]   The *statistical sorter* (and/or tallier) to be discussed in this section resembles the sorter discussed in Sec. 6.14 to the extent that it has 13 stackers and chute blades to guide a card to a selected stacker.   In addition, the statistical sorter has a full set (80) of first-reading brushes, a full set of second-reading brushes, a set of *tally counters,* an accumulator, and a set of type bars for printing totals from the tally counters and the accumulator.

Except for card feeding, which is automatic, the operation of the statistical sorter is controlled by plug-board wiring (see Fig. 6.28). A set of 13 STACKER CONTROL hubs controls the switching of the chute blades.   Each tally counter has a TALLY COUNTER ENTRY hub that controls the incrementing of that tally counter.   Control impulses are emitted each card cycle from the SORT and the TALLY IMPULSE EXIT hubs.   Sorting is effected by wiring a SORT IMPULSE hub via switches to a selected set of STACKER CONTROL hubs.   Tallying is effected by wiring a TALLY IMPULSE hub via switches to a selected set of TALLY COUNTER ENTRY hubs.

[1] The latter rate can be achieved by an electronic calculating punch.

[2] The discussion in this section is based on the fundamental components of the IBM 101 Electronic Statistical Machine.

There are three fundamental switching devices used in the statistical sorter presented here. Two of these, the SINGLE-COLUMN DISTRIBUTOR and the TWO-COLUMN DISTRIBUTOR, may be thought of as variations of the DIGIT SELECTOR discussed in Sec. 6.6. The third, the COMPARING SELECTOR, may be thought of as a variation of the COSELECTOR discussed in Sec. 6.6.

The hubs of a SINGLE-COLUMN DISTRIBUTOR are illustrated in Fig. 6.29. The PU (PICKUP) hub will normally be wired from a FIRST READING hub. In each card cycle, the pickup is energized by the first impulse that its hub receives in that cycle. The impulse causes

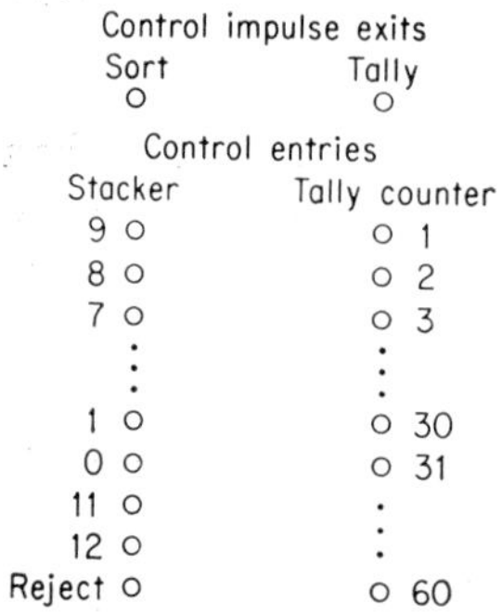

		Entry ○ PU ○	
Control impulse exits		Exits	
Sort	Tally	12 ○—○	
○	○	11 ○—○	
Control entries		0 ○—○	
Stacker	Tally counter	1 ○—○	
9 ○	○ 1	2 ○—○	
8 ○	○ 2	3 ○—○	
7 ○	○ 3	4 ○—○	
⋮	⋮	5 ○—○	
1 ○	○ 30	6 ○—○	
0 ○	○ 31	7 ○—○	
11 ○	⋮	8 ○—○	
12 ○	⋮	9 ○—○	
Reject ○	○ 60	Blank ○—○	

FIG. 6.28. Fundamental control hubs for a statistical sorter.

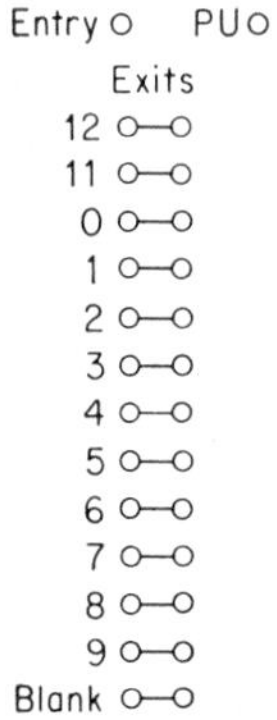

FIG. 6.29. Hubs of a single-column distributor.

the ENTRY hub of the distributor to be internally connected for the remainder of that cycle to the pair of EXIT hubs that are numbered to correspond to the impulse that energized the pickup. If the pickup is not energized in a card cycle, the ENTRY hub is internally connected to the pair of EXIT hubs identified by the word BLANK. The pickup ignores all but the first impulse received in a card cycle.

The ENTRY hub of a SINGLE-COLUMN DISTRIBUTOR is usually wired from either a SORT CONTROL IMPULSE hub or a TALLY CONTROL IMPULSE hub. This wiring may be direct or it may be through intervening switches.

The EXIT hubs are normally wired to STACKER CONTROL or TALLY COUNTER entries. This wiring may be direct or it may be through intervening switches. If a STACKER CONTROL hub receives a SORT CONTROL impulse during a card cycle, the card passing the first set of read brushes in that cycle is routed to the corresponding stacker. If a TALLY CONTROL hub receives a TALLY CONTROL impulse during a card cycle, the corresponding tally counter is incremented by 1 in that cycle.

The TWO-COLUMN DISTRIBUTOR (Fig. 6.30) is analogous to the SINGLE-COLUMN DISTRIBUTOR, but it has two PICKUP hubs, a units position pickup and a tens position pickup; and it has 100 EXIT hubs, numbered 00 through 99. The operation of the TWO-COLUMN DISTRIBUTOR is analogous to that of the SINGLE-COLUMN DISTRIBUTOR. In each card cycle, the ENTRY hub is internally connected to the EXIT hub that is numbered to correspond to the pair of impulses activating the pickups in that cycle. Thus, sort or tally control can be based on the combination of punches in two columns, i.e., a two-digit integer.

The COMPARING SELECTOR illustrated in Fig. 6.31 has two PICKUP hubs and four switch blades. This selector differs from a COSELECTOR

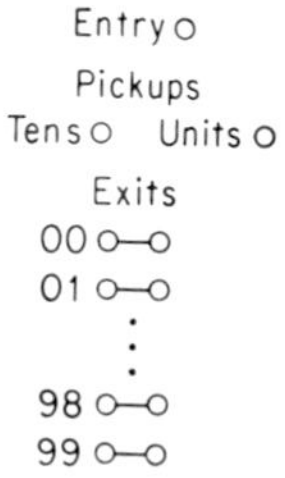

Entry o

Pickups

Tens o   Units o

Exits

00 o—o   Pickups o   o
01 o—o   Switch hubs
  :   T o   o   o   o
98 o—o   N o   o   o   o
99 o—o   C o   o   o   o

FIG. 6.30. Hubs of a two-column distributor. 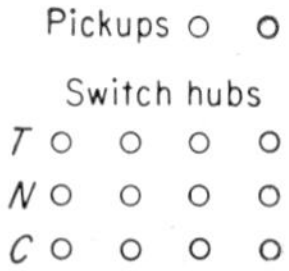   FIG. 6.31. COMPARING SELECTOR hubs.

only in the manner in which the pickups operate. If both PICKUP hubs are impulsed simultaneously in a read cycle, the switch is transferred immediately; i.e., each c hub is connected internally to its T hub for the balance of the read cycle. Otherwise, each c hub is connected internally to its N hub.

Either the column distributor or the comparing selector can be wired to select between two mutually exclusive sets of punches (e.g., between cards punched 1, 3, 5, 7, or 9 in column 23 and those punched 0, 2, 4, 6, or 8 in column 23) for stacker control or for tally counter control. Figure 6.32 shows a column distributor wired to control stacking of cards so that those containing an odd digit in column 23 are routed to stacker 1, those that contain an even digit in column 23 are routed to stacker 2, and those that contain neither an odd nor an even digit (e.g., 12, 11, or blank) are routed to stacker 3. If the c hub had been wired from a TALLY CONTROL IMPULSE hub and the outputs had been wired to TALLY COUNTER ENTRY hubs, the column distributor would have controlled counting of the sets of cards rather than sorting. The TWO-COLUMN DISTRIBUTOR could be wired in an analogous fashion to sort cards into sets or to count the number of cards in sets based on digit punches from two card columns.

Figure 6.33 illustrates how two COMPARING SELECTORS might be wired to control tally counters so that cards with an odd digit in

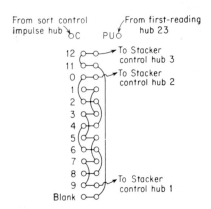

FIG. 6.32. Column distributor wired to sort cards as to odd digits or even digits in card column 23.

column 24 will be tallied in counter 1, those with an even digit in column 24 will be tallied in counter 2, and those with neither an odd nor an even digit in column 24 will be tallied in counter 3. It should be observed that the same selection could be performed by a DIGIT SELECTOR and a pair of PILOT SELECTORS.

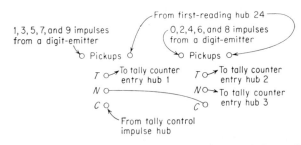

FIG. 6.33. COMPARING SELECTORS wired to selectively control three tally counters.

Each of the sets referred to in Figs. 6.32 and 6.33 was defined on an "or" basis. Each of the sets had several criteria for membership, but membership in a set was achieved by satisfaction of at least one of the several criteria of that set, i.e., the satisfaction of criterion A or criterion B or . . . or criterion K.

Two sets are said to be mutually exclusive if their respective membership criteria are defined so that membership in one set precludes the possibility of membership in another set.   The sets defined in Figs. 6.32 and 6.33 are mutually exclusive if we add a restriction that each card column shall contain not more than one punch.

Figure 6.34 illustrates how two COMPARING SELECTORS may be wired to select elements of a set that is defined on an "and" basis.   A set is defined on an "and" basis if each element of the set satisfies all the criteria for membership, i.e., criterion A and criterion B and . . . and criterion K.

In Fig. 6.34, the criteria for admission to the set are a 5 in column 16 and a 9 in column 63.   The members of the set are tallied in unit 1.

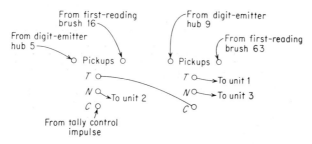

FIG. 6.34. COMPARING SELECTORS wired to select on an "and" basis.

The candidates that fail to satisfy the first criterion are tallied in unit 2, while those that satisfy the first but fail to satisfy the second criterion are tallied in unit 3.

The statistical sorter can be wired to sort cards into mutually exclusive sets whose membership requirements are based on combined "or" and "and" bases.   It can also be wired to tally the number of cards belonging to sets (not necessarily mutually exclusive) whose memberships are based on combined "or" and "and" bases.   The printing unit provides a means of recording the contents of the tally counters.

6.21   The Interpreter.   The interpreter has a set of reading brushes and a set of type bars.   The type bars are controlled by the read brushes to print on the card the characters that correspond to the impulses sensed by the reading brushes.   The relationship between type bars and read brushes is controlled by external plug-board wiring.

Neither the reproducing punch nor the 533 punch unit has type bars. Thus, printing on the statement cards for the data-processing problem would be accomplished on the interpreter before the cards were distributed to customers.

KEYBOARD-CONTROLLED EQUIPMENTS

There are two important punched-card equipments that are basically controlled by keyboards and do not have plug boards. Those are the keypunch and the verifier.

6.22 The Key Punch.[1] The key punch is used to punch alphanumeric data in cards, column by column from left to right. In many respects, the key punch resembles a typewriter. In particular, it is controlled by an operator through the depression of keys on the keyboard. Some automatic control of card positioning, column skipping, and upper and lower case shifting is provided by the program drum.

The principal components are a card hopper, a card feed, a punch-and-print station, a read station, a stacker, a keyboard, and a program drum. The physical location of these components on the IBM 26 Printing Card Punch is illustrated in Fig. 6.35.

The keyboard is illustrated in Fig. 6.36. The principal functions controlled by the keyboard will be discussed in this section. Depression of the FEED key causes a card to be moved from the card hopper to card station 1 (directly below the hopper) in the feed. Depression of the REG (register) key causes the card at station 1 to be registered at the punch station; i.e., the first column is aligned with the punches, and it causes the card at station 2 to be registered simultaneously at the read station.

Typing (key punching) of alphanumeric data can proceed once a card has been registered at the punch station. Depression of a character key will cause that character to be printed at the top of the column at the punch station and the appropriate code to be punched in that column. The cards at the read station and the punch station pass their respective stations synchronously, column by column, with successive depression of the character keys or the space bar. As with a typewriter keyboard, the characters are engraved on the keys. It will be noted that some keys control the punching of two different characters. The upper characters are punched when the keyboard is in numeric shift, and the lower characters are punched when the keyboard is in alphabetic shift. These shifts are basically controlled through the program drum, but the NUM (numeric) shift key and the ALPH (alphabetic) shift keys override program drum control, which will be discussed later.

Depression of the REL (release) key causes the cards at the punch

---

[1] The reader is referred to the operating manual prepared by the manufacturer for detailed information about a particular key punch.

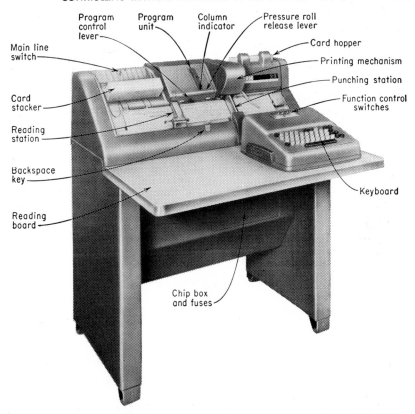

FIG. 6.35. IBM 26 Printing Card Punch. (*Reprinted by permission from "IBM Reference Manual—24 Card Punch, 26 Printing Card Punch," A24-0520, copyright* 1949 *in original notice by International Business Machines Corporation.*)

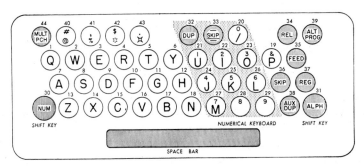

FIG. 6.36. IBM 26 keyboard chart. (*Reprinted by permission from "IBM Reference Manual—24 Card Punch, 26 Printing Card Punch," A24-0520, copyright* 1949 *in original notice by International Business Machines Corporation.*)

station and the read station to be moved to card stations 2 and 3, respectively.

A momentary depression of the DUP (duplicate) key causes the punches from the card column at the read station to be copied (duplicated) into the card column at the punch station. Continued depression of the DUP key will cause copying of successive columns.

The program drum indexes the movement of a card past the punch station (and the simultaneous movement of the preceding card past the read station). A fixed pointer at the bottom of the drum indicates the next column to be punched by reference to a scale at the base of the program drum.

The program drum provides control over such functions as automatic duplication, spacing, and case shifting through a set of four star wheels that ride on a replaceable punched card wrapped around the drum. The four basic program codes are as follows:

Code	Function
1 punch	Alphabetic shift, otherwise numeric shift
0 punch	Start automatic duplication
11 punch	Start automatic spacing
12 punch	Definition of field over which automatic spacing or automatic duplication is to be continued

If the star wheels are raised so they do not ride on the card wrapped around the drum, the key punch is in alphabetic shift unless the numeric shift key is depressed.

6.23 The Verifier.[1] The verifier is used to check the accuracy of key punching. It resembles the key punch in appearance, and the principal difference is that the verifier has a comparing unit in place of the punch unit. One set of inputs to the comparing unit comes from the punches sensed at the "punch station." The other set of inputs to the comparing unit corresponds to the code for the character key depressed. If the two sets of impulses do not correspond, a COMPARING EXIT impulse stops card feeding, turns on an error light, and causes the card to be notched over the column in which the error was sensed. The light turns off and card feeding is resumed if a second attempt at verification is successful; otherwise, it turns off when the third attempt is made. The operator must take the appropriate action when an error is detected.

6.24 Summary. An attempt has been made in this chapter to acquaint the reader with certain basic components of plug-board-controlled punched-card data-processing equipment. It is believed

---

[1] This discussion is based on the IBM 56 Card Verifier.

that the 533 Read-Punch unit has been presented in sufficient detail that with a little practice the reader could wire plug boards for many of the problems with which he may be faced in practice.

This is not true of the other equipments discussed in this chapter. It is hoped, however, that the reader will have gained a general appreciation of the functions that these equipments can perform and the plug-board wiring required to control them. In each case, however, details have been omitted that vary from machine to machine. The reader should refer to the manufacturer's operating manual for specific instructions about a given machine.

PROBLEMS

6.1. Each READ CARD B hub (numbered 1 through 80) in Fig. 6.25 (rows Q through T and columns 1 through 20) is attached to a brush (see Fig. 6.2) that will sense punches in the correspondingly numbered column of a punched card. Assume that each STORAGE ENTRY B hub in Fig. 6.25 (rows K through P and columns 1 through 22) is connected to the corresponding input synchronizer register position by means of a translation unit (see Fig. 6.4). READ CARD B hubs correspond to SECOND READING hubs in Fig. 6.4.

Show the external plug-board wiring that would be required to channel digit punches from card columns 6 through 10 into register positions 5 through 1, respectively, in word 2.

6.2. In Fig. 6.26 each SECOND READING hub (rows G and H and columns 1 through 40) is attached to a read brush (see Fig. 6.2) and each NORMAL PRINT ENTRY hub (rows V through X and columns 1 through 40) accepts impulses to actuate a type bar. The character printed by a type bar is determined by the combination of impulses that actuates it. The type bars, 120 in number, may be actuated simultaneously to print a single line. Successive lines are printed by successive actuations of the type bar.

Show the wiring required if the data from card columns 1 through 5 are to actuate type bars 6, 8, 10, 12, and 14, respectively.

6.3. In Fig. 6.4 what is the relationship between the impulses emitted at FIRST READING and SECOND READING hubs in a single card cycle? What is their relationship on successive card cycles? Explain your answers.

6.4. In Fig. 6.25 the FIRST READING hubs (rows A through D and columns 23 through 42) and the READ CARD B hubs (see Prob. 6.1) are related as the FIRST and SECOND READING hubs in Fig. 6.4. Thus a punch in a card column sensed at first reading is emitted at the corresponding FIRST READING hub and that impulse can be used to control switching of the paths of impulses in the succeeding card cycle.

a. If FIRST READING hub 1 is attached to the c hub of a DIGIT SELECTOR (row R and column 21 of Fig. 6.25), when will an impulse be emitted from DIGIT SELECTOR hub 4 (row Y and column 21 of Fig. 6.25)?

b. Given the wiring specified in (*a*), what would be the consequence of wiring DIGIT SELECTOR hub 4 to the DPU hub (row *F* and column 23 of Fig. 6.25) of PILOT SELECTOR 1 (rows *E* through *Q* and column 23 of Fig. 6.25)?

c. What function does the PILOT SELECTOR HOLD hub (rows *P* and *Q* and column 23 of Fig. 6.25) perform?

d. If either of the common pair of ENTRY B hubs (row *D* and column 21 or 22 of Fig. 6.25) are impulsed in a read cycle, then the assumption (of Prob. 6.1) that STORAGE ENTRY B hubs are connected to the corresponding input synchronizer register positions is realized in the succeeding read cycle. What would be the consequence of wiring DIGIT SELECTOR hub 4 to an ENTRY B hub and wiring the other ENTRY B hub to the DPU hub of PILOT SELECTOR 1? Assume that the connection described in (*b*) has been removed.

6.5. What is the consequence of wiring FIRST READING hubs 6 through 10 (row *A* and columns 28 through 32 of Fig. 6.25) to ALPHABETIC FIRST READ hubs *W*2, row *AK* and columns 18 through 22, respectively, in Fig. 6.25?

6.6. If the CAI hub (row *AK* and column 12 of Fig. 6.25) is wired to the T hub of PILOT SELECTOR 1 and the C hub of that switch is wired to ALPHA IN hub *W*2 (row *AM* and column 11 or 12 of Fig. 6.25), what is the consequence in the event that either the XPU or the DPU hub of PILOT SELECTOR 1 is impulsed in a read cycle?

6.7. What is the effect of wiring WORD SIZE EMITTER hub 5 (row *AK* and column 6 of Fig. 6.25) to WORD SIZE ENTRY hub *C*, *W*1 (row *AQ* or *AR* and column 1 of Fig. 6.25)?

6.8. Prepare a wiring diagram as in Fig. 6.25 to cause data-card columns 6 through 10 to be stored in positions 5 through 1, respectively, of input synchronizer register 1 when card column 1 does not contain a 4 punch and to cause data from card columns 6 through 10 to be stored in input synchronizer register as alphanumeric data when card column 1 contains a 4 punch. Assume that the data in card columns 6 through 10 are strictly numeric when column 1 does not contain a 4 punch.

6.9. What is the consequence of wiring FIRST READING hub 1 (row *A* and column 1) of Fig. 6.26 directly to a DPU hub of PILOT SELECTOR 1 (row *F* or *G* and column 53)? What advantage may be gained by wiring the same sequence of impulses through DIGIT SELECTOR *A* (rows *A* through *M* and column 41 or 42)?

6.10. If an index number is contained in columns 3 through 5 of each card in a deck, describe a sorting procedure that should be used to arrange the deck of cards in ascending sequence on the index number, using the mechanism described in Sec. 6.8 for switching the paths of cards.

6.11. Referring to the 533 timing chart (Fig. 6.19), what, in general, is the distinction between READ EXIT and READ ENTRY hubs?

6.12. Referring to the 533 timing chart (Fig. 6.19), under what circumstances can the CAI impulse (see Fig. 6.5) and the COUPLE EXIT impulse (see discussion of the PILOT SELECTOR in Sec. 6.6) be used interchangeably to activate ALPHA IN hubs?

6.13. Referring to the READ EXITS in Fig. 6.19, could the READ CARD c hubs and the DI hubs be used interchangeably? If so, why? If not, why not?

6.14. In the reproducing punch schematically illustrated in Fig. 6.22, there are 80 FIRST READING hubs that emit impulses sensed by the 80 first reading brushes in unit L. There are also 80 PUNCH hubs that control the 80 punches in unit R. Each set of hubs is numbered 1 through 80, and these numbers correspond to card columns 1 through 80, respectively.

What external plug-board wiring would be required to cause data (punches) from columns 1 through 5 of a card in hopper L to be copied into columns 11 through 15 of a mating card in hopper R?

In addition, there are 80 pairs of hubs, one pair for each of 80 comparing units. What additional wiring would be required to verify that the reproduction was accurate?

6.15. In the reproducing punch schematically illustrated in Fig. 6.22, there are 80 SECOND READING hubs internally connected to the second reading brushes of unit R. There are 80 PUNCH hubs that control the punches in unit R.

What external plug-board wiring would be required to reproduce (gang-punch) data from columns 16 through 20 in the first card of a deck inserted in hopper R to succeeding cards in that deck?

6.16. Column 5 of each card in a deck contains either a 1, a 2, or a 3 punch. Column 10 of each card contains the combination of punches that represent either A, B, or C. Show the external wiring of the statistical sorter (discussed in Sec. 6.20) that you would recommend to tally the following frequency distributions:

a. The number of cards containing a 1, the number containing a 2, and the number containing a 3 in column 5

b. The frequency with which A, B, and C occur in column 10 in cards that contain a 1 in column 5

7

AN ALGORITHMIC LANGUAGE

The reader has discovered by this time that considerable detail work is required to translate the analysis of a data-processing problem to a program written in machine language. An assembly program, such as SOAP II, permits the programmer to delegate a great deal of the detail work to the computer, but it is still necessary for him to write a statement for each operation that the computer is to execute.

It would be quite convenient if the statements from the analysis of a data-processing problem could serve as a program. If so, the programming costs could be considerably reduced. It is conceivable that computers could be designed to accept such statements, provided that the statements conform to specified format restrictions. However, this would undoubtedly increase the cost of the computer.

Another approach is to develop a library of general-purpose subroutines and to introduce these as components of a program. This approach has proved to have considerable merit, but it also has certain limitations. A general-purpose subroutine, once written, may be used in many different programs; however, it may have certain restrictions that make it unusable for a given purpose. For example, the N-percard read and punch routines cannot accommodate alphabetic information; furthermore, their formats may be unacceptable for a particular program.

A third approach is to define a somewhat arbitrary set of operation codes and a somewhat arbitrary instruction format, then program the computer to execute a sequence of such instructions.

Each of the arbitrarily defined operation codes will normally imply the execution of two or more basic computer operations; otherwise, there would be no advantage to its introduction. Because of this many-to-one relationship, such operations are referred to as macro operations. They are also referred to as pseudo operations, because they are not part of the basic machine language.

Similarly, the arbitrarily defined instruction format may permit specification of two or more operands; e.g., we might define an instruction to be of the form MPY ABC, and interpret it to mean multiply A by B and store the result in C.

The program that is written to interpret and execute the pseudo instructions is aptly referred to as an *interpretive routine*. One of its functions is that of interpreting each instruction as it is encountered. If it is a basic-machine-language instruction, it will be executed in the normal manner except that control will be returned to the appropriate instruction in the interpretive routine. If it is a pseudo instruction, control will be transferred to an appropriate subroutine, which in turn will return control to the appropriate instruction in the interpretive routine. Thus, the second function of the interpretive routine is to supply the necessary subroutines for execution of pseudo operations.

The PTSR described in the Appendix is an example of an interpretive routine. Pseudo operation codes have been defined for such functions as N-per-card read (code 50), N-per-card punch (code 51), and block zero (code 52). When operation is in the trace mode, each instruction is analyzed before it is executed and the outcome of this analysis determines the subsequent action. A better example of this approach is the Bell floating-decimal interpretive system, which has been widely used for scientific and engineering calculations.

The operation of an interpretive routine is illustrated in the following diagram.

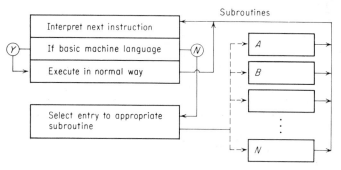

The implementation of the flow diagram may require that a card be read for each instruction executed. This will probably be true if the format of the pseudo instruction exceeds the capacity of a single memory register, but such a restriction is not mandatory. However, the term interpretive routine usually implies successive iterations of a cycle that contains an interpret phase followed by an execute phase.

A fourth approach is to define a general language for describing computational processes, program the specific machine to translate statements written in this language, and compile sequences of basic-machine-language instructions that will cause the computer to perform the operations implied by the statements. Several such compiler systems have been developed and have been successfully used. The essential difference between an interpretive routine and a compiler is that the compiler translates the entire program to machine language before it starts execution, whereas the interpretive routine translates and executes successive pseudo instructions.

An analogy can be made to the normal procedure for translation from one language to another of a speech as contrasted with a book. The difference is that an interpreter repeatedly interrupts the delivery of the speech to perform his function, whereas the translator of a book performs the entire translation and presents the finished product.

In computer operations, interpretive routines are in general easier to conceive and program than compilers. They have the disadvantage that the translation must be repeated each time the program is executed, whereas a compilation need only be performed once.

Both the interpretive routine and the compiler have been effective in permitting the delegation of much of the detail work of programming to the computer. Lest there be any doubt, none of these systems provides for the delegation of the problem analysis to the computer. It should be apparent, furthermore, that the savings in programming cost may be offset in varying degrees by increases in computer time required in the development of the program and in its later execution.

However, there is the possibility of an additional saving in programming cost if programs can be written in a language that is acceptable by all computers or, to be more precise, acceptable by compilers for different computers. This could lead to a reduction in the duplication of programming efforts. It has already been pointed out that the set of basic operation codes will vary from machine to machine; hence it is not surprising that machine-language programs are not interchangeable among computers. On the other hand, it is reasonable that a common language could be developed for describing computational processes and that a compiler could be developed for each computer so that a program written in the common language could be adapted to any computer having such a compiler.

In 1955 a European group[1] was formed which subsequently worked out an algorithmic notation for describing computational processes. A group was formed in the United States for a similar purpose.[2] In a

[1] Known as the GAMM group.
[2] Known as the ACM group.

joint conference which took place in May, 1958, at Zurich, Switzerland, the two groups combined their proposals for algorithmic notations into one preliminary language, which was later given[1] the name ALGOL—a contraction of the words *algorithmic language*. At a conference in Paris in January, 1960, the group prepared a final report defining a language known[2] as ALGOL 60, or simply ALGOL.

The purpose of the remainder of this chapter is to introduce the reader to a language that can be used for describing computational processes.[3] The language is called BALGOL, the algorithmic language used in communicating with the Burroughs 220 Digital Computer. BALGOL is very similar to ALGOL.

The approach followed is to introduce the reader to the language in a step-by-step manner, beginning with very simple concepts and gradually expanding to include all the important features of the language. The introduction of new concepts is brought about in many cases by means of examples. The semantics and syntax of the language are discussed only to the extent necessary to enable the reader to write programs. In other words, this is intended to be an introductory approach by which the reader can learn to use the language.[4]

The examples in the text do not involve sophisticated mathematics; rather, they have been chosen so that the reader will have no difficulty in understanding the problem to be solved and can therefore devote his full attention to the BALGOL description of the computational process.

Obviously, there are many different ways in which the problems in the examples can be solved. Our objective has been to present programs which illustrate certain features of the BALGOL language, and the reader is urged to follow these programs with this thought in mind. Subsequently, the reader may wish to develop for himself one or more alternative programs which solve the same problem.

From this point on, our discussion will be devoted exclusively to BALGOL, which may be considered as a Burroughs 220 dialect of

---

[1] Perlis and Samelson, Report on the Algorithmic Language ALGOL, *Communications of the ACM*, vol. 1, no. 12, December, 1958.

[2] Report on the Algorithmic Language ALGOL 60, *Communications of the ACM*, vol. 3, no. 5, May, 1960.

[3] The remainder of this chapter is taken almost verbatim from "An Introduction to Balgol" by R. V. Oakford and J. M. Gere, pp. 4–87. © 1961 Wadsworth Publishing Company, Inc., Belmont, California. Reprinted by permission of the publisher.

[4] For more detailed definitions of the semantics and syntax than given here, see "Burroughs Algebraic Compiler," Bulletin 220-21011-P Burroughs Corporation, Detroit, 1961.

ALGOL. The "Burroughs Algebraic Compiler" (hereafter called either BALCOM or the compiler for the sake of brevity) for BALGOL was developed by employees of the Burroughs Corporation, and is a proprietary document.[1] The basic input medium for BALCOM is IBM punched cards, and output is by means of either cards or printed pages.

PROGRAMMING IN BALGOL

7.1   An Elementary BALGOL Program.   A program in BALGOL is written by the programmer on standard coding forms (see Table 7.2). All alphabetic characters are written in upper-case letters, except the letter O, which is written with a slash $\emptyset$ in order to distinguish it from zero.   All numeric digits are written in the conventional manner. Other characters, such as $+$, $-$, ., $/$, (, and), are also used with well-defined meanings which will be described later.   The semicolon ; and the dollar sign $ are interchangeable and are used as separators between statements, clauses, etc.

Each line on the coding form will be punched as a single IBM card. In order to distinguish them from other types of cards, program cards must contain a 2 in column 1.   The program itself may occupy columns 2 to 72, while columns 73 to 80 are reserved for identification purposes, such as sequential numbering of the cards.   Data cards are distinguished by a 5 in column 1, with the remainder of the card (columns 2 to 80) available for data.

A program for the following problem illustrates some of the fundamental concepts of BALGOL and also illustrates the steps followed by the programmer in preparing his program and running it on the computer.

Statement of Problem

Let us assume that a set of data cards is available, each card containing four numbers which will be identified as A, B, C, and D.   It is desired to calculate $E = (B \cdot C + D)/(100 - A^2)$ for each set of values of A, B, C, and D.   The results are to be printed on paper with the given values of A, B, C, and D and the corresponding calculated value of E appearing on one line.   Provisions are to be made for identifying the last data card to the computer and for indicating that E is undefined whenever the value $A = 10$ is encountered.   To accomplish the first provision, an extra data card will be appended containing the value 9999.999 for A (it is known that this value of A will not

[1] The designation BAC-220 is widely used in place of BALCOM.

appear elsewhere in the data cards) and, to accomplish the second provision, E will be set equal to 8888.888 whenever A equals 10. The numbers 9999.999 and 8888.888 have been selected arbitrarily.

The flow chart of Fig. 7.1 outlines the sequence of operations to be performed in executing this problem.

The BALGOL program of Table 7.1 describes the computational process illustrated in the flow chart of Fig. 7.1. Note that the 2

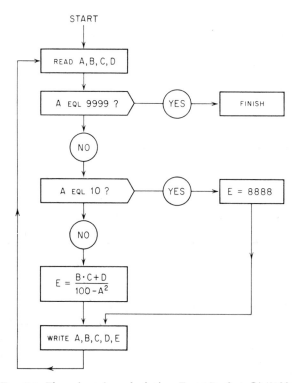

FIG. 7.1. Flow chart for calculating $E = (B \cdot C + D)/(100 - A^2)$.

required in column 1 of the program cards and the 5 required in column 1 of the data cards are omitted for the sake of clarity. The cards in the program are numbered sequentially for convenient reference in the subsequent detailed explanation. These numbers may be omitted in the actual program if desired.

After the program is written on the BALGOL Coding Form (see Table 7.2, which shows the preceding program as written on a typical form), it is punched on cards in the indicated sequence. Then the programmer assembles the deck of cards for processing by the com-

Table 7.1   BALGOL Program for Calculating $E = (B \cdot C + D)/(100 - A^2)$

Program	Card number
JØB card	1
LØDX card	2
L1 . . READ (;;IDS1);	3
INPUT IDS1(A,B,C,D);	4
IF A EQL 9999.999; GØ TØ L3;	5
IF A EQL 10; BEGIN E = 8888.888; GØ TØ L2 END;	6
E = (B·C + D)/(100 − A*2);	7
L2 . . WRITE (;;ØDS1, FØRM1);	8
ØUTPUT ØDS1(A,B,C,D,E);	9
FØRMAT FØRM1(5x11.3,w);	10
GØ TØ L1;	11
L3 . . FINISH;	12

Typical Data Cards				
1.5	1.64	72.439	3.0	13
−12.0	2.34	57.194	7.0	14
10.0	1.91	87.992	−7.0	15
3.5	2.02	−78.700	6.0	16
3.0	2.0	90.0	2.0	17
9999.999	1.0	1.0	1.0	18

Table 7.2   Program as Written on Typical BALGOL Coding Form

puter. The assembled deck consists of the header cards, the program cards, and the data cards (in that order). The assembled deck is placed in the hopper of the card-read input unit of the Burroughs 220 by the computer operator. Successive cards are read automatically into the computer under control of BALCOM. The compiler translates the BALGOL program into machine-language instructions, and the resulting program is stored in memory. This phase of the operation is known as the "compile phase" and is terminated by the FINISH

Table 7.3 Typical Listing of Results of Compilation and Execution of Program

```
$$$  TIME ON   1358
  A-011          JOB  11/10/61   1 MIN    JOHN DOE (ILLUST. PROB.
                     ART. 2.1) BURROUGHS ALGEBRAIC COMPILER
               L1 . . READ($$ IDS1) $                                3
               INPUT  IDS1(A,B,C,D) $                                4
               IF A EQL 9999.999 $ GO TO L3 $                        5
               IF A EQL 10 $ BEGIN E = 8888.888 $ GO TO L2 END $ 6
               E = (B.C + D)/(100 − A*2) $                           7
               L2 . . WRITE($$ ODS1, FORM1) $                       8
               OUTPUT ODS1(A,B,C,D,E) $                             9
               FORMAT FORM1(5 × 11.3, W) $                         10
               GO TO L1 $                                          11
               L3 . . FINISH $                                     12
COMPILED PROGRAM ENDS AT 0279
PROGRAM VARIABLES BEGIN AT 9260
```

1.500	1.640	72.439	3.000	1.246
−12.000	2.340	57.194	7.000	−3.200
10.000	1.910	87.992	−7.000	8888.888
3.500	2.020	−78.700	6.000	−1.743
3.000	2.000	90.000	2.000	2.000

```
  NO CARDS NOT READ
$$$  TIME OFF   1359
```

declaration (which must always appear as the last statement in a program). The program itself is listed during the compile phase (see the upper part of Table 7.3, which shows a typical listing of the preceding program). Many of the possible syntactical errors which can be made by the programmer are detected by the compiler during this phase, and appropriate error messages are interspersed in the listing. This feature is of considerable aid in removing errors from programs (a process usually referred to as "debugging"). Of course, not all errors will be detected during compilation.

When compilation is completed, the "execution phase" begins automatically, and the first statement in the program is executed. The remaining statements in the program are executed consecutively (except as modified by GO TO or conditional statements in the program itself) until the program is completed. The results are printed on paper (or punched on cards), as shown in the lower part of Table 7.3. Note that supplementary information may also be printed, depending upon the particular compiler which is being used. For example, the listing in Table 7.3 includes information pertaining to the time on and off the computer, the last word location in memory occupied by the machine-language instructions (0279), the first word location occupied by the variables in the program (9260) and a message which indicates that all data cards were read.

Throughout this chapter, any word which is part of BALGOL is in small capital letters in the illustrative programs. This makes it simple to distinguish words which are part of the language (called *reserved words*) from those which the programmer has defined. A complete listing of all reserved words is given in Sec. 7.27.

Comments on the Program

Card 1. The job card is required at the beginning of every program. A typical format is as follows:

Columns	Entry
1	2
2–7	(Charge number)
16–18	JOB
21–29	(Date)
30–36	(Estimated running time in minutes)
40–80	(Identifying information, such as name of programmer and phone number)

Card 2. The Load-execute (LODX) card must be the second card in every program. A typical format is as follows:

Columns	Entry
1	2
16–19	LODX
21–26	BALGOL

The job card and the load-execute card are frequently called "header cards" and serve several functions. The job card provides information needed by both the computer operator and the accounting staff of the computation center and also identifies the author of the program.

The load-execute card identifies the program as BALGOL, so that the appropriate compiler (BALCOM) will be called into service.

Card 3.   READ Statement.   A *statement* defines an operation to be performed by the computer.   In this case, execution of the READ statement causes only one data card to be read.   However, in general, card reading will continue automatically until a value has been assigned to each variable in the referenced input-data set.   The READ statement refers to the input-data set by an *identifier*, in this case IDS1. For the present, we shall consider that the READ statement always consists of the word READ followed by a left parenthesis, two semicolons, the identifier of an input-data set, and a right parenthesis. The explanation for the presence of the two semicolons is given at the end of Sec. 7.12.

Identifiers are names chosen by the programmer to identify various entities in the program, e.g., variables, input-data sets, output-data sets, editorial formats, etc.   An identifier must start with an alphabetic character (that is, a letter); otherwise it can be an almost arbitrary combination of alphabetic characters and numeric characters (that is, digits).   However, each identifier must be unique, must not contain more than 50 characters, and must not conflict with the list of reserved words given in Sec. 7.27.   No special characters, such as commas, periods, and plus signs, or spaces can be contained in an identifier.

A *label* is a name used to identify a statement for reference purposes. A label may be either an identifier or an integer (in the case of an integer, leading zeros are ignored; thus, the labels 0027, 027, and 27 are equivalent).   The distinguishing characteristic of a label is the separator . . that follows it and separates it from the statement it labels.   In general, the function of the separators in BALGOL is analogous to that of punctuation marks in the English language.   In this example the READ statement is labeled L1 so that it may be referred to later on in the program.

All statements are separated from one another by semicolons (or dollar signs).

Card 4.   INPUT Declaration.   The purpose of a *declaration* is to define the properties of an identifier used elsewhere in the program. It is not an execution statement.   The declaration always begins with a declarator, in this case the word INPUT.   An INPUT declaration defines one or more input-data sets, each of which is given a name in the form of an identifier.   In this example, there is one input-data set which is arbitrarily given the name IDS1.   The input-data set consists of the list of variables A, B, C, and D to which numeric values will be assigned when the identifier IDS1 is referred to by a READ statement (card 3). Successive values from a data card or cards will be assigned to successive variables in the input-data set. The programmer is responsible for synchronizing the sequence of values on data cards with the sequence of variables in the input-data set.

If more than one input-data set is to be defined in a single INPUT declaration, then commas are used to separate the sets. For example, the following declaration would define three input-data sets:

INPUT IDS1(X1,Y1,Z1), IDS2(X2,Y2,Z2), IDS3(X3,Y3,Z3)

All declarations are separated from each other and from statements by semicolons (or dollar signs).

Card 5. IF Statements. The IF statement is a conditional statement which defines an operation to be performed *only if* a specified condition is satisfied. The IF statement has two parts: first, an IF clause which specifies the condition; and second, a statement (which is actually a statement within the IF statement) which is executed only if the condition is satisfied.

In this example the IF statement specifies that if A equals 9999.999, the statement GO TO L3 is to be executed. If A is not equal to 9999.999, the GO TO L3 statement is not executed and in this example the following statement (card 6) will be executed.

The phrase A EQL 9999.999 is called a *relation*. All the relations that can be specified in the IF clause are shown in Table 7.21. In those relations, E_1 and E_2 are *arithmetic expressions* (see discussion of card 7 below). The operators LSS, LEQ, etc., are called *relational operators* and must be preceded and followed by a space. It is possible to specify more than one arithmetic relation in an IF clause by constructing a Boolean expression, as illustrated in the next section.

The GO TO statement is used to branch to a labeled statement, thereby controlling the sequence of statement execution. The words GO TO are followed by the label of the statement which is to be executed next. Note that the symbol . . following a label (e.g., L3 . .) acts as a separator that distinguishes a label from an identifier and is not considered to be part of the label. Thus the separator . . does not appear after the label in the GO TO statement itself.

Card 6. IF Statement Containing a Compound Statement. For syntactical purposes it is frequently desirable that a sequence of statements be regarded as a single statement. This is accomplished by enclosing the sequence of statements within a pair of "brackets" in the form

BEGIN S_1 ; S_2 ; S_3 . . . S_n END

Such a statement is called a *compound statement*. The symbols S_1, S_2, . . . S_n each indicate either a simple or a compound statement. (Thus a compound statement may be nested within a compound statement.) The symbols BEGIN and END serve as enclosing "brackets" for the compound statement and may be replaced by left and right parentheses if desired. (A semicolon may be inserted between the last statement S_n and the word END if desired.)

In this example the compound statement BEGIN E = 8888.888; GO TO L2 END is executed whenever the condition A EQL 10 is satisfied; otherwise the compound statement is not executed, and in this example the program proceeds to the next statement (card 7).

If the condition A EQL 10 *is* satisfied, the value 8888.888 is arbitrarily *assigned* to E. The symbol = in BALGOL does not have the usual algebraic meaning of equality; instead, it has the meaning *assign*. Hence the relational operator EQL and the assignment symbol = are definitely not interchangeable. The distinction between these quantities will become clearer as the symbol = is used subsequently. After E has been assigned the value 8888.888, the GO TO L2 statement is executed.

Card 7. Assignment Statement. An assignment statement is expressed in general as

$$V = E$$

or

$$\text{Variable} = \text{Expression}$$

In other words, the assignment symbol = means that the current value of the expression on its right-hand side is to be assigned to the variable on its left.

In this example the arithmetic expression on the right must be evaluated for the values currently assigned to the variables A, B, C, D. The result is assigned to the variable E.

The concept of a *variable* in BALGOL is the same as in algebra; namely, it is an identifier that represents a quantity that may assume any one of a series of values.

The concept of an *arithmetic expression* in BALGOL is also the same as in algebra. Furthermore, the symbols and syntax are almost identical. The permissible arithmetic operators are shown in Table 7.4.

Table 7.4

Arithmetic operator in BALGOL	*Meaning*
*	Exponentiation
.	Multiplication
/	Division
+, −	Addition, subtraction

Exponentiation (A*B) is undefined when A = 0 and B ≤ 0 or when A < 0 and B is nonintegral. Otherwise, A and B may be positive or negative, integer or noninteger. Division (A/B) is undefined when B = 0.

The elements of an arithmetic expression are numbers, variables, arithmetic operators, and parentheses. Within parentheses the order of precedence for performing the arithmetic operations is exponentiation, multiplication, division, and addition or subtraction. As in algebra, parentheses should be used to remove ambiguities. For example, A/B/C should be either (A/B)/C or else A/(B/C). Similarly, A*B*C should be either A*(B*C) or (A*B)*C.

Omission of the multiplication operator is permitted whenever this will not result in ambiguity. For example, the product of $2X + 7$ and $3Y + 8$ can be written in the form

$$(2X + 7)(3Y + 8)$$

which is equivalent to

$$(2X + 7) . (3Y + 8)$$

Similarly, the product of 4 and X can be written in the simple form $4X$, which is equivalent to either $4 . X$ or $4(X)$. When constants are multiplied, parentheses must be used to eliminate ambiguities; thus 3 times 6 should be written as 3(6) or (3)6, rather than 3 . 6.

For convenient reference, the rules pertaining to arithmetic expressions are summarized in Sec. 7.16.

Card 8. WRITE Statement. A WRITE statement refers first to an output-data set by its identifier (e.g., ODS1) and second to a format specification by its identifier (e.g., FORM1). The execution of the WRITE statement causes the values currently assigned to the variables in the referenced output-data set (ODS1) to be printed (or punched) as specified in the referenced format specification (FORM1). As in the case of the READ statement, two semicolons are required in the WRITE statement, for reasons which are explained in Sec. 7.12.

Card 9. OUTPUT Declaration. The purpose of an OUTPUT declaration is to define one or more output-data sets, each of which is given an arbitrarily selected name. In this example the data set consists of the variables A, B, C, D, and E and has been given the name ODS1. The values currently assigned to the variables will be printed (or punched) when the identifier ODS1 is referred to in a WRITE statement, provided that an appropriate format (FORM1) is also referred to in the WRITE statement.

Card 10. FORMAT Declaration. The FORMAT declaration defines one or more format specifications (hereafter called formats) and specifies identifiers for the formats. The declaration consists of the declarator FORMAT followed by the list of formats, each of which is preceded by an identifier. Each format is enclosed within parentheses. A format specifies the form of presentation of individual values in the output-data set, the spacing of successive values on the printed page (or on cards), and the output medium (printer or card punch). A format may also be used to define headings in alphabetic form. Because of the complexities of possible formats, only the format used in the example of Table 7.1 will be described at present. Generalizations and variations will be presented in later examples.

The format in this example consists of two parts, an *editing phrase* (5x11.3) and an *activation phrase* (w). There must be a suitable correspondence between editing phrases in the format and variables in the corresponding output-data set. In this case there are five variables (A, B, C, D, E) in the output-data set. The significance of the 5 in the editing phrase 5x11.3 is that the phrase is to be repeated five times. In other words, 5x11.3 is equivalent to writing x11.3, x11.3, x11.3, x11.3, x11.3, and thus it is seen that there is one editing phrase associated sequentially with each variable in the output-data set. The x indicates that the value currently assigned to the variable is to be written as a decimal number; the 11 indicates that the number is to be written in a field 11 columns wide; and the 3 indicates that three digits to the right of the decimal point will be printed (the remaining digits to the right are discarded). The number will be justified right in the field, and the sign, if negative, will be printed to the left of the number. Thus the printed line will have the following appearance:

A	B	C	D	E
±XXX.XXX	±XXX.XXX	±XXX.XXX	±XXX.XXX	±XXX.XXX

The activation phrase w specifies that the results are to be printed with single spacing between lines.

Thus it is seen that the execution of a WRITE statement causes the sequence of values specified in the output-data set to be assembled as specified by the editing phrases in the format and printed or punched as specified by the activation phrase in the format.

Card 11. This GO TO statement specifies that the next statement to be executed is the one having the label L1. Therefore, as long as data cards are available, another data card will be read and the sequence of operations will begin anew.

Card 12. FINISH Statement. The FINISH statement indicates to the compiler the completion of the compile phase. Consequently, the last statement in a program must be a FINISH statement; furthermore, the FINISH statement must not appear elsewhere in the program. After compilation is completed, the first statement in the program (in this example, card 3) will be executed, thus beginning the execution phase.

Execution of the FINISH statement at the end of the execute phase indicates completion of program execution; hence card reading is automatically initiated. In this way the compilation of the next program in the input unit is begun automatically and the computer is not delayed, as is the case when the operator must start each program manually.

Cards 13 to 18. Typical Data Cards. Column 1 of each data card must contain the digit 5. This distinguishes a data card from other types of cards such as program cards, which have a 2 in column 1. Columns 2 to 80 of a data card may be used to store successive values. At least one blank column must separate successive values on the card. Furthermore, each value must be wholly contained on a single card. Successive values from a card are assigned to successive variables in the input-data set as they are encountered, reading from left to right across the card.

In this example four values (A, B, C, D) are punched on each card; hence one card will be read upon each execution of the READ statement. The numbers on the data cards in this example must be written in decimal form; integer numbers will be discussed in Sec. 7.3.

Editorial Use of Blank Spaces and Line Advances. In general, the rules for the editorial use of blank spaces and the starting of a new line in the BALGOL program are intuitive by analogy to the English language, in which a blank space is used to indicate the end of a word or a number. Ambiguity may result if a blank space is inserted within a word or if a space is not inserted to separate adjacent words.

Similarly, in the BALGOL language a blank space may be used when necessary to indicate the end of a "word," e.g., an identifier, a reserved word, or a declarator. Ambiguity will result from the insertion of a blank space such that a single word (or number) is divided into two words (or numbers) or from omission of a blank space such that two words (or numbers) are combined into a single word (or number).

In many places in a program, spaces are optional and the programmer may suit his own convenience. For example, spaces are optional before and after arithmetic operators (A + B and A+B are equivalent), before and after the assignment symbol (A=2 and A = 2 are equivalent), before and after separators, before and after commas which separate items in a list (as in INPUT, OUTPUT, and FORMAT declarations), and before and after parentheses.

An advance from one line (or card) in the program to the next line is not the same as in English writing. There is no counterpart in BALGOL to the use of a hyphen in English to indicate a word that is separated between two successive lines. Furthermore, the compiler does not recognize an advance from one program card to the next. Instead, column 72 of one program card is followed immediately by column 2 of the next card. Thus, if a word is broken at column 72 of one card and continued at column 2 of the next card, it will appear to BALCOM as a single word. Alternatively, if one word ends at column

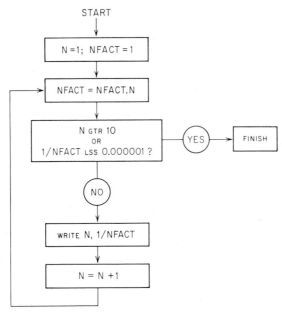

Fig. 7.2. Flow chart for calculating $1/N!$.

72 of one card and the next word starts at column 2 of the next card, the two words will appear to BALCOM as a single word.

Subject to these general restrictions and to a very limited number of other restrictions (e.g., spaces are required to the left and the right of relational operators), spaces and line advances may be used freely by the programmer to enhance the readability of his program.

One or more statements or declarations may appear on a single line, and a single statement or declaration may occupy more than one line.

7.2 A Second Illustrative Program. The following problem illustrates some variations of the concepts discussed in the preceding section, as well as some additional features of the language.

Let us assume that we wish to compute a table of reciprocal factorials $1/N!$ for values of N equal to 1, 2, 3, ... The results are to be printed in two columns with the value of N in the first column and the corresponding value of $1/N!$ in the second column. The calculations are to be terminated when N becomes greater than 10 or when the value of the reciprocal factorial is less than 0.000001, whichever occurs first.

The flow chart of Fig. 7.2 indicates the sequence of calculations to be defined in the BALGOL program of Table 7.5. Note that in this example it is not necessary to read numbers from data cards for use in the program. Instead, all required numbers are either specified as constants or else calculated in the program.

Table 7.5   BALGOL Program for Calculating $1/N!$

Program	Card number
JØB card	1
LØDX card	2
N = 1; NFACT = 1;	3
LA . . NFACT = NFACT.N;	4
IF (N GTR 10) ØR (1/NFACT LSS 0.000001);	5
GØ TØ LB;	6
WRITE (;; RESULT, FØRM);	7
ØUTPUT RESULT (N, 1/NFACT);	8
FØRMAT FØRM (B20, x5.1, B5, x10.8, w2);	9
N = N + 1; GØ TØ LA;	10
LB . . FINISH;	11

Comments on Program

Card 3. The two statements on this card serve the purpose of assigning initially the value 1 to the variables N and NFACT, the latter being the identifier for the variable N factorial.

Card 4. This assignment statement assigns to the variable NFACT a value which is equal to the current value of NFACT times the current value of N. (The expression "current value" refers to the value currently assigned to the variable.) During the first cycle of execution of the program, the values of NFACT and N are equal to 1; hence the "new" value assigned to NFACT is also 1. During the second cycle (after N has been assigned the value 2; see card 10), the execution of this statement will assign to NFACT the value 2, which is equal to the current (or "old") value of NFACT times the current value of N. During the third cycle, NFACT will be assigned the value 6, etc. Thus this single assignment statement serves to calculate the value of N! for each value of N.

Alternative forms for writing the product NFACT.N in this statement are NFACT(N) and (NFACT)N.

Cards 5 and 6. These two cards contain an IF statement consisting of an IF clause (card 5) and a statement (card 6). The clause contains a *Boolean expression* which is recognized by the presence of the *Boolean operator* OR. The expression contains two arithmetic relations, each contained in parentheses. In this case, if either one of the arithmetic relations is satisfied (or is "true"), then the Boolean expression itself is said to be "true"; hence the IF clause is satisfied. Therefore, the statement immediately following the clause (and contained within the IF statement) is executed. If neither one of the two relations is satisfied, then the Boolean expression is said to be "false," the IF clause is not satisfied, and the statement following is not executed. Instead, in this example, the next statement (card 7) is executed.

If it is desired that the cycle of calculations in this program be repeated until *both* the arithmetic relations are satisfied, then the Boolean operator AND will be used in place of OR. In other words, the Boolean expression

$$(\text{N GTR } 10) \text{ AND } (1/\text{NFACT LSS } 0.000001)$$

is true only if both relations are satisfied.

Other Boolean operators are NOT, IMPL, and EQIV. Their meanings are discussed in Sec. 7.17.

An extension of the IF statement is the EITHER IF statement (or the "alternative statement"), which is described in Sec. 7.19.

Card 7. The execution of this statement results in the output-data set identified as RESULT being printed according to the format identified as FORM.

Card 8. This declaration specifies that the output-data set RESULT consists of the values of N and 1/NFACT. Note that an expression (e.g., 1/NFACT) as well as a variable (e.g., N) may be used in an output-data set. The expression may have any degree of complexity. This is in contrast to input-data sets, which must contain variables only, for the obvious reason that only variables can have values assigned to them.

Card 9. This declaration specifies the format for printing the output-data set. The editing phrase B20 specifies that there will be 20 blank columns. The phrase x5.1, which is associated with N, specifies that N is to be printed in a field five columns wide with one digit to the right of the decimal point. The next phrase B5 specifies five blank spaces. The phrase x10.8 specifies that the value of 1/NFACT is to be printed in a field 10 columns wide with eight digits to the right of the decimal point.   Finally, the activation phrase w2 specifies printing of the preceding items with a single space both before and after printing (hence double spacing).   A summary of the various editing and activation phrases is given in Sec. 7.23.

It should be noted that if a few cards in this program are changed, it becomes a program for listing factorials and their reciprocals for values of N covering any desired range.   Also, by making use of numbers of the integer type (discussed in the next section), some slight improvement in the format can be made.

7.3 Numbers and Type Declarations.   Numbers which are punched on data cards or which are incorporated as part of a BALGOL program may be represented in one of three different forms.   These will be referred to as integer form, decimal form, and floating-point form.

A number represented in *integer form* will consist of a string of digits, for example, 17294.   The maximum number of digits permitted is 10, since each word in the memory of the computer contains 10 digit positions.   A plus or minus sign may precede the number.   Leading zeros are ignored; thus, 001234 is treated as if it were 1234.   An integer number is stored in memory in the same form in which it is written as data or as part of a program, except that leading zeros are supplied to fill up the word in memory.   Some examples of numbers in integer form are shown in Table 7.6.

Table 7.6

BALGOL program	Data cards	Computer memory
1234	1234	0000001234
-1234	-1234	-0000001234
-1234512345	-1234512345	-1234512345
123456123456	123456123456	Undefined
0	0	0000000000

A number represented in *decimal form* will consist of a string of digits containing a decimal point (e.g., 12.345).   When the number appears as part of a BALGOL program, it is necessary that the decimal point be imbedded between two digits (for example, 0.5 and 11.0 are acceptable forms, but .5 and 11. are not acceptable).   On the other hand, the decimal point need not be imbedded when a number appears on a data card; thus, .5 and 11. are acceptable decimal forms on a data card.   A plus or minus sign may precede a number in decimal form.

A number which appears in decimal form will automatically be stored in the computer memory in excess-50 floating-point form (see Sec. 3.23).

Some examples of numbers in excess-50 floating-point form are shown in Table 7.7.

Table 7.7

Number	Excess-50 floating-point form
1	5110000000
10	5210000000
$-1{,}234{,}567{,}800{,}000{,}000$	-6612345678
0.0001	4710000000
-0.00000012345678	-4412345678

The largest positive number which can be represented by the excess-50 convention is 9999999999, which is equivalent to $0.99999999 \times 10^{49}$. Thus any number equal to or larger than 10^{49} is undefined by the excess-50 convention. The smallest positive number which can be represented is 0010000000 or 0.1×10^{-50}. The excess-50 convention assigns the value 0 to any positive number smaller than this. Corresponding comments can be made concerning negative numbers.

From the preceding discussion it is apparent that a decimal number can have no more than eight significant digits, inasmuch as it is stored in memory in floating-point form. Leading zeros are not counted as significant digits, but trailing zeros are counted as significant digits.

Some examples of decimal numbers are shown in Table 7.8.

Table 7.8

BALGOL program	Data cards	Computer memory
123.0	123. or 123.0	5312300000
-123.45	-123.45	-5312345000
0.00012	.00012 or 0.00012	4712000000
12345678.9	12345678.9	Undefined
1234567800.0	1234567800	Undefined
0.000012345678	.000012345678	4612345678
0.0 or 0	0. or 0	0000000000

The third way in which a number may be represented is the *floating-point form*, which is analogous to the familiar convention in which a number is multiplied by a power-of-10 scale factor (e.g., 1.5×10^6). Such a number may appear in a BALGOL program as a decimal number (or an integer number) followed by the scale factor. The scale factor is preceded on program cards by a double asterisk, which serves to identify the scale-factor convention to the compiler. In contrast, on data cards the same number must be represented as a decimal number followed by a scale factor which is preceded by a comma. The comma performs the same functions on data cards as the double asterisk used on the program cards. A floating-point number is always stored in memory in excess-50 floating-point form; hence no more than eight significant digits may be used. Some examples are shown in Table 7.9.

Table 7.9

BALGOL program	Data cards	Computer memory
1.23**2	1.23,2	5312300000
12.3**+1	12.3,+1	5312300000
−0.12345**3	−.12345,3	−5312345000
12**−5	12.,−5	4712000000
12345678**2	12345678.,2	6012345678
12345678**−12	12345678.,−12	4612345678
0	0	0000000000
0.12**75	.12,75	Undefined
0.12**−60	.12,−60	Undefined

In the last example the characteristic cc would have to be -10, and in the next-to-last example it would have to be 125. Both of these values are outside the permitted range of cc; hence the resulting numbers in memory are undefined.

It is seen from the above discussion that equivalent numbers in both decimal and floating-point form will have the same representation in computer memory, namely, excess-50 floating-point form.

Because all numbers of the kind discussed in this section are stored in memory in either integer or excess-50 form, it is necessary to distinguish between these two cases only as far as arithmetic operations are concerned. Hence, in the BALGOL language, numeric variables are said to be of *integer type* or *floating-point type*.[1]

However, when reference is made to *numbers* as they appear in the BALGOL program or on data cards, it is necessary to distinguish between the *three forms* previously discussed: integer, decimal, and floating-point.[2]

Since integer arithmetic and floating-point arithmetic are not the same, it is necessary to *declare* in a BALGOL program the *type* of any

---

[1] Boolean variables are discussed in Sec. 7.17.

[2] In the reference manual "Burroughs Algebraic Compiler" these three forms are called integer, floating-point, and floating-point with a scale factor, respectively.

variable. Then the computer will carry out the appropriate type of arithmetic when performing arithmetic operations with that variable.

The type of the variable represented by an identifier is specified by a *type declaration*. For example, FLOATING A, B, C, declares that A, B, and C are of floating-point type. Similarly, INTEGER D, E declares that D and E are of integer type. Another possible type declaration is INTEGER OTHERWISE, which declares that all numeric variables not explicitly declared as floating type shall be considered as integers. Similarly, FLOATING OTHERWISE declares that all variables not explicitly declared as integer type shall be considered as floating type. However, this latter declaration is redundant since any variable not otherwise declared as to type is declared implicitly (or *declared by default*) to be of floating type. Thus, if all quantities which appear in a program are to be treated as floating, no type declaration is necessary.

It should be noted that, in a type declaration, the reserved word REAL is synonymous and interchangeable with the word FLOATING. (This is one of the few redundancies in the language.)

Some of the differences between integer and floating-point arithmetic are shown in the following illustrations.

Example 7.1   (12,345,678) (1000) = 12,345,678,000

In floating-point arithmetic, (12345678) (1000.0), the result is 12,345,678,000 and is represented in memory as 6112345678. In integer arithmetic the result is 2345678000 since only 10 digits can be stored in memory and the number is truncated from the left.

Example 7.2   (11,111,111) (222) = 2,466,666,642

In floating-point, (11111111) (222.0), the result is 2,466,666,600 (represented as 6024666666). In integer arithmetic the result is 2,466,666,642.

Example 7.3 $15/6 = 2.5$

In floating-point, 15.0/6, the result is 2.5 (represented as 5125000000). In integer arithmetic the result is 2, i.e., the quotient is truncated to an integer.

Example 7.4 $2/3 = 0.6666 \ldots$

In floating-point, 2/3.0, the result is 0.66666666 (note that the result is not rounded) and is represented in memory as 5066666666. In integer arithmetic the result is 0.

Example 7.5   12345678/10 = 1234567.8

In floating-point, 12345678/10.0, the result is 1234567.8 (represented as 5712345678). In integer arithmetic the result is 1234567.

Note that this provides a means of isolating certain digits of a number, in this case the first seven digits. The first four digits of a 10-digit number can be obtained by dividing by 1000000 in integer arithmetic.

Example 7.6   5,000,000,001 + 5,000,000,001 = 10,000,000,002
In integer arithmetic the result of this calculation is 2.

Finally, it should be observed that the input and output procedures do not take into account type declarations. In the case of input, the type of a number is determined solely by the form in which it appears in the data card. In other words, a number that is punched in a card in either decimal or floating-point form will be stored in memory in excess-50 floating-point form; a number punched in integer form will be stored in integer form.[1] It is the responsibility of the programmer to ensure that the forms of the values on data cards are consistent with the declared types of the variables to which such values will be assigned.

In the case of output, the form in which the number is to be printed (or punched) is specified by the editing phrase. The output procedure assumes that the type of the value as stored in memory is consistent with the form specified in the editing phrase.

7.4   A Third Illustrative Program.   The following example illustrates the use of type declarations in distinguishing between numbers of integer and floating-point types; it also incorporates some additional features of the language.

Assume that it is desired to calculate a table of values of natural logarithms by using the series

$$ \text{LN } X = 2\left[\frac{X-1}{X+1} + \frac{1}{3}\left(\frac{X-1}{X+1}\right)^3 + \frac{1}{5}\left(\frac{X-1}{X+1}\right)^5 + \cdots\right] $$

for values of X from 1 to 20 in steps of 1; that is, for X = (1,1,20). The latter notation for specifying an orderly sequence of values will be used in subsequent examples. The values within parentheses specify the initial value, the increment between successive values, and the upper limit, respectively, of the sequence of values that X is to assume.

The results obtained from the program are to be printed in three columns, the first containing values of the argument X, the second containing LN X with three digits to the right of the decimal point, and the third containing the number of terms N which were used in the series. The series is terminated when the value of the last term is less than 0.0001. The values of X and N are to be printed in integer form.

[1] The type of a number which appears explicitly in a BALGOL program is also determined by the form in which the number is written.

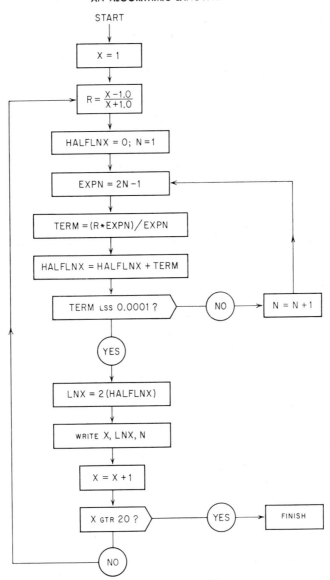

FIG. 7.3. Flow chart for calculating the natural logarithm of X.

It should be noted first that the natural logarithm of a number can be obtained in a BALGOL program by means of the *library procedure* LOG. Hence the following example would not be used as part of an actual program; it is presented solely as a means of illustrating the language. The library procedures include SQRT, SIN, TAN, SINH, etc., discussed in Sec. 7.14. The general form for calling these procedures is ID(E), i.e., the name of the procedure followed by the argument (a number, a variable, or an expression) which is enclosed within parentheses; for example, LOG(X), SQRT(B*2 − 4A.C), SIN(Z/2), etc. These procedures are called, as required, in arithmetic expressions. For example,

$$Z = \text{LOG}(X*2) + \text{SQRT}(\text{SIN}(1 - X*2))$$

As in previous examples, we shall present a flow chart for the program (Fig. 7.3), the BALGOL program itself (Table 7.10), and, finally, line-by-line comments on the program.

Table 7.10 BALGOL Program for Calculating the Natural Logarithm of X

Program	Card number
JØB card	1
LØDX card	2
INTEGER X, N;	3
X = 1;	4
L1 . . R = (X − 1.0)/(X + 1.0);	5
HALFLNX = 0; N = 1;	6
L2 . . EXPN = 2N − 1;	7
TERM = (R*EXPN)/EXPN;	8
HALFLNX = HALFLNX + TERM;	9
IF TERM LSS 0.0001;	10
BEGIN LNX = 2.HALFLNX;	11
WRITE (;; ØUT1, FØRM1);	12
ØUTPUT ØUT1 (X,LNX,N);	13
FØRMAT FØRM1	
(B20, I3, B5, X6.3, B5 ,I4, W0);	14
X = X + 1;	15
IF X GTR 20; GØ TØ L3;	16
GØ TØ L1	17
END;	18
N = N + 1; GØ TØ L2;	19
L3 . . FINISH;	20

Comments on Program

Card 3. Type Declaration. This type declaration specifies that X and N are to be integer quantities. All other quantities are implicitly of the floating type.

Card 5. This assignment statement specifies that R is to be assigned the current value of the expression $(X - 1.0)/(X + 1.0)$. The evaluation of this expression involves three arithmetic operations, namely, addition, subtraction, and division. Each such arithmetic operation involves two numeric operands (that is, values to be operated on). If both operands are of the integer type, then the operation will be performed using integer arithmetic. If both operands are of the floating type or if one operand is floating type and one is integer type, the operation will be performed using floating-point arithmetic. In the latter case, the compiler provides for automatically transforming the integer operand to floating type prior to execution of the arithmetic operation.

In this example the number 1.0 is in decimal form and accordingly is treated as floating type. Therefore, the values of the arithmetic combinations $X - 1.0$ and $X + 1.0$ will be floating type, even though X is integer type. Thus, floating-point arithmetic will be performed when taking the ratio $(X - 1.0)/(X + 1.0)$.

If the statement on card 5 were written as

$$R = (X - 1)/(X + 1);$$

integer arithmetic would be performed, thereby producing the value zero for the variable R for all positive values of X.

Card 7. The variable EXPN is floating-point because it was so declared, even though the arithmetic expression $2N - 1$ consists of terms of integer type. The transformation in type is performed automatically before assignment is made.

Card 10. The IF statement beginning on this card consists of the IF clause followed by the compound statement on cards 11 to 18. If the relationship TERM LSS 0.0001 is *not* satisfied, the compound statement is ignored and the next statement $(N = N + 1)$ is executed. Thus, an additional term of the series is calculated. The series is terminated at the term that contributes less than 0.0001 to HALFLNX.

In this example, the number 0.0001 appears in decimal form in the arithmetic relation TERM LSS 0.0001 and hence is of the same type as the variable TERM, namely, floating type. However, it is not necessary that this always be the case. In general, the form of an arithmetic relation (see Sec. 7.17) is

$$E_1 \, r \, E_2$$

where E_1 and E_2 are arithmetic expressions and r is a relational operator (LSS, GTR, etc.). If the types of the values of E_1 and E_2 are not the same, then the value of the expression (either E_1 or E_2) which is of integer type will be converted automatically to floating type before the relation is tested.

Card 11. Note that the multiplication operator could be omitted without ambiguity.

Cards 12 to 14. The WRITE statement, in combination with the OUTPUT and FORMAT declarations, causes the three variables X, LNX, and N to be printed in the format specified in FORM1. The format is constructed of a string of editing phrases followed by an activation phrase w0. The editing phrases have the following meaning: B20 indicates 20 blank spaces; I3 indicates that an integer number (in this case the value of X) is to be printed in a three-column field; B5 indicates five blank spaces; X6.3 indicates that one floating-point number (in this case the value of LNX) is to be printed in a six-column field with three digits to the right of the decimal point; B5 indicates five blank spaces; and I4 indicates that an integer (N) is to be printed in a four-column field. The activation phrase w0 specifies that the line described by the preceding phrases is to be printed with single spacing. (The zero is redundant and preferably is omitted to avoid confusion with the letter *O*.)

In this and preceding examples, a total of three of the six editing phrases have been illustrated. The three are the I phrase (for integer numbers), the x phrase (for floating-point numbers), and the B phrase (for providing blank spaces). Other phrases are F and S (for floating-point numbers) and the A phrase (for alphanumeric information). For a precise description of the six phrases, see Sec. 7.23. The use of the A phrase is illustrated in Sec. 7.8.

Card 16. Note that this is an IF statement within an IF statement. Note also that it would not be correct to write this statement as

$$\text{IF } X \text{ GTR } 20 \text{ ; FINISH ;}$$

since this would mean that the FINISH declaration would not appear at the end of the program.

7.5 Comments and Headings. The programmer may intersperse descriptive remarks within the BALGOL program by means of the COMMENT declaration if he so desires. Such remarks are solely for the programmer's convenience and have no effect on the compiled machine-language program nor on its execution. As an example, the programmer may wish to begin a program with a COMMENT declaration that describes briefly the purpose of the program. The declaration consists of the declarator COMMENT followed by any *alphanumeric phrase*. The term alphanumeric phrase refers to words or character groups that contain a combination of alphabetic, numeric, and special characters (including spaces). A complete list of these characters as defined in BALGOL is shown in Table 7.13. In the COMMENT declaration the only exceptions are that there cannot be a separator consisting of a pair of dots after the word COMMENT, since this confounds COMMENT . . with a statement label, and there cannot be a semicolon contained within the declaration. As in the case of any other declaration or statement, the separator ; follows the declaration.

For instance, the following line might have been inserted after card 2 of the example in Sec. 7.4:

COMMENT NATURAL LOGARITHMS OF NUMBERS ;

This comment would appear in the listing of the BALGOL program in the same form in which it is written; this would identify the program to the reader.

BALGOL also provides means for interspersing alphanumeric information in the output of the program. One way of accomplishing this is by using an *alphanumeric-insertion phrase* in a format contained in a FORMAT declaration. Such a phrase is enclosed within asterisks and is separated from adjacent editing or activation phrases by commas. The phrase itself may contain any alphanumeric characters (including spaces) other than an asterisk. The use of an alphanumeric-insertion phrase is particularly convenient in providing headings, titles, etc., on the printed output page.

The following illustration makes use of alphanumeric-insertion phrases:

WRITE (;; HEADING) ;
FORMAT HEADING (B22,*X*,B6,*LN X*,B9,*N*,W,W4) ;

The execution of the WRITE statement causes the writing of the headings specified in the format. Note that in this case the WRITE statement does not refer to an output-data set, since none is required, but refers only to a format. The format is as follows: 22 blank spaces, an X, six blank spaces, the expression LN X (note that a space is considered to be a character), nine blank spaces, and an N. The activation phrase w specifies that the preceding is to be printed on a single line after single spacing has occurred. The next phrase w4 specifies that the items to its left (there are none in this case) are to be printed after double spacing. Hence the effect of the two phrases together is to cause single spacing, printing of the desired heading, and then double spacing.

The two cards shown above could be inserted before card 5 in the program shown in Sec. 7.4. The result would be that the headings X,

LN X, and N would appear above the columns of printed output information.

7.6 Arrays and Subscripted Variables. As an illustration of a program containing an array and subscripted variables, let us consider the problem of generating a table that contains the integers 1 to 100, the squares of these integers, and the cubes of these integers:

1	2	3	4	. . .	100
1	4	9	16	. . .	10000
1	8	27	64	. . .	1000000

The table is an ordered *array* of integer values and could have any one of several possible arrangements; for example, the array may have three rows and 100 columns (as indicated above) or it may have 100 rows and three columns. In either case the *subscripted variable* X_{ij} furnishes a convenient method of referring to an element in the array. For instance, one can specify that i is an index over the rows of the array and j is an index over the columns of the array. Then X_{ij} becomes a subscripted variable referring to the value of the element in the ith row and jth column of the array (e.g., X_{23} refers to the value in the second row and third column of the array).

The printing device (the IBM 407 Accounting Machine) used with the Burroughs 220 does not provide for the printing of subscripts. To overcome this difficulty, the common algebraic form X_{ij} is represented as X(I,J) in BALGOL. The list of subscripts is enclosed in parentheses and the subscripts are separated by commas. This particular problem requires only two subscripts, but the language permits as many subscripts as may be required. The number of subscripts must be the same as the dimension of the corresponding array.

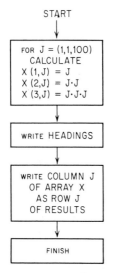

START

FOR J = (1,1,100)
CALCULATE
X (1,J) = J
X (2,J) = J·J
X (3,J) = J·J·J

WRITE HEADINGS

WRITE COLUMN J
OF ARRAY X
AS ROW J
OF RESULTS

FINISH

FIG. 7.4. Flow chart for preparing a table of integers, squares, and cubes.

The flow chart (Fig. 7.4) and BALGOL program (Table 7.11) illustrate the computational process for generating the elements of the table illustrated above and storing them as a 3×100 array (three rows and 100 columns) in memory. After the table is generated, it is printed as a 100×3 array (100 rows and three columns) with a heading over each column.

Table 7.11   BALGOL Program for Preparing a Table of Integers, Squares, and Cubes

Program	Card number
JØB card	1
LØDX card	2
cømment PRØGRAM TØ CØMPUTE SQUARES AND CUBES ØF INTEGERS FRØM 1 to 100;	3
INTEGER ØTHERWISE;	4
ARRAY X(3,100);	5
FØR J = (1,1,100);	6
BEGIN X(1,J) = J;	7
JSQ = X(2,J) = J.J;	8
X(3,J) = JSQ.J	9
END;	10
WRITE (;;HED);	11
FØRMAT HED (B23, *N*, B5, *SQUARE*, B6, *CUBE*, W, W4);	12
FØR J = (1,1,100);	13
WRITE (;;ØDS, FØRM);	14
ØUTPUT ØDS (FØR I = (1,1,3); X(I,J));	15
FØRMAT FØRM (B15, 3I10, W2);	16
FINISH;	17

Comments on Program

Card 3.   This COMMENT declaration identifies the program for the convenience of the programmer.

Card 4.   The type declaration INTEGER OTHERWISE declares that all variables in this program are to be considered as integers.   (In general, this declaration specifies that all variables not otherwise declared explicitly as to type are automatically declared to be integer type.)

Card 5.   ARRAY Declaration.   Before any variable with subscripts may be used in a statement, it is necessary that the array of which it is an element be defined.   This is accomplished by the ARRAY declaration [e.g., ARRAY X(3,100)], which in general consists of the declarator ARRAY and one or more array definitions that are separated from each other by commas.   An *array definition* consists of an identifier (e.g., X) and a list of integers (e.g., 3,100) that defines the dimension and size of the array.   This list is enclosed in parentheses and its elements are separated by commas.   Also, the ARRAY declaration serves the purpose of indicating that the identifier X represents a *multivalued variable*.   A subscripted variable [e.g., X(1,10)] refers to a single element in the array.   Each integer in the list of integers in the array definition represents the upper limit for which the corresponding subscript is defined.   Each upper limit must be 2 or greater; otherwise there is no need for that subscript.   The lower limit of each subscript is automatically assigned the value 1.   The compiler automatically reserves a sufficient number of words in memory to store all elements of the array (in this case 300).

When the type of an array identifier is explicitly declared, it is sufficient to include the identifier in a type list (e.g., INTEGER X), although it is permissible to append parentheses to the identifier [e.g., INTEGER X()].   The latter form is for the convenience of the programmer since it emphasizes that X is an array identifier.

The type declaration for the identifier of the array *must* precede the ARRAY declaration.   Thus, cards 4 and 5 in this example could not be interchanged.

In this example, values were assigned to the elements of the array by means of the assignment statements of cards 7 to 9.   There are occasions, however, when the initial values of the elements in an array must be specified explicitly by the programmer.   This can be accomplished by reading the values from data cards and assigning them to the elements of the array which are specified in an input-data set.   A second method makes use of an alternative form of the array definition, discussed in Sec. 7.21.

Cards 6 to 10.   FOR Statement.   Lines 6 to 10 in this example constitute a FOR statement.   Line 6 contains a FOR clause and lines 7 to 10 contain a compound statement enclosed in the BEGIN . . . END brackets.   In general, a FOR statement comprises a FOR clause, a semicolon (acting as a separator), and a statement (either simple or compound).   The function of the FOR clause is to control iteration (or repeated execution) of the statement that follows the clause.

In this particular example, the clause FOR J = (1,1,100) causes the compound statement contained in lines 7 to 10 to be executed repeatedly for values of J equal to 1, 2, 3, . . . , 100.   After this is done, the statement following the FOR statement is executed (card 11).   Thus the single FOR statement contained in lines 6 to 10 generates the required table of squares and cubes.   The element (1,1,100) is called a *step-until element*, and the details of its operation are discussed in Sec. 7.20.

In addition to step-until elements, a FOR clause may contain a sequence of numbers.   For each such number, the statement contained in the FOR statement will be executed.   Some examples of FOR clauses are as follows:

FOR K = 1, 3, 5, 11, 7, 13, 17
FOR K = (1,1,9), (10,5,50), 100, 200
FOR K = 2, 1.5, (1.0, −0.1, −1.0), −1.5, −2

These examples are self-explanatory and show that the numbers may be positive or negative, of any form (integer, decimal, or floating-point), and that the step-until element may represent either an increasing or a decreasing sequence. Furthermore, any one of the numbers in the above example may be replaced by an arithmetic expression, as discussed in Sec. 7.20. Finally, it should be noted that if the type of the number is not the same as the type of the variable K, then the number will be converted to the type of K.

Card 7. Subscripted Variables. The variable $X(1,J)$ is a subscripted variable, the subscripts specifying the variable to be the jth element of the first row in the array defined by the array declaration $X(3,100)$. The statement $X(1,J) = J$ is an assignment statement that assigns the current value of J to the variable $X(1,J)$.

The general form of the subscripted variable is $ID(E_1, E_2, \ldots, E_n)$, where ID represents an arbitrary identifier and $E_1, E_2, \ldots, E_n$ represent arithmetic expressions. The identifier must have been declared previously (either explicitly or implicitly) as to type, and the array of which the subscripted variable is an element must have been explicitly declared previously as to size. As mentioned above, this is accomplished by the ARRAY declaration, e.g., ARRAY $ID(U_1, U_2, \ldots, U_n)$, in which $U_1, U_2, \ldots U_n$ must be positive integers greater than 1 that specify the upper limits of the corresponding subscripts. A subscript is redundant when its upper limit is 1. The lower limit of each subscript is automatically taken as 1. Thus, the subscript expressions $E_1, E_2, \ldots, E_n$ must satisfy the following restrictions: (1) the value of a subscript must not be less than 1 and (2) the value of a subscript must not exceed its upper limit as specified in the ARRAY declaration. If either of these restrictions is not satisfied, the consequences are undefined but may lead to erroneous results.

A subscript expression E_i may have decimal or floating values, such values being automatically truncated to an integer. For example, the portion of the number 2.356 to the right of the decimal point would be removed in truncation, leaving the integer 2 as the value of the subscript expression.

Card 8. Generalized Assignment Statement. As indicated in this example, two or more variables may be assigned the same value in a single assignment statement. Of course, if the variables are not all of the same type, one must use care in the formulation of a generalized assignment statement. Consider first the simple assignment statement $V_1 = E_1$. If the declared type of V_1 differs from the type of E_1, the value obtained from the evaluation of E_1 will be converted automatically to the type specified for V_1 and the converted value will be assigned to V_1. In particular, a number of the floating type will be truncated to an integer as described above.

Consider next a generalized assignment statement $V_2 = V_1 = E_1$, where E_1 is an expression which yields a number of the floating type, V_1 is integer type, and V_2 is floating type. The result of this generalized assignment is that the value of E_1 will be truncated to an integer for assignment to V_1 and the integer value will then be converted to a floating value and assigned to V_2. However, the decimal-fraction portion of the value of E_1 would have been truncated in the first assignment. If, instead, the statement were written $V_1 = V_2 = E_1$, then V_2 would be assigned the value of E_1 and V_1 would be assigned the truncation of the value of V_2.

In this example the generalized assignment statement and the variable JSQ are introduced into the program solely in order to save computer time during execution. It is more efficient to assign the value of $X(2,J)$ to JSQ and then use JSQ in the next calculation (card 9) than it is to calculate the relative location in the array of the value of $X(2,J)$ for the use in the latter calculation, as would be required if the program were written as follows:

$$X(2,J) = J.J;$$
$$X(3,J) = J.X(2,J);$$

Cards 11 and 12. This WRITE statement in combination with the FORMAT declaration causes the printing of a line of headings for the table of results. The appearance of the line of headings is as follows: 23 blank spaces, the letter N, five blank spaces, the word SQUARE, six blank spaces, and the word CUBE. The spacing has been so arranged that the headings will appear above the appropriate columns of results.

Cards 13 and 14. This is a FOR statement which causes 100 executions of the WRITE statement on card 14. The WRITE statement causes printing of the output-data set ODS (see card 15) in the format FORM (see card 16).

Card 15. OUTPUT Declaration with Subscripted Variables. The FOR clause in the output-data set indicates that the set consists of three variables $X(1,J)$, $X(2,J)$, $X(3,J)$. In other words, the BALGOL language permits the use of the FOR clause to facilitate specification of a sequence of subscripted variables in an output-data set. Note that the FOR clause is followed by a subscripted variable, rather than by a statement, when used in this manner.

The FOR clause may also be used with an INPUT declaration in an analogous manner.

An alternative scheme for use in this illustrative program would be to omit card 13 and replace card 15 by the following:

OUTPUT ODS(for J = (1,1,100); for I = (1,1,3); X(I,J));

If this is done, no change in the FORMAT declaration is needed, since a format enclosed in parentheses (as in card 16) will be repeated indefinitely for the corresponding output-data set (see Sec. 7.23).

7.7   Iterations Controlled by the UNTIL Statement.   Iterative processes occur very frequently in numeric calculations; hence control of iterations is an important part of any computer language.   In the examples of Secs. 7.1, 7.2, and 7.4, it was shown that an IF statement could be used to control an iterative process by specifying that a statement was to be performed conditionally.   Then in Sec. 7.6 the FOR statement was introduced as a means of specifying that a statement was to be performed for a specified set of values of a variable.   Still another means of controlling an iteration is the UNTIL *statement*, which causes a statement to be executed repeatedly until a specified condition is satisfied.

As an illustration of the use of the UNTIL statement, consider the sequence of statements in Table 7.12 for calculating the square root of a number by an iterative process.   It should be noted first that the square root of a number can be obtained in a BALGOL program by means of the library procedure SQRT (see Sec. 7.14).   Hence the example which follows would not be used as part of an actual program. It is selected solely because it provides a very simple example of an iterative process.

Assume that it is desired to calculate values of the variable Y equal to the square root of another variable X, that is,

$$Y = \sqrt{X} \qquad \text{and} \qquad Y^2 = X$$

From these relations it is apparent that

$$2Y^2 = Y^2 + X \qquad \text{and} \qquad Y = \frac{1}{2}\left(Y + \frac{X}{Y}\right)$$

This suggests a recursive formula

$$YNEW = \frac{1}{2}\left(YOLD + \frac{X}{YOLD}\right) \tag{7.1}$$

The recursive formula provides a means of calculating Y for any positive value of X by iteration.   Beginning with the initial approximation for Y, called YOLD, the right-hand side of Eq. (7.1) is evaluated. This produces a new approximation for Y, called YNEW.   Then this new approximation is treated as YOLD and substituted again in the right-hand side of the equation, thus giving a still more accurate approximation for YNEW. This process is continued until the difference between YNEW and YOLD has reached a sufficiently small value, say less than a small number epsilon (EPS).

The statements in Table 7.12 are assumed to be part of a complete BALGOL program. It is assumed that all variables are of the floating type and that elsewhere in the program a value has been assigned to X. It is then desired to obtain the square root of X, if X is positive or zero. If X is negative, it is desired to branch to another part of the program.

Table 7.12   BALGOL Statements for Calculating $\sqrt{X}$

Statements	Card number
EITHER IF X LSS 0; GØ TØ L2;	1
ØR IF X EQL 0; BEGIN YØLD = 0; GØ TØ L1 END;	2
ØR IF X GEQ 1; YØLD = X/2;	3
ØTHERWISE; YØLD = 2X;	4
EPS = 0.00001;	5
DIFF = 1;	6
UNTIL DIFF LEQ EPS;	7
BEGIN YNEW = 0.5 (YØLD + X/YØLD);	8
DIFF = ABS (YØLD − YNEW);	9
YØLD = YNEW	10
END;	11
L1 . . Y = YØLD;	12

Comments on Program

Cards 1 to 4.   EITHER IF Statement.   The statement on these cards constitutes a single EITHER IF statement, which may be considered as a generalization of the IF statement. The reserved word EITHER indicates the start of a special sequence of IF statements, while the reserved word OR indicates a continuation of the sequence. Beginning with the first IF clause, each clause is tested in sequence to determine whether or not its condition is satisfied. When a clause is encountered whose condition is satisfied, the statement immediately following it is executed. Then the entire EITHER IF statement is considered to be satisfied and its successor statement (card 5 in this example) is executed, unless a GO TO statement has caused a branch to some other part of the program. If none of the IF clauses is satisfied, the statement following OTHERWISE is executed.

Thus, in this example, if the relation X LSS 0 is satisfied, the statement GO TO L2 is executed. If it is not satisfied but the relation

X EQL 0 is satisfied, then the compound statement on card 2 is executed. If neither of the first two relations is satisfied but the relation X GEQ 1 is satisfied, then the assignment statement YOLD = X/2 is executed, after which the statement on card 5 is executed. If all three IF clauses are not satisfied, the statement YOLD = 2X is executed, after which the statement in card 5 is executed.

Another form of the EITHER IF statement is discussed in Sec. 7.19.

Card 5. The value of the small quantity EPS must be specified.

Card 6. An initial value for DIFF must be specified (greater than EPS) or else the UNTIL statement may not be executed at all. For example, if DIFF is not assigned a value, it is possible that its current value is zero. Then the condition DIFF LEQ EPS (card 7) is satisfied initially and the UNTIL statement (cards 7 to 11) is not executed.

Cards 7 to 11. UNTIL Statement. These cards contain an UNTIL statement, consisting of an UNTIL clause (card 7) followed by a compound statement (cards 8 to 11). The compound statement is executed repeatedly until the condition specified in the UNTIL clause is satisfied. Then the next statement following the UNTIL statement is executed.

To be more specific, the general form of the UNTIL statement is

$$\text{UNTIL } C; S$$

The letter C indicates a condition (e.g., a relation) and the letter S indicates a statement (either simple or compound). The UNTIL statement operates in the following manner. First, the condition C in the UNTIL clause is tested and one of two results obtains. Either the condition is satisfied (e.g., DIFF $\leq$ EPS) or else the condition is not satisfied (e.g., DIFF $>$ EPS). Second, if the condition is satisfied, then the statement S following the UNTIL clause and contained in the UNTIL statement is not executed. Instead, in this example the next statement is executed (card 12). Third, if the condition is not satisfied, then the statement S is executed. Then the condition is tested again and the cycle just described is repeated until the condition is satisfied. Another possibility is that the statement S contains a GO TO statement, which can break the cycle if that statement is executed. This is illustrated by the flow chart of Fig. 7.5.

Another way of writing the UNTIL statement in the preceding example is to omit card 5 and replace card 7 by the following:

$$\text{UNTIL DIFF LEQ } 0.00001;$$

In addition, the condition C in an UNTIL clause may consist of a Boolean expression as described previously for the IF clause (see Sec.

7.2).   For example, the condition may consist of two arithmetic relations enclosed in parentheses and separated by a Boolean operator,
such as OR or AND.   Thus, one can write

$$(\text{N GTR } 100) \text{ OR } (\text{X LSS EPS})$$

as the condition in an UNTIL clause.   Boolean expressions are described
in Sec. 7.17.

   Card 9.   Intrinsic Function ABS.   This is one of the six intrinsic
functions that are part of the BALGOL language.   The general form
of this function is ABS(E), where E is a number, a variable, or an
arithmetic expression.   The value of ABS(E) is the absolute value
(magnitude) of E.

   The other intrinsic functions are MOD, MAX, MIN, SIGN, and PCS.
For a description of these functions, see Sec. 7.11.

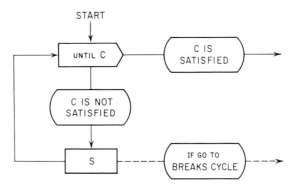

FIG. 7.5. Flow chart for UNTIL statement.

7.8   Alphanumeric Input and Output.   BALGOL provides for the
processing of alphabetic and special characters as well as numeric
characters.   The term *alphanumeric* is used to refer to words or
character groups that may contain a combination of such characters.
It was shown previously that alphanumeric information could be
inserted in the program listing by means of the COMMENT declaration
and that such information could be interspersed within the output
data by means of the alphanumeric-insertion phrase in a format.   The
latter provision is particularly useful for titles and headings.

   In addition to the provisions listed above, it is possible to read alphanumeric information from data cards and also to have such information
printed as output.   In order to understand how this is accomplished,
it is first necessary to observe how alphanumeric characters are coded
for storage in the memory of the computer.   Since information is

stored in memory in the form of 10-digit words, each alphanumeric character is assigned an integer equivalent before it can be stored in memory. Since there are 47 characters to be coded, the integers 00 through 99 more than suffice to provide a unique code consisting of a two-digit integer to represent each alphanumeric character. The convention shown in Table 7.13 has been adopted for the Burroughs 220.

Table 7.13   Integer Equivalents of Alphanumeric Characters

Alphanumeric character in BALGOL	Integer equivalent
A–I	41–49
J–R	51–59
S–Z	62–69
0–9	80–89
+	10
−	20 or 34
=	33
(	24
)	04
.	03
,	23
; or $	13
/	21
*	14
Space	00

Since the numeric equivalent of each alphanumeric character requires two digit positions and since each word in memory contains 10 positions, it follows that each computer word can contain the equivalent of no more than five alphanumeric characters.

It is necessary to adopt a convention that distinguishes alphanumeric information on a data card from numeric information. The BALGOL language requires that alphanumeric information on a data card be enclosed within semicolons (hence a semicolon cannot be contained within the alphanumeric information itself).[1] For example, the following might appear on a data card:

$$;PROBLEM\ NO.\ 37;\ 72.0\ 1914.2$$

[1] This restriction could be eliminated by means of an external procedure (see Sec. 7.15) or a library procedure (see Sec. 7.14). At the Stanford Computation Center, an external procedure named RCARD provides for specifying the format of a data card by means of editing phrases that are analogous to those used in specifying output formats.

The 14 characters within the semicolons would be treated as alphanumeric information; the two numbers following would be treated as numeric data.   When these data are read, the alphanumeric characters between semicolons must be divided into words not exceeding five characters each.   A space is counted as a character.   The first word consists of the first five characters, reading left to right.   The second word consists of the next five characters, etc.   If the last word contains fewer than five characters, it is automatically filled out with spaces, for which the numeric code is 00.

As in the case of numeric values, a variable must be specified to which the value of each word will be assigned when such data are read. It will be recalled that a list of such variables is specified in the definition of an input-data set contained in an INPUT declaration.

In the example given above, the alphanumeric group PROBLEM NO. 37 contains 14 characters (assuming one space after PROBLEM and one space after NO.).   It therefore requires three identifiers in the input-data set.   For example, the INPUT declaration corresponding to the data shown above might be

$$\text{INPUT IDS(ALPH1, ALPH2, ALPH3, X, Y)}$$

where ALPH1 is an identifier corresponding to the first five characters, ALPH2 corresponds to the next five, and ALPH3 corresponds to the last four characters, with a space added automatically to complete the group.   The variable X would be assigned the value 72.0 and Y would be assigned 1914.2.   The identifier IDS refers to the input-data set and would appear in the associated READ statement, e.g., READ (;;IDS).

The reading of the alphanumeric information PROBLEM NO. 37 from a data card would result in the following numbers being assigned to ALPHI1, ALPH2, and ALPH3, respectively:

$$5759564253 \qquad 4554005556 \qquad 0300838700$$

If such values are to be operated on for any purpose other than reading or writing, their identifiers should be declared as integer type.

An alternative way of specifying the identifiers in the INPUT declaration illustrated above is to replace the simple variables ALPH1, ALPH2, and ALPH3 with subscripted variables, as follows:

$$\text{INPUT IDS(FOR } K = (1,1,3)\text{; ALPH(K), X, Y)}$$

This form is useful if the alphanumeric string to be read into the computer is lengthy.   In the example given, the INPUT declaration must be preceded by the ARRAY declaration containing the definition ALPH(3).

Output of alphanumeric information requires a WRITE statement, an OUTPUT declaration, and a FORMAT declaration. In the WRITE statement, alphanumeric information is distinguished from numeric information by an alphanumeric editing phrase (the A phrase) in a format definition. The WRITE statement causes the output-data set identified by the OUTPUT declaration to be printed in the format specified in the FORMAT declaration. Consequently, the identifiers associated with the alphanumeric information must appear in the OUTPUT declaration, and the corresponding editing phrase in the format definition is distinguished by the letter A.

To continue the example, the following portion of a program could be used to cause printing of the information read from the foregoing data card (except for the two semicolons):

WRITE (;; ØDS, FØRM);
ØUTPUT ØDS (ALPH1, ALPH2, ALPH3, X, Y);
FØRMAT FØRM (2A5, A4, B6, 2x10.1,w);

The editing phrase 2A5 specifies that ALPH1 and ALPH2 are to be printed as alphanumeric phrases, each of five characters. The phrase A4 specifies that four characters of ALPH3 are to be printed. These first two editing phrases could be replaced with the single editing phrase A14 and the same results would be achieved. Another alternative is to replace the first three phrases with the phrases A15, B5. The remaining phrases in the format are associated with editing the values of X and Y, which are 72.0 and 1914.2, respectively, and with printing the edited line. The use of a FOR clause in the OUTPUT declaration is also permitted, analogous to its use in an INPUT declaration.

7.9 Subroutines. There are many computational processes that have a wide range of applicability. For example, the need for solving a set of simultaneous linear equations, for multiplying matrices, for inverting a matrix, etc., recurs in a wide variety of problems. It is desirable that an algorithmic language provide for general-purpose descriptions of such frequently used computational processes in order that needless duplication of programming effort may be obviated. The subroutine, the function, and the procedure can be used in a variety of ways to accomplish this purpose. These three types of subprograms will be discussed in this and subsequent sections.

The *subroutine* is useful for intraprogram reduction in programming effort. It is basically a compound statement with a name (rather than a label). It can be used effectively to eliminate repetition of the same compound statement at various points in a single program.

The subroutine is defined by a declaration that consists of the declarator SUBROUTINE, an identifier which serves as a name for the subroutine, and a compound statement. The identifier and the statement are separated by a semicolon. Thus the general form for a subroutine is

$$\text{SUBROUTINE ID; BEGIN } S_1, S_2, \ldots, S_n \text{ END}$$

At least one of the statements in the compound statement must be a RETURN statement, which will be discussed later.

Execution of a subroutine is initiated by execution of an ENTER statement which has the form

$$\text{ENTER ID}$$

in which ID represents the identifier of the subroutine.

The following example is presented as an illustration of a subroutine in a BALGOL program. The purpose of the subroutine is to calculate the square root of a variable X to which a value has been assigned elsewhere in the program. The method of calculating the square root of X is described earlier in Sec. 7.7, and the sequence of statements given in Table 7.12 is incorporated in the subroutine of Table 7.14. It is assumed that all variables are of the floating type. If X is positive or zero, the square root is calculated, but if X is negative, a GO TO statement is executed which causes a branch to another part of the main program.

Table 7.14   A Typical Subroutine Declaration

Statements	Card number
SUBRØUTINE SQUARERØØT;	1
BEGIN	2
EITHER IF X LSS 0; GØ TØ L2;	3
ØR IF X EQL 0; BEGIN YØLD = 0; GØ TØ L1 END;	4
ØR IF X GEQ 1; YØLD = X/2;	5
ØTHERWISE; YØLD = 2X;	6
EPS = 0.00001; DIFF = 1;	7
UNTIL DIFF LEQ EPS;	8
BEGIN YNEW = 0.5 (YØLD + X/YØLD);	9
DIFF = ABS (YØLD − YNEW);	10
YØLD = YNEW	11
END;	12
L1 . . Y = YØLD;	13
RETURN;	14
END SQUARERØØT;	15

Comments on Program

Card 1.   The declarator SUBROUTINE indicates the start of a sub-routine declaration.   It is followed by the arbitrarily selected name of the subroutine, in this case SQUAREROOT.

Cards 2 to 15.   The body of the subroutine is a compound state-ment enclosed with BEGIN . . . END brackets.   The calculations given here for the square root of X are described in Sec. 7.7.

Card 14.   The RETURN statement consists of the single word RETURN.   After the RETURN statement is executed, the next statement in the main program following the ENTER statement that calls the sub-routine will be executed.

Card 15.   As illustrated here, the subroutine identifier may follow the final word END if desired.

To illustrate how the preceding subroutine is called, let us assume that the sequence of statements shown in Table 7.15 is part of a pro-gram containing the subroutine declaration SQUAREROOT.

Table 7.15

Statements	*Card number*
. . .	1
. . .	2
$X = (A - 2)/\text{LØG}(2A);$	3
ENTER SQUARERØØT;	4
IF Y GTR B*2; . . .	5
. . .	6
. . .	7
$X = \text{LØG}(B) + 1/B*2;$	8
ENTER SQUARERØØT;	9
. . .	10
. . .	11
L2 . . WRITE (;;MESSAGE);	12
. . .	13

In the partial program of Table 7.15 it is assumed that X is assigned a value (card 3).   Then the ENTER statement (card 4) calls the sub-routine SQUAREROOT, which must be contained in the program but need not appear prior to the ENTER statement.   After the RETURN statement in the subroutine is executed, the next statement to be executed is the statement (card 5 in the main program) which follows the ENTER statement.   The RETURN statement will not be executed if the value of X is negative, since the GO TO L2 statement in the sub-routine causes a branch to the statement labeled L2.   This might be a WRITE statement which causes printing of a message (see card 12).

Note that an identifier which is used in the subroutine must be defined in the same manner as an identifier in the main program, and it will have the same meaning in both places. Thus, the subroutine is in every sense a component part of the program. Just as compound statements may be contained within compound statements, sub-routines may be defined within other subroutines.

7.10 Functions. The FUNCTION declaration is basically an assignment statement and can be used to eliminate repetition of the same assignment statement at various places in a single program. It may be used for either intraprogram or interprogram reduction in programming effort. It may be adapted for use in several programs since the identifiers used as parameters within the FUNCTION declaration are semi-independent of those used elsewhere in the program.

A function is defined by a declaration that consists of the declarator FUNCTION followed by an assignment statement. The general form is

$$\text{FUNCTION } ID(P_1, P_2, \ldots, P_n) = E$$

The identifier ID chosen as a name for the function is followed by a list of *formal value-parameters* enclosed in parentheses and separated from each other by commas. The formal value-parameters are identifiers of simple variables which serve as the parameters of the function. The expression E on the right-hand side of the assignment symbol is usually formulated in terms of constants and variables in the formal value-parameter list. If desired, any other variables appearing in the program containing the function declaration may appear in the expression; however, this makes the function dependent upon the rest of the program.

As mentioned above, the variables appearing in the formal value-parameter list are semi-independent of identifiers used elsewhere in the program. This is because they must be declared as to type in the main program. However, an identifier that is used in the formal value-parameter list may be used for a different purpose in the main program (i.e., outside of the function declaration). The only restriction is that the two different uses must require only one type declaration for that identifier.

Evaluation of a function occurs whenever its *function designator* appears in an expression in the program. The function designator consists of the function identifier followed by a list of *actual value-parameters* that are enclosed in parentheses and separated from each other by commas:

$$ID(E_1, E_2, \ldots, E_n)$$

The actual value-parameters are expressions defined in terms of constants and/or variables that appear in the program. When a function designator is encountered in program execution, each expression in the actual value-parameter list is evaluated and its current value is assigned to the corresponding variable in the formal value-parameter list prior to evaluation of the expression defined in the function declaration.

It is important to note that a function must be declared before it is referred to by a function designator. Also, a function may be declared inside a subroutine.

To illustrate the FUNCTION declaration, let it be assumed that in a certain program the inverse hyperbolic sine of a number must be evaluated several times. Hence the following FUNCTION declaration is made a part of the program:

$$\text{FUNCTION ARCSINH}(X) = \text{LOG}(X + \text{SQRT}(X*2 + 1))$$

Now let it be assumed that at a later point in the program the inverse hyperbolic sine of a variable BUG is to be calculated and its value assigned to another variable BOG. The following statement could be used:

$$\text{BOG} = \text{ARCSINH}(\text{BUG})$$

The current value of the actual value-parameter BUG is assigned to the formal value-parameter X in the FUNCTION declaration and then the function ARCSINH(X) is evaluated. The resulting value is then assigned to the variable BOG.

As another example, let it be assumed that the assignment statement

$$X = \text{ARCSINH (ARCSINH}(Y*2+))$$

appears elsewhere in the program. In this case two successive evaluations of the declared function would occur. First, the expression $Y*2+1$ is evaluated and its value assigned to the formal value-parameter X is the declared function ARCSINH. The resulting value of ARCSINH(X) is then reassigned to the formal value-parameter X and the function is evaluated a second time. This value is then assigned to the variable X in the main program. In this case the variable X appears in the FUNCTION declaration and also in the assignment statement, with different meanings in each case. A single type declaration (either explicit or implicit) in the program must satisfy both meanings.

Intrinsic functions are discussed in the next section, and functions defined by procedures are discussed in Sec. 7.13.

7.11   Intrinsic Functions. There are six *intrinsic functions* that are part of the BALGOL language and can be designated without the necessity of a FUNCTION declaration.   One of these functions (ABS) was encountered in Sec. 7.7.   The others are MOD, MAX, MIN, SIGN, and PCS. The evaluation of one of these functions occurs whenever the corresponding function designator appears in an expression in the program.

The designator for the function ABS has the form ABS(E), where E is an arithmetic expression (of which numbers and variables are special cases).   The value of the function ABS(E) is the absolute value, or magnitude, of E, and its type (integer or floating) is the same as that of E itself.   The function designator may appear in any arithmetic expression in the program; for example, one can write the assignment statement

$$Y = \text{ABS}(A*2 - B) + \text{ABS}(\text{SQRT}(C - \text{ABS}(D)))$$

or the output-data set X, Y, ABS(Z).   The designator may appear also in a Boolean expression, as illustrated by the following UNTIL clause:

$$\text{UNTIL}(\text{ABS}(X) \text{ LSS } 0.001) \text{ ØR } (N \text{ GTR } 50)$$

The general form of the MOD function is

$$\text{MOD}(E_1, E_2)$$

where E_1 and E_2 may be numbers, variables, or arithmetic expressions, but their values *must* be integer type.   The type of the MOD function is also integer, and the value of the function MOD is the integer obtained as the remainder when the value of E_1 is divided by the value of E_2. For example, MOD(98,10) equals 8 since 98/10 equals 9 plus 8/10; MOD(72,5) equals 2 since 72/5 equals 14 plus 2/5; MOD(24,72) equals 24 since 24/72 equals 24/72; MOD(−72,5) equals −2 since −72/5 equals −14 plus −2/5; MOD(72,−5) equals 2 since 72/−5 equals −14 plus 2/(−5); etc.

In arithmetic two integers are said to be congruent modulo m if they differ by an integral multiple of m.   For example, 8 and 98 differ by an integral multiple of 10; therefore, 8 is congruent to 98(mod 10) or, more concisely,

$$8 \equiv 98(\text{mod } 10)$$

This implies also that

$$98 \equiv 8(\text{mod } 10)$$

From this definition of congruence it is seen that, in general, the intrinsic function MOD has the following meaning:

$$\text{MOD}(E_1, E_2) \equiv E_1(\text{mod } E_2)$$

The MAX and MIN functions are of the form $\text{MAX}(E_1, E_2, \ldots, E_n)$ and $\text{MIN}(E_1, E_2, \ldots, E_n)$, respectively, in which there must be at least two expressions in the list ($n \geq 2$). The value of MAX is that of the algebraically largest expression in the list, and the value of MIN is that of the algebraically smallest expression. The type of the function is integer if all the expressions are integer; otherwise, the type is floating.

The function SIGN has the form SIGN(E), where E is a single expression, and is equal to $+1$ if E is positive (when evaluated), -1 if E is negative, and 0 if E is 0. The type of the function is the same as that of E.

All the above functions may be used in any arithmetic or Boolean expression in a program as illustrated for the function ABS.

The function PCS has the form PCS(E) and is used to determine whether a particular program control switch is on or off. The use of this function is described in the "Burroughs Algebraic Compiler."

7.12 Procedures. The *procedure* is a subprogram which is particularly useful for eliminating duplication of programming effort. Its importance stems from the fact that the identifier notation used within a procedure is completely independent of the notation used outside the procedure. This feature makes it quite simple for a programmer to incorporate in his program a procedure written by another programmer. Except for the identifier chosen as the name of the procedure itself, the programmer may duplicate in his program any identifiers used in a procedure that is to be incorporated. The method for achieving communication between a program and a procedure contained therein will be explained in the discussion of the example that follows.

The example defines a procedure for performing the computations required in matrix-by-vector multiplication. The column vector V, having the form

$$\begin{bmatrix} v_1 \\ v_2 \\ \cdot \\ \cdot \\ \cdot \\ v_{\text{RVMAX}} \end{bmatrix}$$

is to be premultiplied by the matrix M which has RMAX rows and CMAX columns:

$$\begin{bmatrix} m_{1,1} & m_{1,2} & \cdots & m_{1,\text{CMAX}} \\ m_{2,1} & m_{2,2} & \cdots & m_{2,\text{CMAX}} \\ \cdot & \cdot & \cdots & \cdot \\ m_{\text{RMAX},1} & m_{\text{RMAX},2} & \cdots & m_{\text{RMAX},\text{CMAX}} \end{bmatrix}$$

It is, of course, necessary that the number of columns of M be the same as the number of rows of V in order that M and V are compatible for matrix-by-vector multiplication, that is, CMAX = RVMAX. The result of the multiplication $M \cdot V$ is a vector P, which has the form

$$\begin{bmatrix} p_1 \\ p_2 \\ \cdot \\ \cdot \\ \cdot \\ p_{\mathrm{RVMAX}} \end{bmatrix}$$

in which

$$p_1 = m_{1,1}v_1 + m_{1,2}v_2 + \cdots + m_{1,\mathrm{CMAX}}v_{\mathrm{RVMAX}}$$
$$p_2 = m_{2,1}v_1 + m_{2,2}v_2 + \cdots + m_{2,\mathrm{CMAX}}v_{\mathrm{RVMAX}}$$
$$\cdots$$
$$\cdots$$

In order that the multiplication procedure be generally applicable, it is necessary that the size of the matrix M be variable; hence the procedure is defined in terms of the number of rows RMAX and the number of columns CMAX. In the event that CMAX is not equal to RVMAX, the procedure provides an immediate exit from the procedure to a labeled statement in the main program.

The declaration for a matrix-by-vector multiplication procedure named MATVECMULT is shown in Table 7.16.

Table 7.16 Example of a BALGOL Procedure Declaration

Statements	Card number
PRØCEDURE MATVECMULT(RMAX,CMAX,RVMAX;M(,),V(), P();ERR);	1
BEGIN	2
INTEGER RMAX,CMAX,RVMAX,R,C;	3
IF CMAX NEQ RVMAX; GØ TØ ERR;	4
FØR R = (1,1,RMAX);	5
BEGIN	6
SUM = 0;	7
FØR C = (1,1,CMAX);	8
SUM = SUM + M(R,C)V(C);	9
P(R) = SUM	10
END;	11
RETURN END;	12

The PROCEDURE declaration is a self-contained description of the computational process and consists of the declarator PROCEDURE, a procedure *heading*, a semicolon, and the procedure *body*. In this example the heading appears on card 1 following the declarator, and the body appears on cards 2 to 12. The heading includes the procedure identifier (MATVECMULT) and the *formal-parameter list* which is contained in parentheses. The formal-parameter list consists of those identifiers and labels used in the description of the computational process that are to serve as channels of communication between the procedure and a program which contains it. The procedure body is a compound statement. It must contain declarations that are necessary to define the properties of the identifiers used in the procedure declaration (as in this example on card 3) and it must contain a RETURN statement. The RETURN statement serves the same purpose in a procedure as in a subroutine.

The formal-parameter list has three subdivisions that are separated by semicolons, Starting at the left, the first subdivision contains a list of *formal value-parameters* that are separated by commas; e.g., RMAX, CMAX, RVMAX. The second subdivision contains a list of *formal name-parameters* that are separated by commas, e.g., M(,), V(), P(). The third subdivision contains *formal program-reference-parameters*, e.g., ERR. The subdivisions are separated by semicolons.[1]

The value-parameters are variables which will be assigned a single value when the procedure is called. Hence, they permit only one-way communication, namely, from the program to the procedure. The name-parameters are identifiers of variables or arrays and will be replaced by corresponding identifiers from the main program at the time the procedure is called. This replacement results in a two-way communication between the program and the procedure, which is effective for the duration of procedure execution. A name-parameter that identifies an array comprises an identifier followed by parentheses. The parentheses contain one less comma than the dimension of the array; for example, M(,) and V() identify two- and one-dimensional arrays, respectively. No subscript limits are specified and no ARRAY declarations for these quantities are required within the procedure because the actual arrays are defined and contained in the program outside the procedure. The program-reference-parameters are identifiers representing statement labels; identifiers for subroutines, input-data sets, output-data sets, or formats; or identifiers for functions or procedures (in which case the identifier is followed by empty parentheses).

---

[1] In the reference manual "Burroughs Algebraic Compiler," the three subdivisions are called input, output, and program-reference parameter lists, respectively. The terminology used here is introduced because it is descriptive of the functions of the lists and is consonant with the ALGOL terminology.

Execution of a PROCEDURE is initiated by a *procedure-call statement* that cannot precede the declaration for the procedure being called. As an example of a procedure-call statement, consider the following statement which calls for the execution of the procedure MATVECMULT:

MATVECMULT(I,J,K; A(,), B(), C(); LABEL1)

The procedure-call statement contains the name of the procedure and the actual-parameter list. The latter is enclosed in parentheses and must correspond element by element with the formal-parameter list of the procedure declaration. Thus, the actual-parameter list also contains three subdivisions: value-parameters, name-parameters, and program-reference-parameters. These subdivisions are separated by semicolons.

The list of actual value-parameters is a list of expressions, of which variables and numbers are special cases. These expressions are defined in terms of the identifier notation of the main program. It will be recalled that evaluation of an expression results in a single value. When the procedure-call statement is executed, each expression in the actual value-parameter list is evaluated, and the current value for each expression is assigned to its corresponding formal value-parameter prior to execution of the body of the procedure. Thus, in this example the current values of I, J, and K are assigned to RMAX, CMAX, and RVMAX.

The list of actual name-parameters should be a list of variables or array identifiers which are defined in the program outside the procedure. When the procedure-call statement is executed, each formal name-parameter is replaced by its counterpart actual name-parameter prior to the execution of the body of the procedure. The consequence of name replacement is that the procedure can operate directly on the variables and arrays defined in the program outside the procedure. Thus, a two-way channel of communication is set up between the program and the procedure.

Array identifiers in the actual name-parameter list must agree as to dimension with their counterparts in the formal name-parameter list. This means that the number of empty subscript positions must be identical in counterpart identifiers. In this example the dimensionality is identical for the arrays referred to in the procedure and their counterparts in the main program; hence the forms of the counterpart array identifiers in the formal and actual name-parameter lists are strictly analogous.

The dimension of an array in the main program may exceed that of the counterpart array referred to in the procedure. The resultant modification in the form of the array identifier in the actual name-parameter list is illustrated in a later example.

The entities represented by the actual program-reference-parameters must correspond to those of the formal program-reference-parameters, and they must be defined appropriately in the main program. Actual program-reference-parameters may be statement labels; identifiers for subroutines, intput-data sets, output-data sets, or formats; or identifiers of functions or procedures. In the last cases the identifier is followed by empty parentheses. An exception is that an intrinsic function may not be used as an actual program-reference-parameter. If it is desired to do so, the function should be renamed by means of a FUNCTION declaration, after which the name of the function (followed by parentheses) can be used as an actual program-reference parameter.

When the procedure-call statement is executed, the formal program-reference-parameters are replaced by the actual program-reference-parameters prior to execution of the statements in the procedure body. In the preceding example, the label LABEL1 will replace ERR when the procedure-call statement is executed. Thus, whenever the GO TO ERR statement (card 4) is executed within the procedure, the effect will be that of executing the statement GO TO LABEL1. Hence, there must be a statement in the main program carrying the label LABEL1.

For the most part, the body of a procedure is prepared in the same manner as a program. Some restrictions concerning procedures are the following: (1) The procedure body must be enclosed within BEGIN and END brackets. (2) The body must contain a RETURN statement and must not contain a FINISH statement. (3) A PROCEDURE declaration may not contain another PROCEDURE declaration but may contain SUBROUTINE and FUNCTION declarations and may refer to other procedures by means of program-reference parameters. (4) A procedure must be declared before it is called. (5) After a procedure is declared, the identifier which names it is recognized as such throughout the remainder of the program and it becomes (in effect) a reserved word for any program containing that procedure. However, the name of the procedure could be used as a formal parameter for another PROCEDURE or FUNCTION declaration.

As another example of a procedure-call statement, consider the following portion of a program which defines the premultiplication of a matrix B by a matrix A, yielding a product matrix $C = [AB]$. It is assumed that matrix A has m rows and n columns and matrix B has p rows and q columns. Furthermore, it is assumed that the numbers defining the sizes of the two matrices have been stored as elements of an array L:

$$L = \begin{bmatrix} m & n \\ p & q \end{bmatrix}$$

Thus, it is seen that $m = L(1,1)$, $n = L(1,2)$, etc. The execution of the following FOR statement would determine the product matrix C:

FOR $J = (1,1,L(2,2))$;

MATVECMULT$(L(1,1),L(1,2),L(2,1);A(,),B(,J),$
C(,J)$;$ LABEL1$)$;

The formal name-parameter list in the PROCEDURE declaration, MATVECMULT, contains the array identifiers $M(,),V(),P()$. The actual name-parameter list in the foregoing procedure-call statement is $A(,)$, $B(,J)$, $C(,J)$. The form of $M(,)$ is identical to $A(,)$, as in the preceding example. The form of $V()$ is not identical to that of $B(,J)$ but the number of empty subscript positions is the same for both.

This is a case in which the dimension of the array in the main program exceeds that of the counterpart array referred to in the PROCEDURE declaration. In such a case, the dimensionalities of actual and formal name-parameters are made to agree by fixing one (or more) of the subscripts in the actual name-parameter. This has the effect of temporarily reducing the dimension of the array while the procedure is executed.

In this example the counterpart of array $V()$ is the jth column of $B(,)$ and the counterpart of $P()$ is the jth column of $C(,)$. Thus the dimensions of the counterpart actual and formal name-parameters are identical for purposes of procedure execution.

It is not uncommon to find that a procedure is declared in which one or more of the parameter lists is empty. For example, the procedure heading may contain value and name-parameters, but no program-reference parameters. In such a case the semicolon which normally precedes the program-reference parameters should be omitted. The mandatory use of semicolons in the procedure heading is shown by the following forms, in which VP, NP, and PRP represent lists of value-parameters, name-parameters, and program-reference parameters, respectively: (VP; NP; PRP), (; NP; PRP), (VP;;PRP), (VP;NP), (;; PRP), (;NP), or (VP). The fifth form explains the requirement for semicolons in the READ and WRITE statements, which are actually procedure-call statements (see Secs. 7.22 and 7.23).

A procedure such as MATVECMULT, which is written in BALGOL language, is known as a *declared procedure*. In this case, it is a procedure which is written by the programmer himself, punched on cards, and then embodied in the main program.   Another source of declared procedures is the computation center library, in which case the procedure would probably have been written by another programmer.   A deck of cards containing the procedure (in BALGOL) is obtained from the library and is inserted at an appropriate location in the main program by the programmer, just as though he had written the procedure himself.

Other types of procedures are the previously mentioned *library procedures* (see Sec. 7.14) and *external procedures* (see Sec. 7.15).

7.13 Functions Defined by Procedures.   Frequently the computations required to evaluate a mathematical function cannot be defined by a single arithmetic expression and hence cannot be defined in a FUNCTION declaration.   Instead, a PROCEDURE declaration is required to define the computational process.   In such a case it is desirable that the procedure behave like a function in order that a procedure-call statement can be included in an expression as though it were a function designator.

For the procedure to behave like a function, its execution must result in a single value that can be used in the evaluation of any expression containing it.   This is accomplished by including in the body of the procedure a *procedure-assignment* statement that assigns a single value to the procedure identifier.   The statement has the form

$$ID(\ ) = E$$

in which ID is the procedure identifier and E is an expression.   The effect of this statement is to assign to the procedure identifier ID the current value of E.   The procedure identifier must be followed by empty parentheses.   It is mandatory that the procedure-assignment statement be followed immediately by a RETURN statement, if the procedure is to behave like a function.

As an illustration of such a procedure, let us consider the PROCEDURE declaration in Table 7.17, which describes the computation of the series approximation to the exponential function:[1]

$$e^x = 1 + x + \frac{x^2}{2!} + \frac{x^3}{3!} + \cdots$$

The identifiers used in the declaration have the following significance: XABS represents the absolute value of X, N represents the

[1] The library procedure EXP (see Sec. 7.14) employs a rational function that can be computed more rapidly than the series approximation of e^x.

number of the term in the series, TERM represents the value of the Nth term, and SUM represents the value of the sum of the first N terms.

Table 7.17   Example of a Procedure That Behaves like a Function

Statements	Card number
PRØCEDURE EXPFCT(X);	1
BEGIN XABS = ABS(X);	2
IF XABS LSS 112.82666;	3
BEGIN	4
TERM = SUM = N = 1.0;	5
UNTIL (TERM/SUM) LEQ 0.00000001;	6
BEGIN	7
TERM = TERM(XABS/N);	8
SUM = SUM + TERM;	9
N = N + 1.0	10
END;	11
IF X LSS 0; SUM = 1.0/SUM;	12
EXPFCT ( ) = SUM; RETURN	13
END;	14
WRITE (;; ØDS, FØRM);	15
ØUTPUT ØDS (X);	16
FØRMAT FØRM (*X = *, x15.6, B5, *IS ØUT ØF RANGE FØR EXPFCT*, w);	17
RETURN	18
END;	19

Comments on Procedure EXPFCT(X)

Card 1.   The PROCEDURE heading defines the name of the procedure (EXPFCT) and the formal-parameter list.   In this case the list consists of one formal value-parameter, namely, X.   As a consequence, no semicolon appears in the formal parameter list, as explained earlier.

Card 2.   The procedure body appears on cards 2 to 19 and is enclosed by the brackets BEGIN and END.

Card 3.   Since $e^{112.82666} \geq 10^{50}$, e^x is computed only when $|x| <$ 112.82666.   Otherwise, the program skips to the WRITE statement on card 15 and an error message is printed.

Card 5.   Initially, TERM, SUM, and N are set equal to 1, which represents their values when the first term in the series is considered.

Cards 6 to 11.   When this UNTIL statement is executed, the value of e^x is calculated to the accuracy specified by the UNTIL clause and the result is assigned to the variable SUM, representing the sum of N terms.

Card 12.   If x is negative, then $e^x = 1/\text{SUM}$.

Card 13. Procedure-assignment Statement. This statement assigns the value of SUM to EXPFCT( ). A RETURN statement follows immediately, as is required when a procedure is to behave like a function.

Card 15. This WRITE statement provides for printing an error message whenever XABS is outside the permitted range. It is followed by a RETURN statement (card 18) in order to return to the main program.

Card 17. The FORMAT declaration (which is assumed to be punched in one card) provides for printing an output line in the following form:

$$X = dddddddd.dddddd \text{ IS OUT OF RANGE FOR EXPFCT}$$

No type declarations appear in this procedure; hence all variables are implicitly floating.

A call statement for a function defined as a procedure can appear directly in an expression, for example, the assignment statement

$$CF = EXPFCT(LAMBDA)$$

causes the above procedure to be executed with the current value of LAMBDA assigned to X. Then the resulting value of SUM [equal to EXPFCT(X)] is assigned to the variable CF.

The cards containing the function defined as a procedure are incorporated in the program deck in the same manner as a declared procedure.

7.14 Library Procedures. The BALGOL language includes a number of *library procedures* which can be called without the procedure being declared in the program. The general form of the call statement is the same for each of these procedures, i.e., the procedure name followed by the argument (a number, a variable, or an expression) which is enclosed within parentheses, thus:

$$NAME(E)$$

where the NAME is the reserved word used as the name of the procedure. These procedure-call statements are included in arithmetic or Boolean expressions as required, in the same manner as described for intrinsic functions (see Sec. 7.11).

Most of the library procedures are summarized in Table 7.18. In each case the required type of the argument E and the type of the result are given, as well as the value which results from execution of the procedure. For more detailed information pertaining to these and other library procedures, the reader should refer to the manual "Burroughs Algebraic Compiler."

Table 7.18   Library Procedures

Name ID	Type of argument E	Value of result	Type of result
SQRT	Floating	$\sqrt{E}$	Floating
EXP	Floating	e^E	Floating
LOG	Floating	$\ln E$	Floating
SIN	Floating	$\sin E$, E in radians	Floating
COS	Floating	$\cos E$, E in radians	Floating
TAN	Floating	$\tan E$, E in radians	Floating
ARCSIN	Floating	$\arcsin E$, radians	Floating
ARCCOS	Floating	$\arccos E$, radians	Floating
ARCTAN	Floating	$\arctan E$, radians	Floating
SINH	Floating	$\sinh E$, E in radians	Floating
COSH	Floating	$\cosh E$, E in radians	Floating
TANH	Floating	$\tanh E$, E in radians	Floating
ENTIRE	Floating	Largest integer not greater than E	Floating
ROMXX	Floating	$\sqrt{1 - E^2}$	Floating
FLOAT	Integer	E	Floating
FIX	Floating	E	Integer

The READ and WRITE procedures are described in Secs. 7.22 and 7.23.

7.15   External Procedures.   An external procedure is a machine-language program that is stored in a deck of punched cards.   When an external procedure is to be referred to in a program, it must be declared in the program and its deck of cards must be appended to the BALGOL program deck (see Sec. 7.25).   The declaration of the procedure must precede any other reference to the procedure.

The declaration for an external procedure has the following form: EXTERNAL PROCEDURE ID (VP$_1$, VP$_2$, . . . ; NP$_1$, NP$_2$, . . . ; PRP$_1$, PRP$_2$, . . .) where VP, NP, and PRP indicate value, name, and program-reference parameters, respectively.   It is seen from this example that the declaration consists of the declarator EXTERNAL PROCEDURE followed by a procedure heading of the same form as the procedure heading in a declared procedure (see Sec. 7.12).   The identifier ID and the list of parameters would be defined in a description of the external procedure obtainable from the computation center librarian.

Execution of an external procedure is called in the same manner as a declared procedure.

When the external procedure is to behave like a function, then the external procedure declaration must be followed by a type declaration for the procedure identifier ID, thus:

EXTERNAL PROCEDURE ID(parameter list); type declarator ID

A semicolon must be the only symbol (other than spaces) between the two declarations.

The *external statement* is a special case of the external procedure where the parameter list is empty. The primary function of the external statement is to provide a means for inserting a sequence of machine-language instructions (written by the programmer) into a BALGOL program. Since machine language is beyond the scope of this text, external statements will not be discussed further.

ADDITIONAL TOPICS AND SUMMARIES

The following sections contain additional information pertaining to BALGOL, as well as summaries of features of the language which have been described previously. Also included are a list of reserved words and a description of the organization of the input-card deck.

7.16 Arithmetic Expression. The concept of an *arithmetic expression* in BALGOL corresponds to that of an algebraic expression in algebra. Each is formulated in terms of constants, variables, arithmetic operators, and parentheses.

Table 7.19 Simple Arithmetic Expressions

Simple arithmetic expressions in BALGOL	Meaning of arithmetic operator
$V_1 * V_2$	Exponentiation
$V_1 . V_2$	Multiplication
V_1 / V_2	Division
$V_1 + V_2, V_1 - V_2$	Addition, subtraction

A *constant* is a number. It may have any of the three forms (integer, decimal, or floating-point) defined in Sec. 7.3.

The concept of a *variable* in BALGOL is that of a variable in algebra. Thus, a variable is an identifier that represents any unspecified value from a set of values.

The permissible arithmetic operators are illustrated in Table 7.19, in which V_1 and V_2 represent variables.

It is permissible, of course, that V_1 and V_2 be replaced by constants. However, it should be noted that the multiplication operator is identical to the decimal point.   When V_1 and V_2 are both replaced by constants, ambiguity is avoided by requiring that one or the other of the two constants be enclosed in parentheses.

In the cases illustrated in Table 7.20, the multiplication operator is redundant and may be omitted.   In that table, the following notation is used:

ID: Identifier of simple variable, array, or function
V: Identifier of simple variable
C: Constant

Exponentiation $(V_1 * V_2)$ is undefined when $V_1 = 0$ and $V_2 \leq 0$, or when $V_1 < 0$ and B is nonintegral.   Otherwise the values of V_1 and V_2 may be positive or negative and integer or noninteger.

Division (A/B) is undefined when $B = 0$.

It is permissible to replace V_1 and V_2 (in Table 7.19) with function designators (see Sec. 7.10) or with procedure-call statements when the procedures behave like functions (see Sec. 7.13).

Table 7.20   Cases in Which Multiplication Operator Is Redundant

Form with multiplication operator	Equivalent form with multiplication operator omitted
).ID	)ID
).C	)C
).(	)(
V.(	V(
C.(	C(
C.ID	CID

More complicated arithmetic expressions may be formed by composition of simple arithmetic expressions.   Thus it is permissible to replace the variables V_1 and V_2 in Table 7.19 by expressions E_1 and E_2 of arbitrary complexity.

Parentheses should be used freely by the programmer, just as in algebra, to obviate ambiguity with respect to the order in which operations are performed in the evaluation of an expression.   For example, $A/B/C$ should be either $(A/B)/C$ or $A/(B/C)$, and $A*B*C$ should be either $(A*B)*C$ or $A*(B*C)$.   Within parentheses, the order of precedence of performing operations corresponds to the order in which the simple arithmetic expressions are listed in Table 7.19, i.e., expo-

nentiation, multiplication, division, then addition or subtraction·
Subject to these restrictions, operations are performed working from
right to left.

Note that each arithmetic operator requires two operands. The
type of arithmetic in which an operation is performed depends upon
the types of the values of the operands. Each operand must, of
course, represent a single numeric value. An operation will be performed in integer arithmetic if and only if both operands are values of
integer type, and the resulting value will be integer type. In integer
arithmetic, division always yields an integer quotient; e.g., 8/3 results
in the quotient 2, and 4/6 results in the quotient 0 (see Sec. 7.3 for the
examples of integer arithmetic). When the magnitude of the product
of two integers exceeds 9999999999, the result is truncated from the
left and only the low-order digit positions are retained.

If either or both of the operands are values of the floating type,
then the operation will be performed in floating-point arithmetic.
The necessary transformation from integer to floating type will be performed automatically prior to execution of the operation, and the
resulting value will be floating type.

Similarly, when the value resulting from evaluation of an arithmetic
expression is assigned to a variable of a different arithmetic type, the
necessary transformation in type is performed automatically prior to
execution of the assignment operator.

It is permissible to replace E_1 and E_2 with Boolean expressions (see
Sec. 7.17). Evaluation of Boolean expression yields either the value 1
or 0, and when these values are encountered in an arithmetic expression
they are treated in every respect as integers.

7.17 Boolean Expressions. The use of a Boolean expression to
specify a condition in an IF clause has been illustrated in Sec. 7.2.
However, Boolean expressions have a much wider range of application
than is indicated in that illustration. For example, they are used in
problems involving symbolic logic, Boolean algebra, switching circuits,
etc.

Boolean expressions are formulated in terms of Boolean constants,
Boolean variables, Boolean operators, arithmetic expressions, relational operators, and parentheses.

The Boolean constants are the digits 1 (representing true) and 0
(representing false). Boolean variables are named by means of
identifiers in the same manner as arithmetic variables. Since the
rules for formulating identifiers are independent of the properties of
the entity identified, it is necessary to declare Boolean variables as to
type. This is accomplished in a manner that is analogous to declara-

tions for variables of integer type and floating type. The difference is that the declarator in this case is the reserved word BOOLEAN, e.g.,

BOOLEAN S, ABLE, BAKER, B1, B2

A variable may be either single-valued or array-valued. In the latter case, the size and dimensionality of the array is defined in an array declaration in the manner previously described (see Sec. 7.6).

The relational operators are a special set of Boolean operators, for which the operands may be arithmetic expressions. The relations shown in Table 7.21 can be specified in BALGOL.

Table 7.21   Arithmetic Relations

BALGOL	*Mathematical equivalent*
E_1 LSS E_2	$E_1 < E_2$
E_1 LEQ E_2	$E_1 \leq E_2$
E_1 EQL E_2	$E_1 = E_2$
E_1 NEQ E_2	$E_1 \neq E_2$
E_1 GEQ E_2	$E_1 \geq E_2$
E_1 GTR E_2	$E_1 > E_2$

In the foregoing relations, E_1 and E_2 represent arithmetic expressions. The operators LSS, LEQ, etc., are called *relational operators* and must be preceded and followed by a space. The meaning of each operator is indicated by its familiar counterpart shown in the column headed Mathematical Equivalent. Note that the mathematical symbol for EQL is used in BALGOL as the assignment operator, whereas the mathematical symbols for the remaining relational operators are undefined in BALGOL.

As illustrated in Sec. 7.1, a simple relation may appear in an IF clause or an UNTIL clause without being enclosed in parentheses. However, when a relation is to be evaluated as a Boolean expression, it must be enclosed in parentheses. For example IF E1 LSS E2, is a well-defined IF clause; and V = (E1 LSS E2) is a well-defined assignment statement, where (E1 LSS E2) is a Boolean expression. Normally V would have been declared as Boolean type, and it would be assigned the value 1 (true) if the value of E1 is algebraically less than E2; otherwise, it would be assigned the value 0 (false).

The remaining Boolean operators are NOT, AND, OR, IMPL, and EQIV. Each of the first three operators has the same meaning in BALGOL that is attributed to it in symbolic logic. The last two have the meanings attributed to the operators implication and equivalence, respectively, in symbolic logic. These meanings are defined below in terms of the values that result from application of each operator. It is assumed here that B1 and B2 are Boolean variables. However, the meanings hold when either or both are replaced by Boolean expressions.

The expression NOT B1 has the value 1 when B1 has the value 0, and NOT B1 has the value 0 when B1 has the value 1. Note that the operator NOT has only one operand, which always follows and never precedes the operator. The remaining Boolean operators, like arithmetic operators, have two operands each, one preceding the operator and the other following it.

The expression B1 AND B2 has the value 1 if and only if B1 and B2 simultaneously have the value 1. Otherwise the expression B1 AND B2 has the value 0.

The expression B1 OR B2 has the value 0 if and only if B1 and B2 simultaneously have the value 0. Otherwise B1 OR B2 has the value 1.

The expression B1 IMPL B2 has the value 0 if and only if B1 has the value 1 while B2 simultaneously has the value 0. Otherwise B1 IMPL B2 has the value 1.

The expression B1 EQIV B2 has the value 1 if and only if B1 and B2 simultaneously have identical values. Otherwise B1 EQIV B2 has the value 0.

The meanings of the operators are summarized in Table 7.22, which in symbolic logic would be referred to as a truth table. The table shows the values assumed by each expression when the variables B1 and B2 assume each of the four possible pairs of values.

Table 7.22 Truth Table for the Boolean Operators

Operands	Values			
B1	0	0	1	1
B2	0	1	0	1
Expressions				
NOT B1	1	1	0	0
B1 AND B2	0	0	0	1
B1 OR B2	0	1	1	1
B1 IMPL B2	1	1	0	1
B1 EQIV B2	1	0	0	1

It was stated earlier that B1 and B2 could be replaced by Boolean expressions. This will be illustrated in the following example.

Consider the problem of adding two binary integers.[1] This will involve an addend A1, an augend A2, a sequence of "carries" C, and the resultant sum S, as shown below.

Carries	(C	0	1	1	0
Addend	(A1)	0	0	1	1
Augend	(A2)	1	0	1	1
Sum	(S)	1	1	1	0

In order to describe the generation of S in BALGOL in terms of Boolean expressions, let J be an index over the digit positions of the numbers shown above. Thus C, A1, A2, and S become array-valued Boolean variables, and the first element in each array is the units position of the corresponding binary integer, the second element is the twos position, etc.

Now consider the partial sum PS(J) and the partial carry PC(J) resulting from adding the pair of elements A1(J) and A2(J). The following truth table shows the outcome for each possible pair of values of A1(J) and A2(J):

A1(J)	0	0	1	1
A2(J)	0	1	0	1
PS(J)	0	1	1	0
PC(J)	0	0	0	1

Referring back to Table 7.22, which summarizes the meanings of the Boolean expressions, it is seen that the assignment statement

$$PS(J) = \text{NOT } (A1(J) \text{ EQIV } A2(J))$$

results in PS(J) assuming the appropriate value for each pair of values that A1(J) and A2(J) can assume. Similarly, it is seen that

$$PC(J) = A1(J) \text{ AND } A2(J)$$

results in PC(J) being assigned the appropriate values.

To complete the calculation of S(J), it is necessary to add $C(J)$ to PS(J) as shown in the following table. The variable PC2(J) represents the resultant contribution to C(J+1).

C(J)	0	0	1	1
PS(J)	0	1	0	1
S(J)	0	1	1	0
PC2(J)	0	0	0	1

[1] This example illustrates the logic of adding binary integers as it is performed by an electronic computer.

Thus the following assignment statements serve to calculate the values of $S(J)$ and $PC2(J)$:

$$S(J) = \text{NOT } (C(J) \text{ EQIV } PS(J))$$
$$PC2(J) = C(J) \text{ AND } PS(J)$$

Finally, the value of the carry to position $J+1$ is calculated by the assignment statement

$$C(J+1) = PC(J) \text{ OR } PC2(J)$$

Alternatively, the value of $S(J)$ and of $C(J+1)$ could be calculated as follows:

$$PS(J) = \text{NOT } (A1(J) \text{ EQIV } A2(J));$$
$$S(J) = \text{NOT } (C(J) \text{ EQIV } PS(J));$$
$$C(J+1) = (A1(J) \text{ AND } A2(J)) \text{ OR } (C(J) \text{ AND } PS(J));$$

If the sum S is limited to 10 digit positions and if $C(11)$ is 1, then an overflow has occurred. This fact could be identified automatically in an actual accumulator and could be used to signal an overflow error (see Sec. 7.24).

Note that, as in the case of arithmetic expressions, parentheses are used freely to obviate ambiguity. Within parentheses the order of precedence of executing Boolean operations is NOT, AND, OR, IMPL, EQIV.

Since the Boolean values are stored as integers, Boolean expressions may be included in arithmetic expressions where they will behave, in all respects, like arithmetic expressions that may assume only the integer values 0 and 1.

7.18 The GO TO and SWITCH Statements. The normal sequence of execution of statements in a BALGOL program is in the order of their appearance. It has been demonstrated that the normal sequence may be varied by the execution of a GO TO statement which has the form

GO TO SL

where SL represents a statement label. When the GO TO statement is executed, its successor is the statement that is prefixed with the label SL.

The SWITCH statement may be regarded as a generalization of the GO TO statement. The SWITCH statement has the form

SWITCH E, $(L_1, L_2, \ldots, L_k)$

where E represents an arithmetic expression; L_1, L_2, L_3, . . . , and L_k represent statement labels; and k represents the number of labels in the list.

When the SWITCH statement is executed, the expression $E' = |E|$ is evaluated. If E' is of the floating type, it is automatically converted to an integer i; otherwise $i = E'$. The integer i serves as an index for selecting the label of the successor to the SWITCH statement.

If $i = 0$, no label is selected and the normal sequence of statement execution is unaffected.

If $1 \leq i \leq k$, the ith label, counting from left to right, in the list is selected; this identifies the successor to the SWITCH statement.

If $i > k$, the successor to the SWITCH statement is undefined, and the consequences cannot be predicted.

As an example, consider the statement.

SWITCH Y-2, (5, 18, 12)

Table 7.23 shows the relationship between values of Y, the resulting value of the index i, and the successor to the SWITCH statement.

Table 7.23   Successors to a SWITCH Statement

Range of Y	i	Successor to the SWITCH statement
$Y \leq -2$	≥ 4	Undefined
$-2 < Y \leq -1$	3	Statement prefixed with label 12
$-1 < Y \leq 0$	2	Statement prefixed with label 18
$0 < Y \leq 1$	1	Statement prefixed with label 5
$1 < Y < 3$	0	Next statement in normal sequence
$3 \leq Y < 4$	1	Statement prefixed with label 5
$4 \leq Y < 5$	2	Statement prefixed with label 18
$5 \leq Y < 6$	3	Statement prefixed with label 12
$6 \leq Y$	≥ 4	Undefined

Note that Y can be either floating or integer type and can be either positive or negative but that the resulting value of i is always a positive integer. If the value of i exceeds the number of elements in the list, the successor to the SWITCH statement is undefined.

7.19   EITHER IF Statements.   The EITHER IF statement is basically a sequence of IF statements and hence may be considered as a generalization of the IF statement, which has been discussed in Secs. 7.1 and 7.2. In summary, the latter consists of an IF clause followed by a statement. The IF clause specifies a condition, and the statement following the clause is executed only when the condition is satisfied; otherwise that statement is not executed.

The EITHER IF statement has two alternative forms, the difference being in the form of the ending of the statement:

$$\text{EITHER IF } B_1; S_1; \text{ OR IF } B_2; S_2; \ldots ; \text{ OR IF } B_k; S_k \text{ END}$$
$$\text{EITHER IF } B_1; S_1; \text{ OR IF } B_2; S_2; \ldots ; \text{ OTHERWISE}; S_k$$

In both cases each B_i represents either a Boolean expression of arbitrary complexity or a relation, and each S_i represents either a simple statement or a compound statement. The second form of the statement is illustrated in the example of Sec. 7.7.

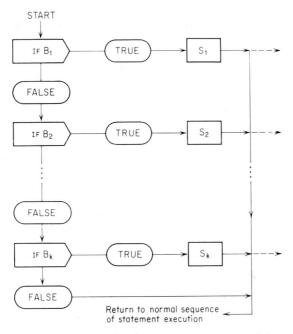

FIG. 7.6. Flow chart for the EITHER IF . . . END statement.

The flow chart in Fig. 7.6 serves to illustrate the execution of the first form (EITHER IF . . . END) of the EITHER IF statement. Successive Boolean expressions B_1, B_2, etc., are evaluated until one is found that has the value true (that is, 1); then the statement immediately following the clause containing that expression is executed. Execution of that statement may result in execution of a GO TO statement that specifies its successor statement, as indicated by the dotted arrows. Otherwise, statement execution returns to the normal sequence, as indicated by the solid arrow. If no Boolean expression is found that has the value true (1), then none of the contained statements is executed, and statement execution continues in the normal sequence.

In the EITHER IF . . . END form, there must be at least one OR IF clause; otherwise the ordinary IF statement should be used instead.

The execution of the EITHER IF . . . OTHERWISE form of the EITHER IF statement is shown in Fig. 7.7. Execution of this form differs from the EITHER IF . . . END form in that the OTHERWISE clause has replaced the kth IF clause. The OTHERWISE clause behaves exactly

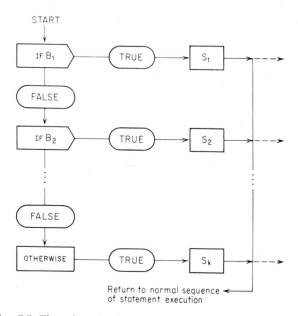

FIG. 7.7. Flow chart for the EITHER IF . . . OTHERWISE statement.

like an IF clause containing a Boolean expression which has the constant value true (1). Thus, whenever the sequence of expressions $B_1, B_2, \ldots, B_{k-1}$ all have the value false (0), the statement S_k is executed.

It is not necessary that the EITHER IF . . . OTHERWISE form shall contain any OR IF clauses. When it does not, one or the other of two statements is executed depending upon the value of the Boolean expression.

7.20 The FOR Statement. The use of a FOR statement was illustrated in Sec. 7.6, and the discussion given there is sufficient for the majority of programming purposes. However, in this section a more detailed discussion of the statement is presented.

The general form of the FOR statement is

$$\text{FOR } V = IL; S$$

where FOR is a reserved word, V is any variable (called the induction variable), IL is an iteration list containing arithmetic expressions and/or step-until elements, and S is a statement that may be a simple statement, a compound statement, a conditional statement, etc. The FOR clause assigns successive values from the iteration list to the variable V. After each assignment, the statement S is executed. This cycle is repeated until either the iteration list is exhausted, at which point it is recognized that execution of the FOR statement has been completed, or a GO TO statement contained in S is executed and the cycle is thereby interrupted.

The iteration list may contain a sequence of arithmetic expressions[1] separated by commas, e.g., $E_1, E_2, \ldots, E_n$. Furthermore, a combination of elements of this type and one or more step-until elements may be used in the iteration list, e.g., $E_1, E_2, (E_I, E_S, E_T), E_3, \ldots, E_n$. In other words, any arbitrary combination of expressions and step-until elements may be used.

The general form of the step-until element is

$$(E_I, E_S, E_T)$$

where E_I, E_S, and E_T are arithmetic expressions that define, respectively, the initial value of the generated sequence, the increment or "step" between successive values, and the test or limiting value. The expressions E_I, E_S, and E_T may assume either positive or negative values. When the sequence passes the test value, the step-until element is deemed to be exhausted.

There are two forms of the step-until element. The following convention has been adopted to distinguish between these two forms. If the first character in the expression E_S is a minus sign, for example, -6 or $-Y*2+B$, then the step-until element will be called a "step-down" element. Otherwise, it will be called a "step-up" element.

In the case of the step-down element, it is necessary that $E_I > E_T$ algebraically, and the element is exhausted when the value of the induction variable V becomes less (algebraically) than the value of E_T. In the step-up element, it is necessary that $E_I < E_T$ algebraically,

---

[1] Throughout this discussion it should be recalled that numbers and variables are special cases of arithmetic expressions.

and the element is exhausted when the value of V exceeds (algebra-ically) that of E_T.

The flow chart in Fig. 7.8 illustrates the functioning of a FOR state-ment while stepping through a step-until element.

The expression E_S is evaluated each time the induction variable V is incremented, and the expression E_T is evaluated each time it is com-pared with V. Thus the increment between steps and the limiting value can be varied from step to step. For example, the values of E_S and E_T can be a function of values calculated by the statements following the FOR clause.

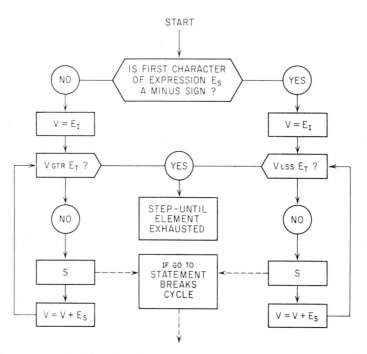

FIG. 7.8. Flow chart for the step-until element.

The only difference between the functioning of the step-up and step-down elements is in the comparison that determines when the step-until element is exhausted, i.e., $V > E_T$ and $V < E_T$, respectively. If a step-up element is to be strictly increasing, it is necessary that $E_S > 0$. If a step-down element is to be strictly decreasing, it is necessary that $E_S < 0$. Note that the minus sign which is used to indicate the step-down element is part of the expression E_S and hence is taken into account in the evaluation of E_S.

Some examples of FOR clauses are as follows:

$$\text{FOR } V = 2,\ 3,\ 11,\ 6,\ 18$$
$$\text{FOR } V = (1,1,9),\ (9.1,0.1,10)$$
$$\text{FOR } V = -25,\ (-20,1,20),\ 25$$
$$\text{FOR } V = (10.0,-0.1,0)$$
$$\text{FOR } V = A,\ B,\ A*2--B,\ C$$
$$\text{FOR } V = (C,\ D,\ E)$$
$$\text{FOR } V = (X*2,-1,3X)$$

These examples should be sufficient to indicate the flexibility that is available to the programmer in constructing a FOR clause for use in a FOR statement.

7.21 Filling an ARRAY. The construction of ARRAY declarations was discussed in connection with the example of Sec. 7.6. In that example, values were assigned to elements of the array by means of assignment statements within the program, and the ARRAY declaration itself served to denote the dimension and size of the array.

An alternative form of the ARRAY declaration permits the programmer to specify in the declaration a sequence of values that are to be assigned to the elements of the array at the time the program is compiled. For example, the declaration

$$\text{ARRAY } X(2,3) = (1,\ 5.0,\ 4,\ 6.0)$$

would result in the integer values 1, 5, and 4 being assigned to the elements $X(1,1)$, $X(1,2)$, and $X(1,3)$, respectively, and the values 6, 0, and 0 being assigned to the elements $X(2,1)$, $X(2,2)$, and $X(2,3)$, respectively, provided that X had been declared as integer type. If, instead, X had been declared as floating type, then each value would be transformed automatically to the excess-50 floating-point form as the assignments were made. Note that only four values are specified in the list, whereas there are six elements in the array. When the list of values is exhausted, the remaining elements in the array are assigned automatically the value 0.

This alternative form of the ARRAY declaration may be generalized for a three-dimensional array as follows:

$$\text{ARRAY } ID(U_1,\ U_2,\ U_3) = (n_1,\ n_2,\ n_3,\ \ldots,\ n_m)$$

where U_1, U_2, and U_3 represent integers that specify the respective upper bounds of the corresponding subscripts of the subscripted variable $ID(E_1,\ E_2,\ E_3)$; n_1, n_2, $\ldots$ represent numeric values; and E_1, E_2, and E_3 represent arithmetic expressions.

During the compilation, the following assignment of numeric values $n_1, n_2, \ldots, n_m$ to elements $ID(I,J,K)$ of the array would be made automatically. In this list it is assumed that the number m of numeric values is equal to the product $(U_1)(U_2)(U_3)$.

Sequence of values	Sequence of elements
The first U_3 values	$ID(1,1,1)$ to $ID(1,1,U_3)$
The second U_3 values	$ID(1,2,1)$ to $ID(1,2,U_3)$
The third U_3 values	$ID(1,3,1)$ to $ID(1,3,U_3)$
.	.
.	.
.	.
The last U_3 values	$ID(U_1,U_2,1)$ to $ID(U_1,U_2,U_3)$

If the list of numeric values is exhausted before each element in the array is assigned a value, the remaining elements are assigned the value 0 automatically.

The following formula defines the sequence number L, counting from left to right in the list of numeric values, of the value that is assigned to the element $ID(I,J,K)$ of the array defined above:

$$L = (I-1)(U_2)(U_3) + (J-1)(U_3) + K$$

where I, J, and K represent integers such that $1 \leq I \leq U_1, 1 \leq J \leq U_2$, and $1 \leq K \leq U_3$. If $L > m$, the sequence number of the last element in the list, then $ID(I,J,K) = 0$. By induction, this formula can be generalized to provide for an N-dimensional array.

7.22 The READ Procedure. The READ statement is actually a statement which calls the READ procedure. Execution of the READ procedure causes one or more cards to be read and assigns the sequence of values thus read to a sequence of variables specified in the input-data set, referred to in the READ statement.

The general form of the READ statement is

$$\text{READ}(;S; IDIDS)$$

where the name-parameter S represents a variable of Boolean type and the program-reference parameter IDIDS is the identifier of an input-data set that is defined in an INPUT declaration. Inclusion of the Boolean variable in the READ statement is optional rather than mandatory. Its purpose is discussed later.

An INPUT declaration is identified by the declarator INPUT and has the general form

$$\text{INPUT } IDIDS_1 (IDS_1), IDIDS_2 (IDS_2), \ldots, IDIDS_k (IDS_k)$$

where IDS represents an input-data set. There may be more than one INPUT declaration in a program. There is no restriction as to the relative locations within the program of an INPUT declaration that defines an input-data set and a READ statement that refers to that input-data set.

In its simple form an input-data set is a list of variables, e.g.,

$$V_1, V_2, \ldots V_k$$

where each element in the list represents either a simple variable or a subscripted variable. In an INPUT declaration, the input-data set is enclosed in parentheses and preceded by an identifier, which may be referred to in a READ statement.

When a READ statement is executed, card reading is initiated. Subsequent events depend upon whether or not a Boolean variable S appears in the READ statement. When there is no Boolean variable in the READ statement, successive values (reading left to right) from the card are assigned to successive variables (reading left to right) in the input-data set. If required, card reading is continued automatically until a value is assigned to each variable in the input-data set, at which point execution of the READ statement is complete. It follows that any unassigned values on the last card read are ignored.

A variation of the basic form of the input-data set permits an iterated element which defines a sequence of subscripted variables, e.g.,

$$\text{FOR } V_1 = IL_1; \text{ FOR } V_2 = IL_2; \ldots ; \text{ FOR } V_k = IL_k;$$
$$V(V_1, V_2, \ldots, V_k)$$

In this form, $V_1, V_2, \ldots,$ and V_k represent induction variables; $IL_1, IL_2, \ldots,$ and IL_k represent iteration lists; and $V(V_1, V_2, \ldots, V_k)$ represents a subscripted variable. The behavior of the FOR clauses in this element is strictly analogous to their behavior in the FOR statement (see Sec. 7.20). The values of variables appearing in the iteration list may be assigned within the program or, alternatively, read from data cards. For example, consider the input-data set

$$K,P, \text{ FOR } I = (K,1,P); X(I)$$

Since K and P are assigned values before the FOR clause is executed' those variables can be used to control the limits of the step-until element in the FOR clause.

A variation of the iterated element (discussed above) permits replacement of the subscripted variable with an input-data set enclosed in parentheses, e.g.,

$$\text{FOR } V_1 = IL_1; \text{ FOR } V_2 = IL_2; \ldots ; \text{ FOR } V_k = IL_k; (IDS)$$

In this form, the FOR clauses control iteration of the input-data set IDS.

When a Boolean variable is included in the READ statement, the operation of the READ procedure differs in the following respects from that described above. Each time a card is read, a check is made automatically to determine whether or not the word SENTINEL appears in card columns 2 to 9. If it does appear, the Boolean variable (S) specified in the READ statement is automatically assigned the value 1, and execution of the READ statement is terminated immediately. Otherwise, the Boolean variable (S) is automatically assigned the value 0 and the operation of the READ procedure assigns successive values read from the cards to successive variables in the input-data set as described above. Thus a SENTINEL card may be used to indicate the end of a sequence of data cards.

The READ procedure is oblivious to type declarations. The form in which values are stored in memory is determined by the form in which they appear in the data card (see Sec. 7.3). The programmer is responsible for determining that the form of each value in a data card is consistent with the type of the variable to which it is to be assigned.

Individual numeric values on data cards must be separated from each other by at least one blank column, and each must be wholly contained within columns 2 to 80 of one data card. In addition, each must satisfy the appropriate restriction as to number of significant digits, as specified in Sec. 7.3.

Alphanumeric values in data cards are bracketed by semicolons to distinguish them from numeric values (see Sec. 7.8 for the discussion of alphanumeric input and output).

7.23 The WRITE Procedure. The WRITE statement actually calls a library procedure which provides three alternative forms of recording output information: printed pages, punched cards, and typed pages. The word "write" as used in this chapter encompasses all three media.

The WRITE procedure requires that the programmer specify three things: (1) an output-data set consisting of the sequence of values to be written; (2) an editing phrase for each value, thereby specifying the form (integer, decimal, or floating-point) and the width of the field in which the number is to be written; and (3) an activation phrase for each line that is to be written, thereby selecting the output medium.

In addition, the WRITE procedure permits the programmer to insert alphabetic and numeric information before, between, or after the values specified in the output-data set. This feature is provided by the alphanumeric-insertion phrase.

In general, the WRITE statement has the form

$$\text{WRITE (;;IDODS, IDFORMAT)}$$

This is the form of a procedure-call statement (see Sec. 7.12) where the value-parameter and the name-parameter lists are empty. The terms IDODS and IDFORMAT are used to indicate that the program-reference-parameter list comprises an identifier for an output-data set and an identifier for a format specification (hereafter called a format).

It is permissible for the output-data set to be vacuous, in which event the WRITE statement has the form

$$\text{WRITE (;; IDFORMAT)}$$

This form may be used for writing page headings, messages, etc., when all the output information is specified in alphanumeric-insertion phrases.

The output-data set itself is defined in an OUTPUT declaration, which is identified by the declarator OUTPUT and contains one or more output-data sets, e.g.,

$$\text{OUTPUT IDODS}_1(E_{11}, E_{12}, \ . \ . \ .), \ \text{IDODS}_2(E_{21}, E_{22}, \ . \ . \ .), \ . \ . \ .$$

Each output-data set is preceded by an identifier which serves as the name by which it is referred to in a WRITE statement. The output-data set itself is enclosed in parentheses and consists of a sequence of variables and/or expressions separated by commas. When an expression is included in an output-data set, it is evaluated during execution of the WRITE procedure. When a variable is included in an output-data set, the value currently assigned to the variable is written by the procedure.

When an output-data set contains a multivalued variable, one or more FOR clauses may be used to specify its sequence of subscripted variables, e.g.,

$$\text{IDODS}(E_1, E_2, \ . \ . \ . \ , \text{ FOR } I = (1,1,P); \text{ FOR } J = (1,1,Q);$$
$$X(I,J), E_n, E_{n+1}, \ . \ . \ .)$$

Note that the entire iterated element of the output-data set [consisting of the two FOR clauses and variable $X(I,J)$] is separated from each adjacent element by a comma. Note also that its form is very similar to that of a FOR statement. The difference is that the second FOR clause is followed by a subscripted variable rather than by a statement. However, the FOR clauses operate in their usual manner (see Sec. 7.20) to control the sequence of values assumed by the subscripts of the variable $X(I,J)$.

The format specification referred to (by means of its identifier) in the WRITE statement is defined in a FORMAT declaration, which, in turn, is identified by the declarator FORMAT and contains one or more formats, e.g.,

FORMAT IDFORMAT$_1$(format), IDFORMAT$_2$(format), . . .

Each format is enclosed in parentheses and is preceded by its identifier.

A format for an output-data set such as IDODS$_1$(E$_{11}$, E$_{12}$, . . . , E$_{1k}$) would provide an editing phrase for each variable (or expression) in the output-data set and an activation phrase for each line to be printed, e.g.,

IDFORMAT(EP$_1$, EP$_2$, . . . , AP$_1$, . . . , EP$_k$, AP$_h$)

where EP$_1$ is the editing phrase for value E$_{11}$, EP$_2$ for E$_{12}$, . . . , and EP$_k$ for E$_{1k}$. Note that successive values specified in the output-data set are paired with corresponding editing phrases. Thus the procedure works from left to right in both lists, editing the sequence of values to be written on a single line. When the activation phrase AP$_1$ is encountered, the edited line is written. The procedure repeats this editing process, and the next sequence of edited values is written when the next activation phrase is encountered. The process continues until all values specified in the output-data set have been edited.

There are four types of editing phrases for numeric values. An editing phrase specifies the form (integer, decimal, or floating-point) and the width of the field (number of spaces) in which the value is to be written. In each of the following definitions of editing phrases w represents an integer number that specifies the width of the field, and d also represents an integer number. The value, when written, is always justified right in the field, and if the number will not fit in the field, an asterisk is written in lieu of the number.

Iw The letter I signifies that the value is to be written in integer form. The field width w must be great enough to accommodate the value and (in the case of a negative number) a sign.

X$w.d$ The letter X signifies that the value is to be written in decimal form, that is, containing a decimal point. The integer d specifies the number of decimal places to which the value is to be truncated when it is written. The field width w must be great enough to accommodate the number and its decimal point, plus a sign if the number is negative.

s*w.d* The letter s signifies that the value is to be written in decimal form. The integer *d* specifies the total number of digits which will be written, including zeros following the decimal point if the number is less than 0.1. The field width *w* must be great enough to accommodate *d* digits, a decimal point, and any possible minus sign.

F*w.d* The letter F signifies that the value is to be written in floating-point form. The integer *d* specifies the number of significant digits to which the number is to be truncated when it is written. In this type of editing phrase it is necessary that *w* be great enough to provide for a possible minus sign, a decimal point, *d* digits, a comma, and a scale factor (which may have a minus sign).

Each of the above phrases edits a single numeric value. The editing process assumes that the value is stored in memory in a form that is consistent with the specified editing phrase. The letter I assumes that the value is stored in integer form while the letters X, F, and S assume that the value is stored in excess-50 floating-point form. The WRITE procedure is oblivious to type declarations; hence the programmer must ensure that the form in which a number is stored is consistent with the corresponding editing phrase.

The alphanumeric editing phrase A*w* signifies that one or more values specified in the output-data set are to be edited as a string of *w* alphanumeric characters. Since a word in memory can store the decimal equivalent for five characters (see Sec. 7.8), the alphanumeric editing phrase A*w* corresponds to *n* successive variables in the output-data set, where *n* is the smallest integer not less than $w/5$. When *w* is not an even multiple of 5, the value of the last variable is truncated automatically.

The format IDFORMAT, shown above, can be modified by interspersing blank-insertion phrases and alphanumeric-insertion phrases.

The blank-insertion phrase B*w* in a format causes *w* spaces to be inserted in the edited line (see card 9 in the example of Sec. 7.2).

The alphanumeric-insertion phrase is an arbitrary string of characters (the asterisk excluded) enclosed in bracketing asterisks. It causes the string of characters between the asterisks to be inserted in the edited line (see Sec. 7.5).

The editing phrases for numeric and alphanumeric values and for the blank-insertion phrase can be converted to definite repeat phrases by prefixing the basic phrase with an integer that specifies the number of repetitions. For example, 3I5 is equivalent to I5, I5, I5.

As stated earlier, an activation phrase causes the edited line to be written. The following activation phrases are commonly used, but additions and modifications may exist at a particular computation center.

w*s*   The letter w signifies that the edited line is to be written by the line printer. The letter *s* indicates an integer which is defined below and is used to control spacing between lines.

p   The letter p signifies that the edited line is to be punched in a card.

c*s*   The letter c signifies that the edited line is to be both written by the line printer and punched in a card. Only the first 80 characters in the edited line will be punched.

t*c*   The letter T signifies that the edited line is to be typed on the typewriter (supervisory printer). The value of *c* specifies the number of carriage returns to be executed prior to typing.

Values of s	Result
0 or blank	Single-space before printing
1	Eject page after printing
2	Single-space before and after printing
3	Eject page before printing
4	Double-space before printing

If one activation phrase follows another, the effect of the second one will be to cause writing of a blank line.

Two or more consecutive phrases in a format may be enclosed in parentheses to form a compound editing phrase. Thus a format specification itself is a compound editing phrase. Compound editing phrases may be nested in a manner analogous to the nesting of algebraic expressions. A compound editing phrase is automatically an indefinite-repeat phrase, i.e., it will be repeated until the output-data set is exhausted. Any compound phrase nested in the format specification may be converted to a definite-repeat phrase by prefixing it with an integer that specifies the number of repetitions.

There are two particular cases that should be noted. If the number of values specified in the output-data set exceeds the effective number of editing phrases in the format specification, the entire format specification is repeated until the output-data set is exhausted. If, on the other hand, the output-data set is exhausted before the editing phrases are exhausted, the surplus editing phrases are ignored.

A line is limited to 120 spaces on the line printer and 80 spaces on a card. If an edited line exceeds the limit for the output medium specified in the activation phrase, the excess data are lost.

7.24 Error Messages. It was stated in Sec. 7.1 that error messages are printed automatically during the compilation phase, when certain errors in syntax are recognized by the compiler. In addition, error messages are printed automatically when certain events transpire in the execution of a program. These error messages are discussed in detail in the reference manual "Burroughs Algebraic Compiler."

When an error is detected during compilation, the corresponding message is printed. Thus the error messages are interspersed among the lines of the program listing that is printed automatically as compilation proceeds. The message itself, e.g., CONSTANT OUT OF RANGE, indicates the nature of the error, while the location of the message indicates the relative location of the error in the program.

The following error messages are printed automatically during program execution when the indicated error is detected:

> RESULT OUT OF RANGE "procedure name"
> RESULT UNDEFINED FOR "procedure name"
> RESULT ILL-DEFINED FOR "procedure name"

Note that in each case the indicated error is detected during execution of the library procedure named in the message. The precise meaning of a specific error message can be found in the reference manual "Burroughs Algebraic Compiler."

The error message ARITHMETIC OVERFLOW indicates that in the execution of some statement an attempt has been made to calculate a result R such that $R \geq 10^{10}$, when R is of the integer type, or $R > 0.99999999 \times 10^{49}$, when R is of the floating type. The computer automatically detects such an overflow error at the instant of its occurrence, at which time an overflow switch is set to the ON position. However, the message ARITHMETIC OVERFLOW is printed only when the overflow switch is tested at some later time during program execution and is found to be in the ON position. Each time the overflow switch is tested it is automatically reset to the OFF state.

Provision is made for automatically testing the overflow switch at the start and at the completion of execution of certain library procedures. However, there are other circumstances during program execution in which the overflow switch may be reset to the OFF state without an error message being printed. Thus the absence of the ARITHMETIC OVERFLOW message does not guarantee the absence of overflow errors during program execution.

7.25 Assembling the Card Deck for Processing. The input-card deck comprises at least a JOB card, a LODX card, and a set of BALGOL program cards. This file is supplemented, as required, by one or more card decks containing data cards, declared procedures, and external procedures. It is imperative that the various decks shall enter the input unit of the computer in the sequence shown in Fig. 7.9 if the desired results are to be obtained. However, items 3, 5, and 6 in that figure are included only if required.

After the BALGOL program is written on the coding form as illustrated in Table 7.2, each line is key-punched into an IBM card.

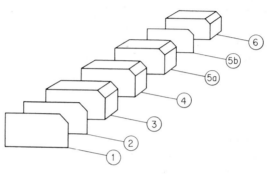

Item No.	Item
1	JOB card.
2	LODX card.
3	If required, declared procedures obtained from computation center library or other sources.
4	The BALGOL program, which always concludes with a FINISH statement.
5a	If required, a deck for each external procedure declared in the program.
5b	If any external procedure decks are included, the last one must be followed by a card containing the word FINISH.
6	Data cards.

FIG. 7.9. Organization of the input-card deck.

The first and second cards of the resulting deck of cards should be a JOB card and a LODX card. The remaining cards constitute the BALGOL program deck and will include any subprograms written by the programmer. It is good practice to prepare a listing of these cards; this listing should be proofread to detect, among other things, apparent errors in syntax or in card sequence.

If there are data cards to be processed, it is normally necessary to key-punch them or, in some instances, they may be available in punched cards from another source. For example, they may have been produced as results from a previous execution of a BALGOL program.

Finally, the BALGOL program may contain call statements for

declared procedures whose declarations are not included in the BAL-GOL program or declarations for external procedures. In this event, card decks for these procedures must be obtained and inserted in their appropriate relative locations in the input-card deck. Frequently, the computation center library is the source from which such card decks are obtained.

7.26 Summary of Rules of Precedence for Declarations. The type of an identifier must be declared (explicitly or by default) before that identifier is used in any statement or in any other declaration.

The type of an identifier for an array must be declared (explicitly or by default) before the ARRAY declaration.

An array must be described by an ARRAY declaration before the use of any variable with subscripts which represents an element of that array.

The declaration of a FUNCTION must precede any statement in which the function is called.

The declaration of a PROCEDURE must precede any statement in which the procedure is called.

A FINISH statement (declaration) followed by a semicolon must terminate the program and must not appear elsewhere in the program.

7.27 List of Reserved Words. There are certain combinations of alphabetic characters that have a definite meaning within BALCOM and cannot be used by the programmer for any other purpose. These are referred to as reserved words and include declarators, operators, separators, names of library procedures, intrinsic functions, etc. The following list of these words is complete as of the time that this text is written. As library procedures are developed to increase the versatility of BALGOL, it will be necessary to reserve additional words.

ABS	EITHER	FLOATING	
AND	END	FOR	LEQ
ARCCOS	ENTER	FORMAT	LOG
ARCSIN	ENTIRE	FUNCTION	LSS
ARCTAN	EQIV		
ARRAY	EQL	GEQ	MAX
	ERROR	GO	MIN
BEGIN	EXP	GTR	MOD
BOOLEAN	EXTERNAL		MONITOR
		IF	
COMMENT	FINISH	IMPL	NEQ
COS	FIX	INPUT	NOT
COSH	FLOAT	INTEGER	

OR	READ	SIN	TAN
OTHERWISE	REAL	SINH	TANH
OUTPUT	RETURN	SQRT	TO
OVERLAY	ROMXX	STATEMENT	
		STOP	UNTIL
PCS	SEGMENT	SUBROUTINE	
PROCEDURE	SIGN	SWITCH	WRITE

Most of the words in the above list are explained elsewhere in the text. For a discussion of the remaining words, such as ERROR, MONITOR, OVERLAY, and SEGMENT, the reader should refer to the manual "Burroughs Algebraic Compiler."

7.28 Definition of Algorithm

The word algorithm, like several other mathematical expressions, comes from the Arabic, being a corruption of Al Khowarizmi, the name of an Arabian mathematician of the ninth century, whose writings were prominent in bringing the present method of numeration to the Occident. During the middle ages the word algorithm referred simply to the use of Hindu-Arabic numerals, but at present it applies to any formalized procedure whereby requested mathematical objects are found by a definite chain of operations, each operation requiring the results of preceding ones.[1]

PROBLEMS

7.1. (*a*) Which of the following may be used as a label?   (*b*) Which may be used as an identifier?   (*c*) Which are reserved words?

A729	ABCDEFG	001	2DELTA
BEFØRE	FINISH	AB + BA	12.5
1000	1	BESSEL	BRØWN

7.2. Assume that A, B, and THETA are identifiers representing simple variables. Which of the following are syntactically correct as arithmetic expressions for:

a. The product of 7 and A:

7A	A7	A.7	7.A

b. The product of A and B:

AB	BA	A.B	A(B)

c. The product of 2.5 and A:

2.5A	A2.5	A.2.5	A(2.5)

d. The product of A and THETA:

A.THETA	THETA.A	ATHETA	THETA(A)

e. The product of 2.5 and 3.5:

(2.5)(3.5)	2.5(3.5)	2.5.3.5	2.53.5

[1] J. V. Uspensky and M. A. Heaslet: "Elementary Number Theory," p. 26, McGraw-Hill Book Company, Inc., New York, 1939.

7.3. (a) Why are compound statements needed? (b) In the following compound statement, is there any ambiguity in the last arithmetic expression? (c) Write a single assignment statement for Z (as defined in the following statement) in terms of numbers and the variable A only.

$$\text{BEGIN } X = 2.5A + 4.0; \; Y = X*4; \; Z = X(Y + X/2) \text{ END}$$

7.4. Prepare an arbitrary number of data cards, each containing one number (in decimal form, e.g., 2.756). It is desired to calculate the squares of the numbers on the cards. Write a BALGOL program which provides for reading the numbers from the cards (one at a time), squaring the numbers, and writing each number and its square on a single line. Thus, the pages of results will contain two columns with the original numbers in the first column and the corresponding squares in the second column.

7.5. Write a BALGOL program to calculate the cross-sectional area A and polar moment of inertia J for circular tubes of various sizes. Prepare a number of data cards that contain the outside and inside diameters (D2 and D1) for various sizes of tubes. (The numbers on the data cards should be in decimal form.) Read the diameters from the cards, calculate A and J, and list the results in four columns (D2, D1, A, J).

7.6. Prepare a number of data cards, each containing two (decimal) values A and B. It is desired to calculate values of the variables Y and Z defined as:

$$Y = (A + B)^3/3.5$$
$$Z = (A^3 - 8A^2B + 3AB^2 - B^3)/3.5$$

Write a program in BALGOL to read exactly five sets of values of A and B from cards (assuming that the number of data cards that follows the program is greater than five) and to calculate the corresponding values of Y and Z. List results in four columns with corresponding values of A, B, Y, and Z appearing in each row.

7.7. Prepare a BALGOL program for calculating by direct addition the sum of the numbers 0.1, 0.2, 0.3, . . . , 10.0, and writing the result.

Answer: SUM $= 505.0$.

7.8. Write a BALGOL program for calculating by direct addition the sum of the numbers 0.1, 0.2, 0.3, ... Terminate the calculations at the number N such that the sum is less than or equal to 100, but the addition of the next number (N + 0.1) would produce a sum greater than 100. The results to be printed consist of the number N and the corresponding sum.

Answer: N $= 4.4$; SUM $= 99.0$.

7.9. Prepare an arbitrary number of data cards each containing one number (in decimal form, e.g., 2.756). It is desired to calculate the sum of all the numbers. Write a BALGOL program which provides for reading the numbers from the cards, writing the numbers in a column, and writing the sum of the numbers on a new line but not in the same column.

7.10. Write a program in BALGOL to calculate a table of values of the dynamic magnification factor MF equal to

$$\frac{1}{1 - r^2}$$

where r is the ratio of the frequency of the forcing function to the natural frequency of vibration of the dynamic system. Write the results in two columns, the first giving the value of r and the second giving the corresponding value of MF. Select values of r from 0 to 3 in intervals of 0.2, and provide for the fact that MF becomes infinite when $r = 1$.

7.11. Write a BALGOL program to compute the value of e by using the series

$$e = 1 + \frac{1}{1!} + \frac{1}{2!} + \frac{1}{3!} + \frac{1}{4!} + \cdot \cdot \cdot$$

Terminate the series when the number of terms exceeds 200, or when the last term included is less than 0.00001. Write the calculated value of e and the number of terms used in the calculations.

7.12. Write a BALGOL program to compute the sine of $\pi/6$ from the series

$$\sin x = x - \frac{x^3}{3!} + \frac{x^5}{5!} - \frac{x^7}{7!} + \cdot \cdot \cdot$$

Terminate the calculations when the number of terms exceeds 50 or when the last term included is less than 0.000001. Write the calculated value of the sine and the number of terms used to calculate it.

7.13. Write a program for preparing a table of squares and cubes of the numbers 1, 2, 3, . . . , 10. Print the results in three columns (numbers, squares, and cubes) with the numbers appearing in integer form.

7.14. Write a program for preparing a table of factorials $N!$ and reciprocal factorials $1/N!$ for $N = (1,1,10)$. Print the results in three columns $(N,N!,1/N!)$. The values of N and $N!$ are to be printed in integer form and the values of $1/N!$ in floating-point form with eight digits to the right of the decimal point.

7.15. Assume that a set of eight-digit, integer numbers are available on consecutive data cards. Write a BALGOL program which will produce two new numbers corresponding to each of the original numbers such that the first number consists of digit positions 1, 3, 5, and 7 and the second number consists of digit positions 2, 4, 6, and 8. List the numbers in three columns (original number, digit-positions 1-3-5-7 number, and digit-positions 2-4-6-8 number). For example, if one of the numbers read from a card is 72942736 the corresponding output will be:

$$72942736 \qquad 7923 \qquad 2476$$

7.16. Write the statements and declarations which must be added to the illustrative example of Sec. 7.1 in order to print the headings A, B, C, D, and E over the printed columns of results.

7.17. Revise the illustrative example of Sec. 7.2 in order to provide for printing the headings N and Reciprocal Factorial above the two columns of printed results.

7.18. Solve Prob. 7.11 and print the results in the form

$$E = d.dddd \qquad N = ddd$$

where each d represents a digit.

7.19. Solve Prob. 7.10 by making use of a FOR statement.

7.20. Solve Prob. 7.13 by making use of a FOR statement and subscripted variables.

7.21. Solve Prob. 7.15 by making use of a FOR statement and subscripted variables.

7.22. Prepare three data cards, each containing six decimal numbers. The numbers on the first card are to be identified as $p_1, p_2, \ldots, p_6$; on the second card as $q_1, q_2, \ldots, q_6$; and on the third card as $r_1, r_2, \ldots, r_6$. Write a BALGOL program which will print a 5×6 array of numbers having the following values:

$$
\begin{array}{cccc}
p_1 & p_2 & \cdots & p_6 \\
q_1 & q_2 & \cdots & q_6 \\
r_1 & r_2 & \cdots & r_6 \\
p_1 q_1 & p_2 q_2 & \cdots & p_6 q_6 \\
q_1 r_1 & q_2 r_2 & \cdots & q_6 r_6
\end{array}
$$

7.23. Write a program for multiplying a 4×5 matrix A by a 5×1 column matrix B, the result being a 4×1 column matrix C. Assume that the elements of matrices A and B are to be read from cards in the following manner: Data card 1 contains in sequence the four elements in the first column of A, data card 2 contains the elements in the second column of A, etc.; and data card 6 contains the elements of B. Arrange the results on the printed page in the following manner (with headings):

MATRIX A	MATRIX B	MATRIX C
$A_{11}\ A_{12} \ldots A_{15}$	B_1	C_1
$A_{21}\ A_{22} \ldots A_{25}$	B_2	C_2
$A_{31}\ A_{32} \ldots A_{35}$	B_3	C_3
$A_{41}\ A_{42} \ldots A_{45}$	B_4	C_4
	B_5	

7.24. Write a program for multiplying two 4×4 square matrices A and B, assuming that the elements of each row of A and B are to be read from punched cards.

7.25. Solve Prob. 7.11 by making use of an UNTIL statement.

7.26. Solve Prob. 7.12 by making use of an UNTIL statement.

7.27. Write a program to calculate the value of π from the series

$$\frac{\pi^2}{8} = 1 + \frac{1}{3^2} + \frac{1}{5^2} + \frac{1}{7^2} + \cdots$$

7.28. Modify the square-root program used as an illustrative example in Sec. 7.7 to calculate imaginary roots for negative values of X.

7.29. An iterative method for determining the roots of an algebraic equation is illustrated by the following problem. Assume that we have the equation

$$X^3 - 5X^2 + 6X - 1 = 0$$

Rewrite the equation in the form

$$X = \frac{1 + 5X^2 - X^3}{6}$$

which gives the recursive formula

$$X_{i+1} = \frac{1 + 5X_i^2 - X_i^3}{6}$$

Then, from the latter equation, calculate an approximate value for X_{i+1} by substituting into the right-hand side a trial value of X_i. Then, using the value of X_{i+1}, repeat the process.

Write a BALGOL program for calculating the smallest positive root of the above equation to an accuracy of six significant figures. (Suggestion: Take $X_0 = 0$ on the right-hand side of the equation as the first trial value.) Since this method for calculating roots may converge slowly, include in the program a provision for limiting the number of iterations to 10. List the consecutive approximations to the root in the output of the program.

Answer: $X = 0.198062$.

7.30. Write a BALGOL program which will read your name and street address from a single data card and will then print the same information on two output lines (name on first line, address on second line).

7.31. Write a BALGOL program which will read the alphabet $(A,B, \ldots ,Z)$ from one data card and then will print two lines of results, the first containing the alphabet in usual order (with a space between letters) and the second containing the alphabet in reverse order.

APPENDIX

THE PROGRAM TEST SUPERVISORY ROUTINE

The program test supervisory routine (PTSR) was developed primarily for the purpose of testing batches of programs with a minimum of manual intervention by the 650 operator. It was designed so errors (other than read or punch feed) that normally result in a machine stop will, instead, result in the automatic execution of an error routine.

The error routine provides for punching of a trace card for the last instruction executed and for an N-per-card memory dump of locations *FFFF* to *LLLL* as specified by the programmer in a header card that precedes the test program deck. It also provides for automatic readout (without processing) of the remaining cards in the test-program deck in which the error was encountered. The read-out continues until the next header card is encountered, at which point the program load cycle is automatically initiated.

The program includes a trace routine, a zeroing routine, a general-purpose read routine that reads either N-per-card format or SOAP II assembled format cards, and an N-per-card punch routine. Entry to and exit from these routines may be programmed, except that exit from the read routine is provided by a transfer card.

A channel of direct communication is thus provided between the programmer and the computer, whereby he can program N-per-card punch-outs or limited traces at any step in the execution of the program. Provision is made, also, for programming continuous surveillance of an arbitrary register. The identification of the register to be surveyed is programmed, hence may be changed by programming. Whenever the surveyed register is referred to in either the D address or the I address of an instruction, a trace card is punched for that instruction.

It is expected that during the testing of batches of programs, operation will be continuously in the trace mode but that trace cards will be punched only on programmed demand or in case of an error condition. This will be done not only to take advantage of the automatic read-out when an error is encountered but also to protect the registers (1550 through 1999) reserved for the PTSR from inadvertent invasion by the program being tested. The more sophisticated user would be expected to run the proved sections of his program at machine speed and program entry to and from the trace mode only for those sections that are unproved.

OPERATING INSTRUCTIONS FOR THE PROGRAM TEST SUPERVISORY ROUTINE

I. The routine occupies registers 1550 through 1999. These locations must not be referred to by the test program.
Rate of operation:
A. Trace without punch mode.
400 instructions per minute traced.
B. Trace with punch mode.
100 instructions per minute traced.
C. No trace mode.
Machine speed.
II. Loading the PTSR program.
Set 8000 equal to 70 1951 1951 ±, and set the control switches from left to right to STOP, RUN, RUN, PROGRAM, STOP, STOP.

When the machine stops with 01 0001 1950 in the program register, set 8000 equal to 00 0000 1997 +, and set the control switches from left to right to RUN, RUN, RUN, PROGRAM, RUN, RUN. Depress PROGRAM START. When loading is complete, control is transferred automatically to 1964, 70 1962 1962; succeeding cards are read until an STPL card, defined below, is encountered.
III. Processing the test package.
A test package is organized as follows:
A. The STPL (start test program load) card.
Columns 1–10: 9999999998+.
Columns 11–20: ONFFFFFLLLL+.
Columns 21–30: 00000 0/1 nnnn+.
1. 9999999998 is used to identify an STPL card.
2. FFFF to LLLL (FFFF < LLLL) defines the range of memory registers to be occupied by the test program

and tables. The range is zeroed automatically before the test program is loaded. N specifies the number of words per card for the memory punch-out that is automatically made when the error routine (discussed in item VIII) is entered.

3. 00000 0/1 *nnnn*+

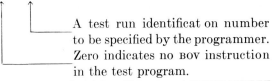

       A test run identificat on number to be specified by the programmer. Zero indicates no BOV instruction in the test program.

B. The test program may be either N-per-card (00000*NFFFF* in columns 1 to 10) or one-word memory load (69 1954 1953 in columns 1 to 10) format or a combination of the two. A transfer card should not follow the program deck, because the STPE card contains the transfer instruction.

C. The STPE (start test program execution) card.

Columns 1–10: 9999999999. STPE card identification code.

Columns 11–20: *rr dddd iiii*. Transfer instruction.[1]

Columns 21–30: 00000 0/1 *nnnn*. Must be same as STPL card.

Columns 31–40: *rr dddd iiii*. Setting of STORAGE ENTRY SWITCHES normally required during execution of test program.[2]

D. The deck of data cards to be processed by the program being tested.

E. The last card in any test package must be an STPL card. If this card is omitted, the end of the test routine will not be executed for the last program tested.

IV. Restrictions on the programmer.

A. Locations 1550 through 1999 must not be referred to by an instruction in the test program.

B. Location 0000 must not be referred to as an I address by any instruction in the test program, nor as a D address by any branch instruction in the test program.

---

[1] The transfer instruction may be the first instruction in the test program or an instruction that transfers control thereto.

[2] Columns 31 to 40 should be nonzero only if a validity exception routine is included in the test program. If 31 to 40 are nonzero, they should contain the entry instruction for the validity exception routine, or an instruction transferring control thereto.

C. Location 8000 will always contain 00 0000 1997+ and should be used by the test program only as an entry to a validity exception routine. If columns 31 to 40 of the STPE card are nonzero, register 1997 will provide for re-entry to the trace mode with the execution of the instruction specified by 31 to 40. Otherwise, the error routine will be entered when a validity exception is encountered during the execution of the test program.

D. When an STPE card is encountered, the transfer instruction (columns 11 to 20) is executed in the trace mode (without trace-card punching) of the PTSR. Succeeding instructions will be executed in the same mode unless the programmer changes the mode by executing an instruction containing a pseudo code permitted by the supervisory routine.

E. A halt instruction will be treated as a no-op.

F. Any card that enters 9999999998 in storage entry register 1 in any read operation executed in the trace mode or in the read routine will be identified as an STPL card. Any card read by the read routine that contains 9999999999 in columns 1 to 10 will be identified as an STPE card.

V. Pseudo operation codes that can be interpreted in the trace mode.

50   Read a sequence of cards via the general-purpose read routine.

Cards read can be either N-per-card format (e.g., 00 000N FFFF in columns 1 to 10) or one-word memory load card format (e.g., 69 1954 1953 in columns 1–10) or any combination of the two. The program is automatically re-entered in the trace mode whenever a transfer card (e.g., 00 0000 $iiii$ in columns 1 to 10) is encountered.

51   Punch a sequence of registers N (consecutive registers) per card.

When this instruction is executed, the L register must contain 0N FFFF LLLL+, where $1 \leq N \leq 7$ defines the number of registers per card and $FFFF \leq LLLL$ defines the range of the sequence of registers to be punched. The next instruction to be executed after punching is completed is specified by the I address of the instruction containing the pseudo operation code 51.

52   Store minus zero in a sequence of registers.

When this instruction is executed, the L register must

contain $XX\ FFFF\ LLLL+$, where XX is arbitrary (but not blank) and $FFFF \leq LLLL$ defines the range of the sequence of registers in which minus zero is to be stored. The next instruction to be executed after zeroing is completed is specified by the I address of the instruction containing the 52 pseudo operation code.

53 End of program.

Cards are read until the next STPL card is identified; a card is punched for the last instruction executed in the trace mode; then loading of the next program is started.

54 Survey location specified by the D address.

The D address of the instruction containing the pseudo operation code 54 is stored in location 1993. This address is compared with the D address and I address of each instruction traced. Whenever an equality occurs, a trace card is punched. The location of the next instruction is specified by the I address.

55 Punch trace cards.

A card is punched for each instruction executed in the trace mode until either a stop punch (56) code is executed or the limit on the number of trace cards is reached. This limit is specified in the D address positions of 1994 and is set at 150. The location of the next instruction is specified by the I address.

56 Stop punch of trace cards.

Punching of trace cards is discontinued. The location of the next instruction is specified by the I address.

57 Stop trace.

The trace mode is left and execution of instructions at machine speed is resumed at the instruction specified by the I address. This operation code may be deleted by storing zeros in 1821.

VI. Entry to the trace mode.

The trace mode can be entered from any point in the program by inserting the following pair of instructions:

$$\underline{\hspace{2cm}} \text{ STD } 1970 \underline{\hspace{1.5cm}}$$
$$\underline{\hspace{2cm}} \text{ LDD } iiii \ 1975$$

where $iiii$ specifies the location of the first instruction to be executed in the trace mode. The blank addresses may be specified by the programmer. Manual entry may be accomplished by dialing the second instruction into the STORAGE ENTRY SWITCHES and transferring control thereto.   The pseudo-operation code 57 provides an exit from the trace mode.

VII. Limit on number of instructions that can be executed in the trace mode.

The limit is specified by the five high-order positions, $XXXXX00000$, of location 1886 and is included in order to control closed loops.   The limit is set at 2000; when this number is reached, program execution is discontinued and the error routine is entered.

VIII. Error routine.

The error routine is entered from the trace mode when any of the following conditions are encountered:

A. An invalid character is encountered during the execution of a test program that contains no validity exception routine.

B. The OVERFLOW switch is set and the test program contains no BOV instruction.   See STPL card for indication of BOV instruction in the test program.

C. An instruction is to be executed that contains an invalid operation code (other than the pseudo codes defined above) or an unpermitted D or I address (including 0000 and 1550 through 1999).

D. A divide operation is to be executed that would lead to a quotient overflow.

E. A BDX operation in which digit position X of the D register contains neither an 8 nor a 9.

F. The number of instructions executed in the trace mode reaches the limit.

G. Control is transferred to 1857.

The error routine causes cards to be read until the next STPL card is identified.   Before loading of the next program is started, a trace card is punched for the instruction leading to the error condition, and a memory dump is executed as defined by $0N\ FFFF\ LLLL$ in word 2 of the STPL card.

IX. Format of the trace card.

Columns 1–5	Count of instructions executed in the trace mode
Columns 6–10	As specified in columns 26–30 of the STPL card
Columns 11–20	Location of instruction executed

Columns 21–30   Instruction
Columns 31–40   Contents of U register after execution
Columns 41–50   Contents of L register after execution
Columns 51–60   Contents of D register after execution
Columns 61–70   Count of number of trace cards punched
Columns 71–80   Instruction to be executed next

X. 533 plug board.

If no load cards (i.e., 12 punch in column 1) are to be read by the test program, a general-purpose board will suffice for the requirements of program test supervisory routine. If a general-purpose board is used, the last two cards in the PTSR deck must be relocated in front of the card immediately preceding them. Otherwise a special board must be used (see Fig. 6.25), or the trace will be broken whenever an L card is read.

XI. Entry to the general-purpose read routine.

If operation is in the trace mode, code 50 must be executed; otherwise, transfer control to 1996.

Any card format other than N-per-card, one-word memory load, STPL, or STPE will be bypassed. A card that specifies storage of information in a location past 1560 will be bypassed. If the STORAGE ENTRY SWITCHES are set at 00 0000 1997, the ERROR switch is at SENSE, and a validity error is sensed, the card being processed is bypassed. An exception card is punched for each card that is bypassed.

XII. Entry to the N-per-card punch routine.

If operation is in the trace mode, code 51 must be executed. Otherwise, programmed entry requires that

$$\text{U register} = 00\ 0000\ 0000$$
$$\text{L register} = 0N\ FFFF\ LLLL+$$

Then control is transferred to 1971.

Manual entry requires that $0N\ FFFF\ LLLL+$ be entered to the STORAGE ENTRY SWITCHES. Then control is transferred to 1972. When punching is complete after manual entry, the machine stops with 01 9000 8000 in the program register.

If the STORAGE ENTRY SWITCHES are set to 00 0000 1997 and the ERROR switch is set at SENSE, the punch-out will not be halted at a register (e.g., $dddd$) containing an invalid character. Instead, 69 $dddd$ 1878 will be stored and punched in lieu of the contents of the register.

XIII. Entry to the zeroing routine.

If operation is in the trace mode, code 52 must be executed. Otherwise, programmed entry requires that

$$\text{U register} = 0\ 0\ 0000\ 0000$$
$$\text{L register} = XX\ FFFF\ LLLL+$$
$$\text{D register} = r\,r\ dddd\ iiii \qquad \text{the exit instruction}$$

Then control is transferred to 1973.

Manual entry requires that $XX\ FFFF\ LLLL+$ be entered to the STORAGE ENTRY SWITCHES. Then control is transferred to 1974. When zeroing is complete after manual entry, the machine stops with 01 9000 8000 in the program register.

The upper limit LLLL of the block of registers to be zeroed must not exceed 1549.

INDEX